MENDIP

A New Study

MENDIP
A New Study

EDITED BY ROBIN ATTHILL

Contributors:

Robin Atthill
P. J. Fowler
Frances Neale
D. I. Smith
Michael Williams
A. J. Willis

David & Charles:
Newton Abbot   London   North Pomfret (VE)   Vancouver

ISBN 0 7153 7297 1
Library of Congress Catalog Card Number: 76-45509

Set in 11 on 13pt Baskerville
and printed in Great Britain
for David & Charles (Publishers) Limited
Brunel House Newton Abbot Devon

Published in the United States of America
by David and Charles Inc.
North Pomfret Vermont 05053 USA

Published in Canada
by Douglas David and Charles Limited
1875 Welch Street North Vancouver BC

Contents

Note on Metrication

THIS BOOK HAS been written and published at a time of gradual transition to the metric system in Great Britain. It has seemed undesirable in a symposium such as this to aim at a rigid uniformity in matters of measurement, which might well make for difficult reading and alienate the general reader, for whom the book is intended, at a moment when the metric system is not yet fully in current use.

Much of the book is concerned with the history of Mendip, and here and in the general descriptive passages, such as the Gazetteer, we have seen fit to retain the traditional units of measurement: yards, miles, gallons, tons—and feet above sea level. In the more specialised sections, such as those on Geology, Climate or Archaeology, metric figures have been used, as now being more or less obligatory within these fields—with some non-metric equivalents to help the reader who is not yet familiar with the new units of measurement. All maps and diagrams, however, show both scales.

The overruling consideration has been to achieve consistency and readability within each chapter, without, we dare to hope, infringing the dictates of common sense.

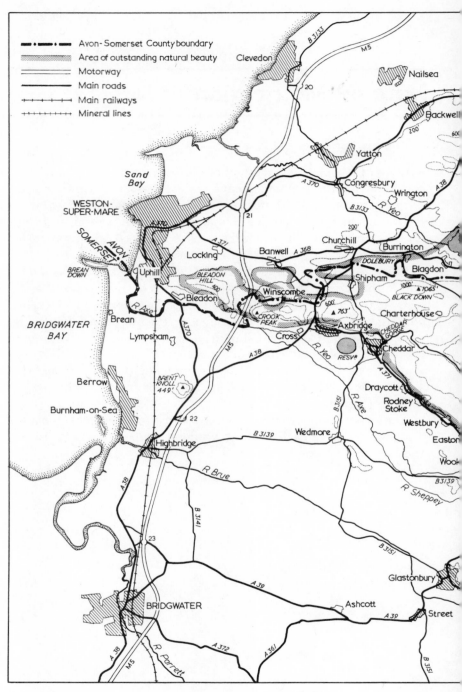

Fig 1. M

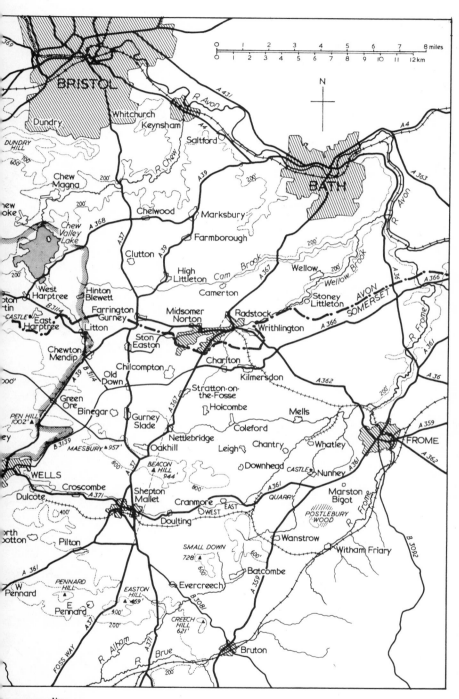

...e surrounding area.

1

Mendip Today

Robin Atthill

THOMAS HARDY DESCRIBED Mendip as 'a range of limestone rocks stretching from the shores of the Bristol Channel into the middle of Somersetshire'. The traditional boundaries of Mendip run 'from the place which is called Kotellisasch to the rock which is called Le Blacston in the Western Sea'. Black Rock is still there, in the estuary of the Axe between Uphill and Brean Down; Cottle's Ash has in course of time become Cottle's Oak on the western edge of Frome.

Here indeed, standing at the top of Egford Hill, one's eye naturally follows the rising contours of the main Mendip ridge as far as Cranmore Tower, 925ft above sea level, while immediately below, the Egford Brook cuts down into Vallis Vale where the Mountain Limestone disappears eastwards under newer geological formations. Thus Frome is the eastern gateway to Mendip, and because of its geographical, historical and economic importance it has been considered as an integral part of the Mendip scene over many centuries, unlike Weston-super-Mare at the other end of the range, which was no more than a fishing village until the nineteenth century and falls outside the scope of this study.

Brean Down (like the island of Steep Holm) is geologically part of Mendip, though separated from it by the estuary of the Axe, and at this western end the bounds of Mendip are clear for all to see: a series of isolated hills—Bleadon Hill, Banwell Hill, Sandford Hill, Crook Peak and Wavering Down—rising sharply from the low-lying moors which are often no more than 20ft above sea level.

To the east of the Bristol–Bridgwater road (A38) between Churchill and Cross, the main massif, broken into at this western end by combes and gorges, climbs towards Black Down, the highest point on the range (1,065ft); and thereafter the high plateau stretches away south-east, mostly at about 800–900ft but rising to 1,000ft at North Hill and Pen Hill, with steep escarpments falling on either side into the valleys of the Axe, the Yeo and the Chew. The main roads along the foothills, the A368 and A371, link together an almost continuous string of villages, sited along the spring line, as far as Chewton Mendip to the north and Wells to the south.

The Bristol–Wells road (A39) marks the eastern boundary of the recently defined Area of Outstanding Natural Beauty. Although much natural beauty lies to the east of this arbitrary line, the eastern half of Mendip is very different country and its boundaries are much harder to define. East of Masbury the plateau has narrowed to a single ridge which continues as far as Cranmore Tower before beginning its gradual descent towards Frome. To the north and south lies broken landscape, a series of lower ridges divided by valleys, often deep and wooded, carved out by the fast-flowing streams on which the industrial prosperity of the area depended for so many centuries.

On the north side a peregrination of Mendip will take one from Litton round the edge of Chewton Plain to Farrington Gurney, where Rush Hill very definitely marks the edge of Mendip; then eastwards along the Wellow Brook past Midsomer Norton and Welton into Radstock, where both the Fosse Way and the Somerset & Dorset Railway began their long climbs to the crest of the range at Beacon Hill and Masbury respectively.

The branch line of railway from Radstock to Frome followed the natural boundary between the outlying ridges of Mendip and the rolling hill country to the north and east. For the last mile or so the railway runs along the valley of the River Frome which swings round the older part of the town and picks up another line of railway, the main line from Paddington to the West. This line follows a geological boundary which corresponds closely to the county boundary, finding the natural gap along the clay lands between the Wiltshire downland to the east and the limestone range to the west.

Brewham summit on the railway marks the great divide between the headwaters of the Frome which flows northwards into the Bristol Avon and those of the Brue which flows south-west and eventually reaches the Bristol Channel at Burnham-on-Sea. It is tempting to follow the river down and include Bruton and the villages that cluster round Creech Hill, but this is not Mendip country. The southern boundary of Mendip has sometimes been taken to be the line of the Frome–Shepton Mallet rod (A361), but this climbs far too high up the eastern flank of the main ridge—650ft above sea level near Cranmore—and ignores some splendid Mendip scenery and delightful villages in the deep valleys to the south.

From Brewham one must strike westwards past Upton Noble, down through Batcombe and along the valley of the Alham as far as what was once Evercreech Junction. Here, as at Radstock, one is very much aware that both road and rail were beginning a long and arduous climb to the summit of the main ridge 6 or 7 miles away to the north. (Incidentally the 1817 os map with its heavy hachures makes this southern boundary very much more obvious than the modern One-inch.)

From Evercreech Junction the Somerset & Dorset branch to Glaston-bury cut through the gap between the Mendip massif and the isolated Pennard ridge to the south. Pilton (like Pylle on the other side of the valley) is the harbour-town where the hills end and the moors begin. Working round the outlying hills past North Wootton, one is soon back in Wells under the main southern escarpment of Mendip.

The bounds of Mendip have been variously defined at various times and for various purposes. There was the Royal Forest of Mendip and the Mining Forest, both of which are dealt with in later chapters. (Today there is another Mendip Forest: 500 acres of woodland near Priddy, planted and watched over by the Forestry Commision.) Mendip as an Area of Outstanding Natural Beauty, so designated by the Department of the Environment, is confined to the western half of the main range, from the Bristol–Wells road (A39) as far as Bleadon Hill. The southern boundary of this area follows the foot of the escarpment westward from Wells; on the north side Blagdon Lake and the Chew Valley Lake are included, but the thickly populated valley between Shipham and Winscombe is excluded.

The Local Government Act of 1972 brought great changes to Mendip from the point of view of administration. The urban and rural district councils based on Frome, Shepton Mallet and Wells, the rural districts of Axbridge and Clutton and the urban district of Norton–Radstock were abolished. Since 1 April 1974 the new Mendip District Council has served the needs of almost all the people of Mendip, from Frome as far west as Black Down. There are two main areas of Mendip excluded from its jurisdiction. Norton–Radstock and Farrington Gurney, and the villages lying under the northern escarpment from the Harptrees westward to Burrington, which were formerly in Clutton or Axbridge rural districts, have now been included in the new county of Avon, despite the bitter opposition of many of the inhabitants; the county boundary now runs along th edge of the escarpment between the 500ft and 800ft contour lines, and six Mendip parishes are thus divided between the counties of Somerset and Avon. Avon also includes all the parishes at the western end of the hill from Churchill to the mouth of the Axe, except for Cheddar, Axbridge, Shipham and Compton Bishop, which remain in Somerset (as does Brean Down), served by the new district council of Sedgemoor. Of the Avon parishes, those from Blagdon westwards are served by Woodspring District Council; those from Ubley eastwards by Wansdyke.

Although geologists may wish to make some qualifications, Hardy's description of Mendip as a limestone range stretching from the Bristol Channel into the middle of Somerset is fair enough, for Mendip, as its name, which is cognate with the Welsh *mynydd* (hill), indicates, is hill country above all. The highest points of the range are rounded uplands of Old Red Sandstone, generally heather-covered; these are less typical of Mendip than the steep hillsides and the hilltops near them, where the thin soil covering the Mountain Limestone is the reason for the beautiful soft turf, the habitat of rare flowers, insects and birds; elsewhere there are still large areas of 'gruffy ground', torn and spoiled by centuries of mining activity, but by far the largest proportion of the hills is now enclosed and farmed.

Farming indeed is the chief occupation on Mendip today. The western plateau is thinly populated: Priddy and Charterhouse are the only villages—and Charterhouse is little more than a scattered hamlet; elsewhere the habitations are isolated inns or farmhouses set in the new enclosures which were made late in the eighteenth century. Day & Masters' map of 1782 shows hardly any of the roads or dwellings which we see today—only a network of unfenced tracks crisscrossing the plateau. East of the Bristol–Wells road, however, the plateau narrows to a single ridge on whose slopes the villages begin: Binegar, Oakhill, Cranmore and Leigh, all 600ft or more above sea level.

The uplands are ringed by an almost continuous chain of populous villages, the villages that are grouped around the oval mass of Mendip on the old mining maps. The eastern end of the range has always been more thickly populated, for settlements grew up in the sheltered valleys and water-power was available for industry from the fourteenth century onwards. This industry was primarily rural industry, and Mendip has remained almost completely rural. Frome has a population of 13,400 and the Norton–Radstock conurbation on the north-east fringe now totals 15,229; Wells (8,600) and Shepton Mallet (5,921) are the only other towns. Axbridge, for all its proud past and impression of urban dignity, has a population of only 1,094, while Cheddar, Winscombe, Banwell and Coleford are sprawling overgrown villages rather than urban areas.

Industry is concentrated in the urban areas today. The mills have gone, except for rare survivals like the paper mill near Wookey Hole. The mines have gone, leaving their spoil heaps littered along the north-east slopes. An occasional factory has grown up in a village environment, like the milk factory at Evercreech, or stone and concrete works on abandoned colliery sites.

The one exception is quarrying, about which much has been written and much more will doubtless be written. It is a subject which arouses strong passions on Mendip, and the history of the industry and the implications of its future development are dealt with at some length in later chapters. The main issue can be stated briefly. Certain villages are considered as quarry villages—Stoke St Michael, for instance, or Nunney, or even Cheddar—in the sense that a noticeable proportion of the working population finds employment in the quarries. But over the whole area of Mendip quarrying employs only a small percentage of the working population. Except in a few villages the economic benefits are minimal: the profits go to the large groups who now own most of the quarries, some of them even belonging to international combines. Against this must be offset the ever-increasing loss of amenity: the scarred hillsides, the lunar landscape gouged out and dotted with spoil tips, the hideous noise of giant crushing plant, the dirt and pollution, and the traffic generated on the highways and byways.

There are alarming juxtapositions: the Nature Reserve in Asham Woods consists of 33 acres hemmed in by quarries that are eating away one of the most beautiful and least-known areas of eastern Mendip. Above Cheddar, Batts Combe quarry is removing the southern escarpment of the hill within half a mile or so of the world-famous Gorge, Mendip's chief scenic splendour. Quite apart from further development, the quarrying concessions so rashly granted in the postwar period seem doomed to destroy, or at least do irreparable harm for many years to come, to the landscape which we know and enjoy today.

Year by year more people come to explore Mendip and to enjoy themselves there, to relax and to recuperate from

> this strange disease of modern life
> with its sick hurry, its divided aims,
> its heads o'ertax'd, its palsied hearts.

Burrington Combe and Cheddar Gorge, Wookey Hole and the incomparable cathedral city of Wells have for centuries evoked feelings of awe and delight from tourists who have visited them; since 1956 the beautiful setting of the Chew Valley Lake has drawn Bristolians in their thousands to the foothills of Mendip and doubtless tempted many to explore farther.

There are no lions on Mendip and no stately homes open to the public, but there are many beautiful villages, some well known, others hidden away unvisited in remote valleys at a distance from the main roads, full of pleasant buildings in a variety of styles and in a variety of local materials, often centring upon a notable church or manor house. Above all, it is the sense of openness and freedom of the hills that is Mendip's chief attraction—the long straight roads with their wide grass verges, the subtle easy curves of the hills, the breath-taking views from either side of the ridge—whether the visitor is merely driving about, or relaxing at some favourite picnic spot like Priddy Pool or Deerleap or Beacon Hill; or more actively committed to walking, riding, camping, orienteering; or in more specialised forms of study or recreation: the caver, the naturalist, the industrial archaeologist—each finds his own fascination on Mendip.

The day tourists come mostly from Bristol or Bath or Weston. So, now, do many of the newer residents. Many of the villages along the northern escarpment from Harptree to Churchill and beyond are within the Bristol commuter zone. The western end of the hill is under pressure from the overspill from Weston. Many of the villages under the southern slopes from Wells to Cheddar are filling up with new residential development; less so at the eastern end of the hill, except for the Holcombe-Highbury area.

Not without trepidation, one watches the impact of the motorway upon Mendip. Inevitably much of the through traffic that found its way from the Midlands to the South West through Frome and Shepton Mallet, or down the Fosse Way from Bath, or down the A38 from Bristol to Bridgwater and beyond, now uses the motorway. On the other hand, Mendip is instantly made accessible to a very much greater number of people who are likely to find there all sorts of satisfaction for their leisure hours; many too may be attracted to settle in a largely unspoiled stretch of countryside from which they can travel to work from a distance that would have been inconceivable a few decades ago.

Mendip is thus a danger area under considerable pressure from conflicting interests of development and conservation: development, because of the continual demand for new housing to meet the population explosion, and because of the seemingly insatiable demand for aggregates with which to build the motorway system which in turn brings more and more people through the countryside; conservation, because, unless we are determined and able to conserve the beauty of the hills with all their natural attractions, the opportunities for recreation and refreshment which they offer, and something of the quality of the traditional and rural way of life that has grown up there over long centuries, then our own life and the lives of our children will indeed be the poorer.

This book is deliberately called *A New Study*. It sets out to present an overall picture of Mendip as it is today, seen in its historical framework.

It is a survey and a summary and an interpretation of our existing knowledge about the whole of Mendip; recognising that for several thousand years life has ebbed and flowed eastwards and westwards along the hill, from Brean Down to Frome, from 'Kotellisasch to the rock which is called Le Blacston in the Western Sea'.

Because of the complexity of the subject, it is clearly not possible for one writer to deal with all aspects of Mendip. This study therefore takes the form of a symposium to which a number of experts in their own fields have contributed. But if the different chapters are written *by* specialists, they are not written *for* specialists. This is a general study for the general reader, but chapter by chapter the bibliographies will guide the general reader who may wish to inquire more deeply into any particular aspect of the subject. The bibliographies, indeed, are an essential part of the book, providing a basis for further study, thought or discussion.

The book is not primarily concerned with the controversies of today or the political issues involved. To be at all worthwhile, a study such as this must aim to be long-term rather than up-to-the-minute. Mendip, as we have already seen, is today an area of pressure. Each of the authors must make his own response to the pressures upon the area about which he is writing, but all have attempted to paint a broad picture based on accurate knowledge and understanding of Mendip in terms of the past and of the present—and, indeed, of the future.

Notes to this chapter are on pages 263-4

2

The Physical Environment and Natural History of Mendip

D. I. Smith and A. J. Willis

Part I Geology and Climate
D. I. Smith

The landscape of Britain is composed of numerous small regions, each of which has a certain measure of distinctiveness. A detailed explanation of the differences between regions is complex, and involves the interplay between the history of man's activities in the area and the physical features of the environment. There is little doubt, however, that the salient feature of the physical environment is the geology. The character of Dartmoor is determined by the underlying granites, the scarps of the Midlands faithfully reflect the variations from limestone to clay, and the green waterless swards of Salisbury Plain the extensive outcrop of the Chalk. Mendip likewise owes its character to the geology of the region in which the massive limestones are dominant.

Geology

Geology, like most sciences, can be subdivided into many branches. For our purposes the important aspects are the lithology (the type of rock) and the distribution of the rocks in the landscape. A detailed account of all aspects of the geology, and an extensive bibliography, is given by Green and Welch (1965) in the memoir which describes the geology of the map of the area around Wells and Cheddar. Geology maps normally portray the stratigraphical age of the rocks and this does not necessarily correspond to the lithology. The oldest rocks represented on Mendip are of Silurian age and the youngest Jurassic. The idealised sequence of rocks for Mendip is shown in the stratigraphical column in Fig 2. This diagram also gives the approximate age and thickness of the various stratigraphical units and presents a guide to the dominant elements of the lithology associated with each unit.

GEOLOGICAL PERIOD		AGE	STRATIGRAPHIC SUB-DIVISIONS		LITHOLOGY	THICKNESS
MESOZOIC	JURASSIC	180	Lias and Inferior Oolite		Mainly limestones, often oolitic and shelly	
	TRIAS (New Red Sandstone)	230	Keuper Marl Dolomitic Conglomerate		Red silty sandstone	1500 m 4920 ft
PALEOZOIC	CARBONIFEROUS		Coal Measures		Mainly shales	
			Millstone Grit		Quartzitic sandstones	
		Approximate time in millions of years	Carboniferous Limestone		Massive limestones, mainly composed of calcite. Some local dolomitization and thin chert and shale bands	1000 m 3280 ft
		350	Lower Limestone Shale		Shales with limestone bands	
	DEVONIAN (Old Red Sandstone)				Quartzitic sandstones and conglomerates with mudstones	500 m 1639 ft
	SILURIAN	400			Volcanic material, lavas and tuffs with minor mudstone bands	0

Fig 2   Stratigraphical column for the Mendip Hills, showing the thickness and age of the major lithological units; this figure is *not* applicable to the Coal Measure strata of the Radstock Coal Basin.

Before the geology map, illustrated in Fig 3, can be fully understood, it is necessary to have a broad understanding of the tectonic deformation (the folding and faulting) that has affected the rocks. The oldest strata (of Paleozoic age) on Mendip were deposited in a layered sequence over long periods of time during which there was little significant tectonic activity. However, in the later part of the Paleozoic the area underwent a major phase of folding and faulting. This is referred to in a general sense as the Armorican (or Hercynian) orogeny. This resulted in a series of large folds, the upfolds of which are termed anticlines and the troughs synclines. The original near-horizontal beds of the individual rock units show this deformation, and from their tilted aspect it is possible to reconstruct the form of the folding on Mendip. There are four major anticlines which in the modern landscape form the summits of Black Down, North Hill, Pen Hill and Beacon Hill. The anticlinal crests run in an approximately west to east direction, and the nature of the folds, and their relationship to the modern land surface, can be seen in the cross sections shown in Fig 4. In detail the anticlines show a degree of asymmetry which is compatible with the major forces causing the folding acting from the south. In extreme cases the strata on the northern limbs of the anticlines are near-vertical or in some cases overturned (see for example, the northern limbs of the sections through the

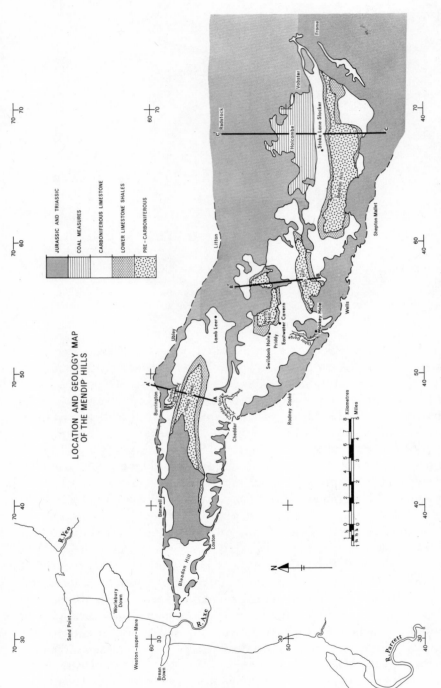

Fig 3   Geological map of the Mendip Hills; the lines correspond to the cross-sections shown in Fig 4.

North Hill anticline, Fig 4). When the deformation exceeds the capacity of the rocks to fold, the strata fracture and faults occur. The Emborough Thrust Fault on Fig 4 illustrates such a case. The nature of the faulting to the south of Norton–Radstock is undoubtedly the most complex in the region and was described by geological surveyors in the 1860s as 'an amount of confusion and distortion which literally baffles description'.

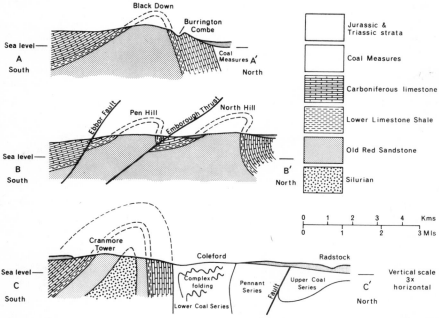

Fig 4   Geological cross-sections showing the structure of the Mendip anticlines; the lines of the cross-sections are marked on Fig 3.

The later rocks of Triassic and Jurassic age were deposited upon an eroded surface cut across these folds. As tectonic activity since the Armorican orogeny has been minimal, these later rocks are little affected by folding and faulting.

The lithology of the rocks that comprise the major stratigraphical units is presented in Fig 2. The oldest rocks, of Silurian age, are dominantly composed of volcanic material which consists not only of the actual lava but also includes ash and small rock fragments, which are described by Van de Kamp (1969). There is evidence that the deposits were laid down in a marine environment and some interbedded mudstones occur. Silurian strata outcrop only on the Beacon Hill anticline and are well exposed in the roadstone quarries at Moons Hill. The Devonian rocks of Mendip, as in much of Britain, are all essentially of a sandstone lithology and are not the product of marine sedimentation. In fact, geologists often refer to this type of Devonian as the Old Red Sandstone, and to its intimates it is simply known as the 'Old Red'. The grain size of the rock varies, but it consists essentially of the mineral quartz (SiO_2), and where fractures occur along bedding planes to give rough flagstones, the glint of small flakes of mica can be seen. The Old Red Sandstone encircles each of the Mendip anticlinal cores. However, if one wishes to see the rock in outcrop, one is forced to search for sections in the stream beds; the exposures in the West and East Twin Brooks adjacent to Burrington Combe, for example, are particularly fine.

The main stratigraphical unit on Mendip is the Carboniferous Limestone which forms the lower part of the Carboniferous system. However, as the 'Carboniferous Limestone' (with a capital 'L') is a time-based stratigraphical division, there is no reason why the lithology of rocks of this age should be limestone. For lithological purposes the Carboniferous Limestone can be divided into two major units. The older of these is the Lower Limestone Shale. This consists of some 120m (400ft) of dark shales, with interbedded bands of limestone. The juxtaposition of these dominantly shaley rocks with the older sandstones and the overlying limestones, as shown in the cross-sections in Fig 3, is basic to an appreciation of the distribution of soils, vegetation and cave development of much of the higher parts of Mendip. The overlying limestones that complete the Carboniferous Limestone succession have a total thickness in excess of 600m (2,000ft). The limestones show many minor variations, but throughout the succession they are distinguished by their purity. The rock is composed almost entirely of the mineral calcite ($CaCO_3$), though locally the rock is modified so that it consists of the double carbonate of calcium and magnesium, the mineral form of which is dolomite, $CaMg(CO_3)$. The Mendip limestones are composed of well over 90 per cent carbonate, and in some localities, as at Batts Combe quarry, this figure rises close to 99 per cent (Plate 1). The second important feature of these limestones is that they are 'massive' rocks. The pattern of the bedding planes and joints causes the rock to be divided naturally into large blocks. The massive character can be seen in any of the numerous limestone quarries and it is clear in the natural exposures of Cheddar and the other gorges. Locally bands of chert occur within the main limestone mass. Chert is composed of silica (SiO_2) and is comparable in mineralogy and origin to the flints that occur within the Chalk. On the plateau surface of Mendip the strata are buried beneath a thick soil cover, but even here the abundant dry stone walling bears testimony to the underlying bedrock.

The Millstone Grit, of Upper Carboniferous age, on Mendip has little relation to its equivalent in South Wales or the Pennines, where it is an important landscape element. Rocks thought to be of this age are reduced to a thickness of some 50m (165ft) and are only found in eastern Mendip where their landscape significance is minimal. The lithology is composed of resistant quartzitic sandstones.

Within the region, rocks of Coal Measure age are only preserved in the broad synclinal basin of the Radstock area. The thickness in the basin exceeds 2,000m (7,500ft) and this is greater than the total thickness of the rock of the main Mendip uplands shown in Fig 2. It is likely that the Coal Measure strata were originally deposited over the whole of the Mendip area, but after the Armorican folding the upfolded strata were removed by subsequent erosion. The proportion of the Coal Measure rocks that are actually composed of seams of coal is probably less than 1 per cent of the total, and many of these seams are too thin to be of economic importance. The Coal Measure sequence can be divided into three major units: the Lower Coal Series, the Pennant Series and the Upper Coal Series. The Pennant Series is almost devoid of coal seams and consists of a coarse grey sandstone. It must be stressed that most of the Coal Measure strata are 'concealed' beneath a cover of younger rocks (see Fig 4). The early coal workings, however, were associated with the exposed coal seams of the Lower Coal Series that outcrop at the surface between Gurney Slade and Mells. These were certainly worked in the fourteenth century by means of bell pits and may well have been exploited in Roman or even pre-Roman times. As mining technology and an understanding of sub-surface geology improved, working was from shafts which tapped deeper and deeper seams. The mines then tended to spread to the north of our region to work the coal that lay beneath the overlying Triassic and Jurassic strata in the neighbourhood of Norton–Radstock. The working of coal in the Somerset coalfield has had to contend throughout its history with two major adverse factors. Firstly, the seams were among the thinnest worked anywhere in Britain, and secondly, the complexity of the geological structure is also unmatched in other coalfields in the British Isles (see Chapter 7, pp 152).

The Triassic rocks of Britain are comparable to those of the Devonian in that the rocks were laid down under terrestrial conditions after the tectonic upheaval of the Armorican orogeny. The main stratigraphical unit on Mendip is the Dolomitic Conglomerate. This is a classical geological misnomer as the rock is rarely dolomitic and is not strictly a conglomerate! The deposits are formed of angular fragments deposited as screes on, or at the foot of, steep slopes that formed the landscape of Triassic times, or along former valley lines. The fragments are therefore composed of Carboniferous or Devonian material, usually

loosely cemented with finer particles of sand with a diagnostic red stain-
ing. Around the periphery of Mendip, and in the lowlands of
Winscombe Vale, there are deposits of a uniformly red silty clay known
as the Keuper Marl.

The Jurassic strata which form the impressive escarpment of the
southern Cotswolds between Bath and Cheltenham are very much
reduced where they cross eastern Mendip. Here the Jurassic forms only
a thin cover over the Paleozoic rocks, as can be seen where the river
valleys and quarries have locally cut through to expose the older rocks
beneath. The junction of the Jurassic and the Carboniferous Limestone
is well displayed in the valleys and quarries at Vallis Vale. The lithology
of the Jurassic is varied, but the most important elements are the Liassic
limestones and the oolitic limestones of the Inferior Oolite. These
limestones are chemically and mineralogically similar to the limestones
already described, but are totally dissimilar in colour, and do not show
the massive nature of their Paleozoic equivalents. Locally the Jurassic
limestones have been quarried for building stone or lime burning, and
two of these are worthy of individual mention, namely the White Lias
and Doulting Stone. The White Lias forms the lowest unit of the Jurassic
sequence and comprises a white, or pale grey, fine-grained limestone
which has, in the past, been much quarried for lime or building stone, in
the area to the south of Radstock. Doulting Stone, however, has a very
much wider reputation, and locally was used in the construction of
Glastonbury Abbey and Wells Cathedral (see Chapter 7, p 156). This
limestone is of Inferior Oolite age and is largely composed of shell
fragments and ooliths set in a calcite cement.

Minerals and Mineralisation

It can be argued that the geology of a region is a major determinant of
subsequent human development, and such a statement is undoubtedly
true for the relationship of mineralisation to mining. For Mendip the
mining of lead and zinc ores has played an important role in the
development of the landscape. It is perhaps surprising that geologically
little is known of the details of the process of mineralisation. The simplest
model is to assume that after the rocks were deposited and consolidated,
hot solutions originating at depth in the earth's crust migrated upward
through the overlying strata. These solutions were enriched with particular elements and differing minerals were formed as the solutions
cooled to their crystallisation temperature. On Mendip the minerals
tend to occur in veins, which are termed lodes if the minerals are of
economic significance. Thin veins formed of calcite, often less than a

centimetre in width, can be observed in rock exposures over most of Mendip. These are clearly of no economic importance, but can be regarded as representing, on a small scale, the pattern that the much thicker lodes would have. The early miners would search out these lodes at the surface and then follow them to whatever depth their technology would permit. The long 'grooves' that can still be seen on parts of Mendip, for example at Shipham, are due to surface exploitation of these mineral lodes.

The distribution of the mineralised areas on Mendip is discussed in detail by Green (1958), and the history of mining by Gough (1967), and it is apparent that the lodes were localised. The worked areas show a strong tendency to be associated with certain lithologies. The most important of these is the Dolomitic Conglomerate and the other is the main outcrop of the limestone. There is little economic mineralisation of the other lithological units. It would appear that the ascending solutions passed up through the whole stratigraphical sequence, but major mineralisation occurs only in the lithologies mentioned above. The mineralisation is most marked where major faults occur, along the crests of the major anticlines, and the local pattern, especially in the limestone, is determined by the joints. There is dispute about the age of the ore emplacement. It is possible that the major phase of primary mineralisation was associated with a late phase of the Armorican orogeny; this would correspond to the postulated situation for many of the ores in Cornwall. In this case the lodes that occur within the Triassic deposits (the Dolomitic Conglomerate), and the limited mineralisation in the Jurassic rocks, would represent a secondary movement at a much later date. An alternative hypothesis would suggest that the mineralisation is Tertiary in date; this would then correspond to similar ores in Derbyshire.

The main ores worked on Mendip were for lead or zinc. The main mineral from which the lead was extracted was galena (PbS); this would be associated with primary sulphide mineralisation. Other lead minerals occur, of which cerussite ($PbCO_3$) is the most common and may represent secondary mineralisation and weathering. There are two major zinc ores, calamine ($ZnCO_3$) which was extensively worked in the eighteenth century, and zinc blende (ZnS) which was mined at a later date, as earlier technology could not separate out the zinc metal from the ore. A range of other rarer lead and zinc minerals are known, two of which are worthy of mention. The first is pyromorphite which is also known as the 'green lead ore' and it is likely that occurrences of this mineral played a part in the naming of the hamlet of Green Ore. Secondly, an extremely rare mineral, an oxy-chloride of lead, was first described from finds on the Mendip Hills and is known as Mendipite.

There is a regional variation in the distribution of the main masses of lead and zinc ore. The Shipham area was particularly associated with zinc mineralisation, while Priddy and Charterhouse were predominantly worked for lead.

Other minerals occur on Mendip although in very reduced quantities compared to the lead and zinc. Red ochre, which is a form of the iron mineral hematite (Fe_2O_3), is found at a number of localities, as is the manganese mineral pyrolusite (MnO_2). These minerals are found together at an old small working near Higher Pitts Farm at the head of Ebbor Gorge. Ores of the mineral silver are very rare indeed. The metalliferous ores are usually associated with masses of calcite and sometimes with barytes $(BaSO_4)$; these uneconomic minerals are often referred to as gangue minerals. (See Chapter 7, pp 149-50).

This account of the mineralogy should not be interpreted as indicating that Mendip is a good site for the collection of ore specimens. Indeed it is a poor area, mainly because the miners cleared out virtually all the surface ores, and the waste products of early smelting were re-worked at later dates. For example, despite the probable association of Green Ore with pyromorphite, even experienced mineralogists have failed to locate specimens of this mineral anywhere on Mendip.

It is most unlikely that any serious proposal to recommence mining on Mendip will ever be ventured, but if it were, the best prospects are in the Dolomitic Conglomerate and the Carboniferous limestones that lie concealed beneath a thin cover of Jurassic rocks in eastern Mendip.

LANDSCAPE EVOLUTION

Geology is concerned with an account of the age, distribution and lithology of the rocks. The development of the present physical landscape is the major aim of geomorphology. There are many physical processes involved in the evolution of landscape, and their relative significance is determined by the lithology and by the climate experienced at various phases in the past. The understanding of the geomorphological evolution of a region generally increases in difficulty as we probe farther back into time.

Mendip was undoubtedly buried beneath a thick cover of Upper Jurassic, and particularly Cretaceous, strata and it is possible that the sedimentation would have continued into the early Tertiary. All these strata have now been removed by a variety of processes. It is difficult to make any detailed comment on the exact nature of the erosive activity for these early phases of landscape evolution. The earliest phase for which comment is possible is represented by the Plateau Surface which forms the salient feature of the higher portion of Mendip. This surface is dominant at an altitude of 250–260m (820–860ft). The Plateau Surface clearly truncates the folded Carboniferous strata and therefore is not directly controlled by the geology. The origin of this surface has given rise to very considerable debate (see Ford and Stanton, 1968, and Donovan, 1969). Fundamentally the argument can be divided into two schools of thought. One group of workers consider that the Plateau Surface is essentially a geologically determined feature. In short, the surface represents an exhumed surface of erosion. The surfaces would, in this case, have evolved at some distant geological period, have been by later strata, but re-exposed by erosion at a more recent date. The original date of the surface could then be considered as Triassic, Jurassic or Mid-Cretaceous, depending on which authority is followed. The alternative school argues that the Plateau Surface was eroded in much more recent times and has never been covered by later strata. The date favoured for formation in this case is late Tertiary, either the end of the Miocene or the beginning of the Pliocene.

These early phases of the genesis of landscape are, by their very nature, speculative. As we move to more recent events, the precision increases, although there is still considerable room for debate.

The Pleistocene period, which approximately covers the last 1–2 million years, was a time of marked climatic variation. At various times ice sheets mantled much of Britain, and these cold phases were interspersed with longer periods when the climate was less severe than that encountered at tt the present day. Not surprisingly these climatic variations have left their mark on the landscape. Recent investigations, notably by Hawkins and Kellaway (1971), have produced evidence that glacial ice undoubtedly reached the Bristol region. That glacial ice overtopped Mendip is unlikely. What is without dispute is that the climate of Mendip at various times during the Pleistocene would have been severe, comparable indeed to that of arctic Canada today; such conditions are referred to as periglacial. It was likely that the vegetation cover on Mendip at this time was sparse, that rocks were fractured by frost action, and that the sub-surface water was perennially frozen to give a condition that is referred to as permafrost. The landscape modification due to these periglacial processes is still manifest in the local physiography. The most recent effects of Pleistocene activity are minor oscillations of sea level which have affected the sedimentation of the lowlands overlooked by Mendip. An account of such changes for the Somerset Levels is given by Godwin (1955).

The Limestone Scenery and Its Development

The geology and geomorphological evolution of Mendip may be complex, but the individuality of the scenery is a reflection of the presence of the massive crystalline limestones. Limestones of this type, wherever they occur in the world, give rise to a landscape pattern that is particularly impressive and differs from the morphology developed on juxtaposed lithologies. The most striking feature is the absence of surface streams, although 'dry valleys' are prolific. Drainage is subterranean and often there is a network of caves and underground stream systems. A diagrammatic representation is given in Fig 5. An extensive review and bibliography of the geology, landforms and caves of the Mendip Hills is available (Smith and Drew, 1975).

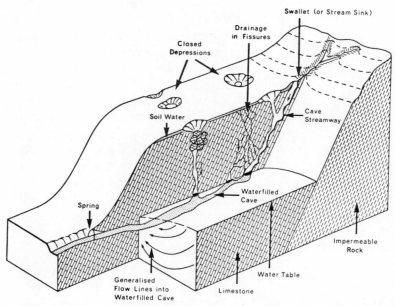

Fig 5   Subterranean drainage of the Carboniferous Limestone and its relationship to the surface landforms.

Limestone scenery is distinctive because of the relative ease with which the constituent minerals are weathered by chemical action. The purity of the limestones has already been mentioned, and it is possible to describe the erosion that occurs under natural field conditions in terms of a simple chemical reaction. The basic equation is as follows:

$$CaCO_3 + H_2O + CO_2 = Ca(HCO_3)_2$$
Limestone + water + carbon dioxide = Calcium bicarbonate
(which goes off in solution)

In words, the solution is due to the action of water enriched with the gas, carbon dioxide, reacting with the limestone (which is dominantly composed of the mineral calcite) to give the soluble product, calcium bicarbonate. Of limestone there is ample, and therefore the controlling factors are the quantity of water that passes through the limestone and the degree to which this is enriched with the gas, carbon dioxide. If we imagine a simple laboratory beaker containing water and limestone rock chippings in contact with the normal atmosphere, the maximum amount of calcium that can be dissolved at a temperature of 10°C (the mean annual temperature for Mendip) is the equivalent of some 70 milligrammes of $CaCO_3$ per litre. However, if water samples are analysed from the caves and springs of Mendip, the calcium figure is often close to 240 milligrammes per litre. The reason for this apparent contradiction is that the carbon dioxide concentration that occurs under field conditions is greater than that found in the normal atmosphere. The normal value is close to 0.03 per cent while the concentration to give the observed field values is approximately 1 per cent, and this is the carbon dioxide value that is commonly found deep in the soils overlying the main limestones of the Mendip Plateau. Thus we have a situation where the rain falls on the soil surface and percolates into the soil with its enhanced carbon dioxide values due to plant and bacteriological activity. The water then passes through the soil to dissolve the underlying limestone bedrock. Reliable estimates of the rate of solutional weathering suggest that the annual loss of limestone is equivalent to some forty cubic metres of limestone from every square kilometre. It is this long continued solution of the bedrock that is fundamentally responsible for the particular character of limestone landforms.

The origin of the dry valleys and gorges on Mendip has excited scientific speculation and investigation for well over a century. Such valleys only become active surface watercourses after exceptionally heavy rainfall. Such occurrences are rare and often associated with considerable flood damage. A recent example was the 'Great Flood' of July 1968, described by Hanwell and Newson (1970). Earlier texts consider that the gorges at Cheddar, Burrington and Ebbor were not formed by *surface* water at all, but are the result of the collapse of underground caverns formed as the result of *underground* water action. However, most recent writers reject this cavern collapse hypothesis on a variety of grounds. The first of these is that caverns of the size necessary to promote a collapse to give a valley of the magnitude of Cheddar Gorge are not found in any known cave system on Mendip today. Secondly the form and pattern of the gorges is similar to that of surface streams, but dissimilar to that associated with contemporary cave streams.

Others seek to find a mechanism to explain how the valleys could have supported surface stream flow in the past, when today all the drainage on the limestone is underground. The simplest reason is that under colder climatic conditions the ground was frozen to considerable depths (this would necessitate a mean annual temperature somewhat below 0°C), and that the runoff was compelled to flow on the surface. Studies of the world's cold regions suggest that this does occur in limestone areas when a permafrost condition exists. Attractive as this explanation may be, especially as recent research suggests that southern Britain would have 'enjoyed' a permafrost climate in the colder phases of the Pleistocene, it is *not* an all-embracing answer to the problem. Limestones far away from the Pleistocene permafrost, for example in the tropics, have dry valley systems exactly comparable to those of Mendip. The best explanation would be to suggest that the total dry valley network is of some antiquity and results from an earlier phase of landscape evolution *before* the chemical erosion had opened up the limestone by solutional processes acting along the joints and bedding planes. There is clear evidence, however, that the dry valleys were re-activated during the permafrost phases of the Pleistocene (see Findlay, 1965, p 15), and the gorges may owe their present morphology to this particular time, although the valley pattern was a pre-existing feature.

The other recurring feature of limestone terrain is the occurrence of closed depressions (see Fig 5). These are relatively common on Mendip and while most are natural, some are due to the collapse of old mine shafts. Ford and Stanton (1968) discuss these features in some detail for central Mendip, and recognise a larger form (which they term a closed basin) which can exceed a square kilometre in area. There is no doubt that the closed depressions are due to collapse, but rarely are the depressions due to roof fall in a major cave. They represent adjustment of surface rocks where concentrated limestone solution has led to the settling of loose limestone blocks. The closed depressions are still actively forming and are a minor irritant to farmers, but a source of joy to most cavers, who hope to gain access to new cave systems by digging out such features.

The subterranean drainage follows flow paths formed by the solutional activity of the groundwater. A simple case is seen when a surface stream flowing over the Lower Limestone Shales disappears into a cave entrance on reaching the limestone (see Fig 5). Such features are known locally as 'swallets' or 'slockers'. These Mendip terms are now widely used in the limestone literature, often far away from Mendip. Stoke Lane Slocker is a particularly clear example of this kind. Over the past decade a detailed programme of water tracing has been pursued to establish the pattern of the underground flow from swallet to spring. Maps of the results can be seen in Smith and Drew (1975, p 194), and Atkinson *et al* (1973). The flow-through time from the swallets to the springs is generally very fast, several kilometres per day. It is without dispute that the water that emerges at the springs at, say, Cheddar or Wookey Hole is not the naturally filtered, pure water that local opinion would often have us believe. There is little time for any natural filtration, and the dumping of wastes in slockers or closed depressions on Mendip is a certain way to ensure polluttion of the water resources (see Atkinson, 1971).

Despite the detailed observations for the tracing of the underground streams of Mendip, which is probably without parallel in any other limestone region, it must be added that less than 5 per cent of the water appearing at the springs passes through the swallets. The remainder percolates directly through the soil into the groundwater circulation. Little is known of the nature and speed of flow of this contribution to the groundwater. Such information is of direct significance, for as the limestone quarrying industry expands, it is likely to conflict with movement of underground water which is an important resource for Avon and Somerset. However, discussion and research into this special problem of limestone hydrology is under way (Stanton, 1971; Atkinson *et al*, 1973). The water movement under Mendip, with its caves and fast flow-through times, is conditioned by the massive nature of the rocks, so that much of the water flows along selected solutionally enlarged joints and bedding planes. Thus limestone solution processes and the development of the underground flow net are the keys to the understanding of the limestone scenery of Mendip.

CLIMATE

Within a region the size of the Mendips macro-climate variations are small, although the local climate, or micro-climate, affects all forms of life and will show great variety. There is a general paucity of long-term climatic observations for the Mendip Plateau, and for most of the climatic factors it is necessary to extrapolate from the records obtained by climate stations peripheral to the main Mendip mass. The most appropriate figures are available from Weston-super-Mare where the meteorological station is located at only 9m (30ft) OD and is therefore affected by its proximity to the sea. The mean monthly temperature figures are given in Table 1. The corresponding figures for the Mendip Plateau can be estimated by assuming that the temperature decreases by some 1°C for every 150m of ascent (5.4°F for every 1,000ft). Thus the

Table 1

**AVERAGE MONTHLY TEMPERATURE AND AVERAGE DAILY SUNSHINE
HOURS FOR WESTON-SUPER-MARE**

	Jan	Feb	March	April	May	June	July	Aug	Sept	Oct	Nov	Dec
Average monthly temp in °C	5.2	5.4	6.9	9.5	11.9	15.2	17.0	16.8	15.0	11.6	7.9	5.9
Average daily sunshine hours	1.68	2.47	3.93	5.32	6.19	7.06	6.18	5.99	4.74	3.33	2.06	1.53

The temperature data is based on records for the periods 1921-26 and 1938-50 and the sunshine figures for 1921-50.

(*Source:* Findlay, 1965)

1 The town of Cheddar spread out below the southern escarpment of Mendip. Strawberry fields fringe the lower slopes below Batts Combe Quarry and the Gorge, beyond which the plateau rises to the Black Down ridge.

2 The cliffs of the lower section of Cheddar Gorge

3 Burrington Combe and the northern slope of Black Down, cut by the valleys of the East and West Twin Brooks. On Burrington Ham *(left)* are the earthworks of a hill-fort. On the right are firebreaks protecting the afforested area of Rowberrow Warren

4 The rare grass *Koeleria vallesiana* growing in a rocky limestone site on Purn Hill, Bleadon; also present *(top left)* but not flowering is the white rockrose (*Helianthemum apenninum*) and just below this a scrap of honewort (*Trinia glauca*)

5 The Cheddar pink (*Dianthus gratianopolitanus*) growing in a rock pocket at Cheddar Gorge

monthly temperatures in Table 1 should be *decreased* by about 1.5°C to obtain long-term averages for the higher parts of Mendip. The mean annual temperature for Weston-super-Mare is 10.7°C. The temperature of the major caves on Mendip and for the groundwater is fractionally less than 10°C. Underground temperatures of this type show no detectable seasonal variation and correspond to the long-term mean annual temperature. Thus the assumptions about the extrapolation of temperature with altitude appear to be valid.

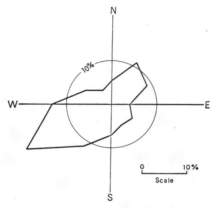

Fig 6   Wind rose showing the frequency of the winds experienced on Mendip.

The sunshine hours are also given in Table 1. It is likely that the sunshine hours received for the higher parts of Mendip are also slightly less than for the immediate coastal area. The greatest lack in the available information is for wind speed and direction. The wind rose, showing the frequency of winds from differing directions, given in Fig 6, is drawn from values presented in *Quarrying in Somerset* (Somerset County Council, 1971, p 36). The information on which this data is based is from various discontinuous records from Avonmouth, Filton, Boscombe Down and Weston-super-Mare. From the data presented from Hannell (1955, p 49) it would appear that winds from the south-west have a consistently higher velocity than those from other directions.

Of the various climatic elements the most significant variable is that of rainfall, together with the linked concept of the availability of water as runoff. The rainfall recording stations for Mendip and the immediate area are, as for most of Britain, very much more numerous than those which have a full climate record including temperature and wind. Maps showing the mean annual precipitation for Mendip based on long-term figures are available (for example see Hannell, 1955, p 63). In general terms the higher areas of Mendip receive some 1,200mm (47in) of precipitation per year and the remainder of Mendip in excess of 900mm

(35in). The corresponding value for the Somerset Levels to the south is some 750mm (30in) and approximately 800mm (32in) for the valley of the Bristol Avon between Bristol and Bath. The mean monthly figures show a tendency for spring and early summer to be slightly drier than the remainder of the year. However, when the long-term records are studied, it is apparent that in any one particular year it is possible for any month to prove the wettest, and that the difference between months is not great. The incidence of summer thunderstorms is relatively high, and a particularly severe storm of this type occurred on 10 July 1968. The prevailing meteorological conditions, a detailed study of the likely recurrence of such storms and an account of the flood damage of the 'Great Flood' of 1968, are given by Hanwell and Newson (1970). The rainfall maximum of some 170mm (7in) occurred a little to the north of Mendip, and the value for Black Down was in excess of 130mm (5in) with a peak intensity of 70mm (2.7in) per hour.

Virtually all the precipitation in an average year falls as rain and, although no detailed figures exist for Mendip, snow is only likely to be found lying on about ten to fifteen mornings a year.

In recent years the attention given to rainfall has been widened to include observations of the overall water budget. The aim is to obtain good estimates for the proportion of the precipitation that is available as runoff. Much of the precipitation is either lost by direct evaporation or is transpired by the plants; the combined quantity is referred to as evapotranspiration. The annual runoff is therefore the annual precipitation less the annual evapotranspiration value. The evapotranspiration will vary markedly throughout the year (from as low as 1–2mm in January to possible maxima of 100mm in June or July) in relation to temperature and to the seasonal water need of the plants, both natural and cropped. Evapotranspiration is a notoriously difficult quantity to obtain by direct measurement, and in the last few years the Bristol Avon River Authority (since 1974 a part of the Wessex Regional Water Authority) has established two sophisticated, automated climate stations to measure the relevant meteorological factors to allow an accurate determination of evapotranspiration. One of the stations is located at Downhead, to the east of Beacon Hill, and the other near Chew Stoke, just to the north of Mendip. These stations form part of a national network and were among the first of their kind to be installed in Britain. In future years the climate record, not only for evapotranspiration, but also for temperature and wind speed, will be very much improved.

At present, however, evapotranspiration estimates for Mendip are based on short-term records. In general terms the annual elevapotranspiration value for the Mendip Plateau is likely to lie within the range of 375–500mm (15–20in) per year. Thus for an average year some 60 per cent of the annual precipitation is available as runoff, although naturally this concept of 'runoff' is complicated for the limestone uplands of Mendip, as the water drains from those areas as groundwater to reappear at the springs at the periphery of the hills. A detailed study by Atkinson for the 'Water Year' of October 1960 to the end of September 1970 for central Mendip gave precipitation values of 1,065mm (4win) and an evapotranspiration loss of 48emm T.9in5g 1969–70 was, however, a dry year with precipitation some x2 per cent less than average and the evaporation 10 per cent greater. Data from Drew (see Smith and Drew, 1975, p 178) for the year 1969 for eastern Mendip gave an annual precipitation of 1,035mm (41in) and a runoff of 578mm (23in); an effective runoff of some 55 per cent.

For agricultural purposes the balance of precipitation and evapotranspiration can be used, on a monthly basis, to highlight periods of the year when there is a strong possibility of a soil moisture deficit. Such a lack of soil water can cause adverse effects on plant growth and crop yield, but under average conditions on Mendip is only likely to occur in June and July (Findlay, 1965, p 23).

In presenting these broad climatic values for Mendip it must be stressed that, for the naturalist and the specialist agriculturalist, microclimates can be of overwhelming significance. The mean monthly temperatures are no real guide to the strawberry grower with his protected, south-facing fields on steep slopes which obtain nearmaximum values of incoming radiation. Similarly, the large closed depressions that occur on the limestones of the Mendip Plateau act as natural frost hollows. The local channelling of the wind by the deep gorges and other topographic features greatly modifies the wind rose shown in Fig 6. The macro-climate based upon long-term averages only sets the broad regional scene.

Soils

Published soil maps, at a scale of one inch to the mile, and their accompanying memoirs, are only available for a relatively small area of England and Wales. The Mendip Hills, however, are covered by two such maps (nos 279 and 280) and by a consolidated soil memoir (Findlay, 1965). The maps and memoir not only describe the soils in detail, but present a fund of information on land use, farming practice and the effects of agriculture on the soils over many centuries.

A broad account of the Mendip soils can be given on the basis of the distribution of the major lithological divisions together with the salient features of the climate and geomorphological history. The two major lithologies are sandstone, of Devonian age, and the limestones of the Carboniferous. The sandstones form the summit areas of Mendip (for example, Black Down, Plate 3) which receive the highest rainfall and are well drained by virtue of the permeable nature of the underlying rock. These soils are particularly distinctive and are representative of a major soil group, namely the podzols. Podzols are markedly acidic soils which have a surface layer of organic material or raw humus. Water draining down through the surface humus acts as a powerful solvent, causing not only the bases such as calcium and magnesium, but also the iron and aluminium oxides, to be dissolved. Fully developed podzols have a surface organic layer of raw humus underlain by a horizon that consists essentially of bleached silica grains. Beneath the bleached layer there occurs an iron pan which can vary in thickness from several centimetres to a thin discontinuous rusty stain. The soils, known as the Ashen series, which cover the broad summits of the Old Red Sandstone on Mendip, have many of these characteristics; the pH (a measure of acidity) is about 4.0 and a thin discontinuous iron pan is present. Podzols of this kind are more usually associated with the wetter areas of upland Britain.

The Ashen series is the only well-developed podzolic soil on Mendip. The other soils are all varieties of 'brown earth'. Brown earth soils are well drained, slightly acidic and show none of the marked variations with depth associated with the podzols; they are usually brown or red-brown throughout the soil profile. Away from the higher summits the Old Red Sandstone gives rise to the Maesbury series which is a freely draining brown earth, although from the agricultural viewpoint it is rather acidic with a surface pH of about 5.0, and it is frequently very stony.

A simple correlation of lithology to soils is not valid for the periglacial head deposits that mantle the lower slopes below the Old Red Sandstone areas. These deposits, often several metres in thickness, cover the low-lying Lower Limestone Shale. The soils developed on these head deposits show many variations depending on their depth and the nature of the underlying geology, but are broadly similar to the Maesbury series. For example, where the periglacially transported sandstone material overlies shaley strata, the Ellick series is recognised. This is normally free draining, but wet flushes occur where the head deposits are thin and the drainage is impeded by the shales beneath.

In contrast to the sandstone-derived soils there are several series developed on the main Carboniferous limestones. The most extensive of these is the Nordrach series which forms the main soil of the Mendip Plateau. It is a brown earth, from 50cm to 1m in thickness and very slightly acidic, with a surface pH of from 6.0 to 7.0. It is typically a silty clay loam and the clay content increases down the soil profile, but despite its relatively heavy texture it is free draining. Soil pits dug on the Nordrach invariably show a very sharp junction with the limestone bedrock beneath, and the soil often continues down into the solutionally enlarged fissures beneath the general base of the profile. The genesis of deep limestone soils is a problem in many regions and the Nordrach is no exception. It is possible that the mineral particles that form the bulk of the soil may represent the insoluble residue left after an extensive period of limestone solutional weathering. If this is the case, the soil would represent the erosion of a very considerable thickness of limestone, as the insoluble content of the bedrock is of the order of 1 per cent. Findlay (1965) considers that this residual origin is unlikely on geomorphological grounds and also because the size analysis of the Nordrach series indicates that much of the soil is composed of particles in the coarse silt range (0.02 to 0.06mm). This size range corresponds to that expected from wind-blown periglacial material, often termed loess. Studies of the mineralogy of these fine grains also support a loessic origin. If this is indeed the case it would be expected that other soils in the region would show a corresponding concentration of particles of this size. The Nordrach series is usually low in stone content except where the underlying limestone is particularly rich in insoluble material such as chert.

The other major limestone soil is the Lulsgate series which often grades imperceptibly into the Nordrach soils. A typical Lulsgate soil is very much shallower than the Nordrach and is also the main soil developed on the Dolomitic Conglomerate, especially where it is dominantly composed of limestone fragments and is coarse-grained. The Lulsgate too, has a high silt content and it can be considered as a thinner, and perhaps younger, form of the Nordrach. The limestone slopes of Mendip are mantled with Lulsgate soils, and they form the major soil for the strawberry fields of Cheddar. As the soil is thin and overlies limestone, it is extremely free-draining and in periods of drought has a tendency to become parched.

Thus in a general way a map of lithology is a key to the soils, but it is necessary to take into account the overall topography as well as the effects of the mantling of the slopes with head deposits and the possible influence of loessic contribution to the limestone soils. It would be possible to continue a description of the soil types with progressively finer local detail; the Silurian volcanics of Moons Hill, for example, give rise to a particularly base rich loam, and the Inferior Oolite of eastern Mendip has its own distinctive soil. The soils of the region incorporate the whole physical background as well as giving a guide to former vegetation cover and, perhaps, early agricultural development.

Conclusion

The landscape of any region at any point in time is an amalgam of a multitude of varying factors. Before the coming of man the physical aspects of the environment were clearly dominant and change in the landscape was slow. In the contemporary landscape the activities of man have clearly played a more important role and the rate of change is rapid. However, the activities of man, from the earliest time to the present, are moulded to some degree by the restraints of the local physical environment.

These views are true of any region, and much of the attraction of the British landscape is the marked diversity from one local area to another. The physical environment of the Mendip Hills is, in many respects, different from that of adjacent regions. There is little doubt that these differences stem from variations in the physical background. The individuality of the character of Mendip is undoubtedly due to the surface outcrop of large areas of massive, pure limestones. The broad outline of the landscape and the distinctive nature of many of the landforms are due to the control of this particular rock type. In some respects the control is direct (the gorges and caves are examples of such features), in others the influence is more complex. The soils are a product not only of rock type but also of climate and of the modifying effects of man's agricultural activities over many centuries. The flora shows a similar response to soil and climate, but in this case man's modification of the original 'natural' landscape is more evident. Other features of the personality present a more complex man–land relationship and the interpretation is the province of the historian, always provided that he works within the framework of the restraints imposed by the physical environment.

Part II   Natural History and Ecology
A. J. Willis

In view of its diversity of habitat conditions, including a variety of soil types and coastal as well as inland sites, it is not surprising that Mendip is rich in plant and animal life. Distinctive plant assemblages are present in the woodlands, on the grassy slopes, on the limestone and upland heath which constitutes much of the vegetation of the Mendip plateau, and on the coastal headland. In addition to these types of vegetation with their associated fauna, Mendip is famous for its gorges, notably Cheddar Gorge, long well-known not only for its spectacular scenery but also for its unique flora, containing many rare species. As in most parts of Britain, the activities of man, in both the past and the present, markedly affect the environment on Mendip. The ecological conditions and the occurrence and performance of plants and animals may be altered in many far-reaching ways. Indeed, a knowledge of past events may help to explain the present-day distribution of species: for example the restricted distribution of Cheddar rarities may represent survival from a much wider former distribution; the presence of sea campion *(Silene maritima)* on old lead workings at Priddy, a considerable distance from the sea, may possibly reflect a shoreline of some six or seven thousand years ago when the sea covered much of the Somerset Levels; the sea storksbill *(Erodium maritimum)*, too, occurs well inland.

VEGETATION

Many of the plants of Mendip may be referred to as calcicoles—plants typical of highly calcareous soils in which calcium carbonate is plentiful. However, leaching (washing out of soluble components) may have been extensive in the past, and much calcium carbonate may thus have been removed from the surface layers of the soils. Consequently in some Mendip habitats, the leached surface soils on the Carboniferous Limestone lack free calcium carbonate and have become acidic; these bear a flora of calcifuge (calcium-hating) species.

Woodland

A moderate proportion of the steeper slopes of the main range of Mendip is covered with deciduous woodland, the majority of the woods being semi-natural, although some, such as Cheddar Wood, may be of considerable antiquity. Formerly most of the Mendip slopes were probably wooded, and doubtless served as a source of hazel poles used, together with timber of, for example, oak, by man in the Neolithic and also in the Bronze Age to build trackways across the bog area south of Mendip as it became increasingly swampy. Moss, who studied the Mendip woodlands early this century, regarded them as fundamentally ash woods, although he also recognised oak as a common component. A more recent survey of the woodlands, mostly on slopes of 20° to 30°, showed the three most frequent trees to be ash *(Fraxinus excelsior)*, which regenerates freely, oak (mostly pedunculate oak, *Quercus robur*) and, in smaller quantity, the small-leaved lime *(Tilia cordata)*. The wych elm *(Ulmus glabra)* is frequent in some parts, being an important hedgerow tree on Mendip slopes, but in the last few years many trees have been killed by a virulent strain of Dutch Elm disease. Among other trees and shrubs which commonly occur are the yew *(Taxus baccata)*, maple *(Acer campestre)*, hazel *(Corylus avellana)*, spindle *(Euonymus europaeus)*, holly *(Ilex aquifolium)*, dogwood *(Thelycrania sanguinea)*, hawthorn *(Crataegus monogyna)*, blackthorn *(Prunus spinosa)*, whitebeam *(Sorbus aria)* and guelder rose *(Viburnum opulus)*. The beech *(Fagus sylvatica)*, so abundant on the Cotswolds, is infrequent, and the ash—oak canopy is frequently open enough to allow strong growth of shrubs and the existence of a well-developed ground flora.

Recent quarrying is adversely affecting Asham Wood, near Frome, an extensive tract where the ash is a strong dominant. Besides a varied shrub layer, including the climbers old man's beard *(Clematis vitalba)* and honeysuckle *(Lonicera periclymenum)*, the diverse ground flora contains many less common and attractive species. Among these are the lily-of-the-valley *(Convallaria majalis)*, the Solomon's seal *(Polygonatum multiflorum)*, the small teasel *(Dipsacus pilosus)* and, together with its parents, the hybrid between the water avens *(Geum rivale)* and the wood avens *(G urbanum)*. Mosses and liverworts are abundant; besides those of widespread occurrence on Carboniferous Limestone, such as *Camptothecium sericeum*, *Ctenidium molluscum*, *Frullania tamarisci*, *Madotheca platyphylla*, *Neckera complanata* and *N crispa*, there are some less common species, including the handsome *Rhodobryum roseum*.

Cheddar Wood is rich in the small-leaved lime, and has a substantial shrub layer including dense privet *(Ligustrum vulgare)* in places, the purging buckthorn *(Rhamnus catharticus)* and spurge laurel *(Daphne laureola)*. The diverse ground flora includes most of the herbaceous plants and ferns common in Mendip woodlands, such as dog's mercury *(Mercurialis perennis)*, wood spurge *(Euphorbia amygdaloides)*, wood sage *(Teucrium scorodonia)*, hart's tongue fern *(Phyllitis scolopendrium)* and buckler fern *(Dryopteris dilatata)*; also present are the meadow saffron *(Colchicum autumnale)*, whose autumn flowers precede the leaves which do not appear until spring, the wild madder *(Rubia peregrina)*, here a common scrambler of more open parts, but restricted in Britain to the South, and the blue gromwell *(Lithospermum purpurocaeruleum)*. This rare gromwell is strongly characteristic of Mendip woodlands, being quite well represented here, but of very local occurrence elsewhere in Britain. Its striking flowers give colour to small woodland clearings and hedgerows, and its porcelain-like, shining, persistent fruits attract attention. Another colourful plant of Mendip, especially of verges on lower slopes to the east, is the meadow cranesbill *(Geranium pratense)*.

Conifer plantations, some of which are extensive, clothe part of the Mendip plateau, particularly where the soils are well-developed podzols (see p 36). For successful establishment here, it is necessary for the roots of the conifers to penetrate beneath the highly cemented pan which must therefore be broken either by deep ploughing or by other means. The dense shade cast by the conifers and the deep carpet of shed needles result in a poor ground flora in these plantations.

Vegetation of the Gorges

The precipitous slopes, rock ledges, and associated grassy areas of Cheddar Gorge and Ebbor Gorge bear a remarkable assemblage of rare plants, no doubt favoured here by the special habitat conditions. No less than a dozen plants give particular distinction to the flora of Cheddar Gorge, two of them being unknown elsewhere in Britain. Of major interest is the Cheddar pink *(Dianthus gratianopolitanus)*, whose colourful flowers enliven the rock ledges in spring (Plate 5). Now native in Britain only in the Cheddar Gorge, it is occasionally naturalised elsewhere, and is a component of the Western and Central European flora. A second rarity, a hawkweed *(Hieracium stenolepiforme)*, is entirely restricted (endemic) to Cheddar, occurring together with a number of other unusual species of hawkweed. Another Cheddar rare plant is the mossy saxifrage *(Saxifraga hypnoides)*, present only in a small quantity here at its southernmost distribution limit in Britain. First described as a component of the British flora from near Cheddar is the cut-leaved self-heal *(Prunella laciniata)*; this occurs in grassy areas, together with the common self-heal *(Prunella vulgaris)* which with it hybridises. Other notable and conspicuous Cheddar plants include the rock stonecrop *(Sedum forsteranum)*, Curtis's mouse-ear chickweed *(Cerastium pumilum)*, the Welsh poppy *(Meconopsis cambrica)*, and the lesser meadow-rue *(Thalictrum minus)*. Among the ferns, the limestone polypody *(Thelypteris robertiana)* is frequent on the scree slopes. The whitebeam *(Sorbus aria)*, and several of its relatives which are much less common, grow on the cliffs, and make the Cheddar Gorge one of the richest sites for these Sorbi in the country. Besides all these less common plants, there is good representation of the more widespread species typical of the limestone, so that the attraction of Cheddar for the botanist is in no way surprising. There is evidence that this unique community of plants may exist because the Gorge is acting as a refugium by virtue of its precipitous nature resulting in 'open' vegetation in which competition is not severe.

Only relatively little woodland is present, as at Burrington Combe, but the flora of the latter area, although having many calcicoles of interest, does not include the rare species.

The Ebbor Gorge, part of which is a National Nature Reserve, has many features in common with Cheddar Gorge, but contrasts rather sharply in being well wooded and also in lacking the extreme rarities among the flowering plants. Of note here are the greater butterfly orchid *(Platanthera chlorantha)*, the nettle-leaved bellflower *(Campanula trachelium)*, the bloody cranesbill *(Geranium sanguineum)* and a rich assemblage of bryophytes (as regards both species and abundance) including the epiphytic liverwort *Nowellia curvifolia*.

Grassland Vegetation

Many of the drier slopes of Mendip bear limestone grassland made up very largely of typical calcicole plants. The most important grasses include sheep's fescue *(Festuca ovina)*, often the dominant, creeping fescue *(F rubra)*, meadow oat *(Helictotrichon pratense)*, quaking grass *(Briza media)* and crested hair-grass *(Koeleria cristata)*. The heath false-brome *(Brachypodium pinnatum)* and the upright brome *(Zerna erecta)*, grasses which are very important on the Cotswold Oolite, are uncommon as dominants on Mendip, although the former may be increasing on Cross Plain and Compton Hill. Many other plants give considerable variety to the flora in the species-rich turf and provide colour on the grassy slopes. Most of these plants, too, are typical of calcareous habitats, such as the bird's-foot trefoil *(Lotus corniculatus)*, thyme *(Thymus drucei)*, mouse-ear hawkweed *(Hieracium pilosella)*, the salad burnet *(Poterium sanguisorba)*, the purging flax *(Linum catharticum)* and the stemless thistle *(Cirsium acaulon)*.

On the Mendip plateau the vegetation is much more heath-like, and in places a transition between calcareous grassland and heath-type vegetation is evident. At Dolebury Warren, for example, the soil shows quite marked changes in depth, related to slope, and the amount of wind-blown material overlying the limestone rubble and bedrock; the vegetation here shows strong correlations with the soil depth. On steep south-facing slopes and on the exposed summit ridge the soil is shallow, and typical limestone vegetation is present. Where the soil is deeper, more leached and more acidic, heath plants such as ling *(Calluna vulgaris)*, bell-heather *(Erica cinerea)* and, in places, bilberry *(Vaccinium myrtillus)* occur, and the vegetation is taller. Some of these calcifuge plants, such as ling and heather, are known to lead to acidification of the soil as a result of the acidic nature of the litter which they produce.

Upland heaths developed on outcrops of Old Red Sandstone are present in several parts of the Mendip plateau. One such area near Priddy has a vegetation rich in ling, heather, the mat-grass *(Nardus stricta)*, wavy hair-grass *(Deschampsia flexuosa)* and the purple moorgrass *(Molinia caerulea)*. Other members of this community include the heath rush *(Juncus squarrosus)* and the dwarf furze *(Ulex gallii)*. In the bog and pond area here, the cotton-grass *(Eriophorum angustifolium)*, the bog asphodel *(Narthecium ossifragum)*, the water horsetail *(Equisetum fluviatile)*, the beaked sedge *(Carex rostrata)* and several species of bog moss *(Sphagnum)* occur.

The 'gruffy' ground of the abandoned lead workings at Charterhouse and elsewhere on Mendip is well known botanically for the presence of several plants characteristic of sites of high lead content. Thriving here, for example, is a distinctive Mendip race of the Alpine penny-cress *(Thlaspi alpestre)* which, like the vernal sandwort *(Minuartia verna)* which may accompany it, is a rare plant in Britain.

Coastal Vegetation

The rocky slopes at Uphill and, more especially, the headland of Brean Down, are subject to maritime influences. The vegetation includes many plants typical of the Carboniferous Limestone, but also includes some which are coastal.

The steep, south-facing rocky slope of Brean Down bears vegetation contrasting with that of the more gentle north-facing slope where the soil is deeper and there is an extensive cover of bracken *(Pteridium aquilinum)*. On the south-facing slope the rather rare dwarf sedge *(Carex humilis)* is abundant in places, and in early summer some areas here are conspicuous with the flowers of the white rockrose *(Helianthemum appenninum)* which dominates locally and also grows on Purn Hill. This attractive plant is known elsewhere in Britain only near Torbay in Devon. Another rarity, restricted in Britain to the coastal Mendip area, but by no means uncommon on Brean Down, is Dillenius' hair-grass *(Koeleria vallesiana)*; this grass, at its most northerly world limit here like the white rockrose, is present also in several places on the Limestone as far inland as Shute Shelve and Fry's Hill (Plate p 4). A recent finding is that in this coastal area it hybridises with the much commoner species *K cristata*.

Indicative of the maritime influence is the presence of the sea carrot *(Daucus carota* ssp *gummifer)* together with the more common wild carrot *(D carota* ssp *carota)*. In the rock clefts nearer to tide level the sea spleenwort *(Asplenium marinum)* may be seen, this fern being set well back in crevices where the illumination is much reduced. A rarity of the coastal limestone is the Goldilocks *(Crinitaria linosyris)*, present in a very small quantity; this area represents one out of a total of only five localities for the plant in Britain. Not present on Brean Down, but growing in several neighbouring sites inland (Uphill, Purn Hill, Crook Peak), is honewort *(Trinia glauca)*, another plant of very restricted distribution in Britain.

The island of Steep Holm supports an interesting flora, and is also noted as a breeding site for large numbers of gulls. A striking botanical feature is the abundance of Alexanders *(Smyrnium olusatrum)*, an umbelliferous plant which dominates an unusual community. The peony *(Paeonia mascula)*, for which Steep Holm is well known, is naturalised here; also present are the golden samphire *(Inula crithmoides)* and a distinctive form of the buck's-horn plantain *(Plantago coronopus* var *sabrinae)*.

ANIMAL LIFE

Information about the distribution and numbers of animals on Mendip and their ecological behaviour comes mostly from the observations of naturalists interested in particular groups of animals, notably the insects (especially Lepidoptera—the butterflies and moths), the birds and the mammals. It is convenient here, therefore, to give some account of these animals group by group, rather than to attempt descriptions of the diversity of animal life of particular habitats, although mention is made of certain localities. Not all groups can be covered; also information is scanty on some groups of organisms. However, the frequent occurrence of common lizards, slow-worms, adders and grass-snakes on Mendip may be noted. Cast skins of grass-snakes and adders can be picked up quite frequently in the autumn, and at Priddy there is an unusual black strain of adders; indeed adders are a common feature of the old walls and rocky areas. The Priddy and Charterhouse areas are rich in spiders, notably *Araneus quadratus*, a big orb-spinner with interesting colour variations. In the ponds there are sticklebacks, roach and perch (most of these heavily parasitised); other inhabitants include the common frog, newts (common, great crested and palmate), dragonflies, *Dytiscus* beetles, the water spider *(Argyroneta)*, midges and mosquitoes.

The Chew Valley and Blagdon lakes support a diverse fauna, being stocked and fished extensively for trout; they are very rich in bird life, including many migrant species. These nutrient-rich reservoirs support large populations of oligochaete worms and chironomid larvae.

Insects

Mendip is rich in insect life, but only a small selection can be covered here.

The bush-crickets and grasshoppers (Orthoptera) are well represented, with four species of bush-cricket, four species of grasshopper and the common groundhopper *(Tetrix undulata)* being abundant or at least locally common. The great green bush-cricket *(Tettigonia viridissima)* is widespread and especially common around Cheddar, Ebbor and Shipham as well as on Bleadon Hill and Crook Peak; the males can be heard in late summer stridulating noisily from clumps of brambles and hawthorns and in the hedgerows. On Crook Peak an attractive variegated grey form of the common field grasshopper *(Chorthippus brunneus)* may be seen frequently on the stonier places.

More than forty species of butterfly are currently known on Mendip, although the list is shorter than formerly and the populations, especially of those butterflies with specialised ecological requirements, have diminished as a result of destruction of habitat during this century. Nevertheless, in spite of these losses, Mendip remains an area where butterflies are well represented.

Species common in woods, at their borders, or in shady lanes, include the speckled wood *(Pararge aegeria)*, the hedge brown *(Maniola tithonus)*, the ringlet *(Aphantopus hyperanthus)*, the pearl-bordered and silver-washed fritillaries *(Argynnis euphrosyne* and *A paphia* respectively), the comma *(Polygonia c-album)*, the holly blue *(Celastrina argiolus)*, the orange tip *(Anthocharis cardamines)*, the brimstone *(Gonepteryx rhamni)* and the large skipper *(Ochlodes venata)*. Particularly good sites for many of these and others are Cheddar and, to the north of the main area of Mendip, Brockley Combe and Goblin Combe. Of very local occurrence are the high brown fritillary *(Argynnis cydippe)* and the white admiral *(Limenitis camilla)*. The purple emperor *(Apatura iris)*, at one time feared extinct in Somerset, was fortunately rediscovered in 1969, after a gap of fifty-one years, in a north Mendip wooded locality where it appears to be safe as long as there is no extensive spread of conifer plantation.

The grassy limestone slopes and more open downland also carry a number of interesting species of butterfly. Among these are the chalkhill blue *(Lysandra coridon)* and the small blue *(Cupido minimus)*, regrettably much less plentiful than formerly, no doubt partly because of the ranker growth of coarse grasses associated with the diminution of rabbit grazing because of myxomatosis. Other downland species include the wall brown *(Pararge megera)*, the marbled white *(Melanargia galathea)*, which is apparently increasing, the dark green fritillary *(Argynnis aglaia)* and the brown argus *(Aricia agestis)*.

Among the many moths on Mendip, the hawkmoths are well represented, the large and small elephant hawkmoths *(Deilephila elpenor* and *D porcellus)* being common. The emperor moth *(Saturnia pavonia)* is best represented on the heathy areas, and the conspicuous oak eggar *(Lasiocampa quercus)* and the drinker *(Philudoria potatoria)* are frequent. Among day-flying moths, the cinnabar *(Callimorpha jacobaeae)* and three species of burnet moths *(Zygaena* spp) are abundant. The cistus forester *(Procris geryon)* is known from Cheddar. The attractive chalk carpet moth *(Ortholitha bipunctaria)* is a typical and common species of the limestone downland.

Among dragonflies (Odonata), the black sympetrum *(Sympetrum danae)* breeds in small numbers at Priddy pools; here also is a well-established colony of the rather scarce downy emerald dragonfly *(Cordulia aenea)*, for which there is only one other known Somerset locality. The migratory common sympetrum *(Sympetrum striolatum)* may appear in hundreds in September along tracks, and the four-spotted Libellula *(Libellula quadrimaculata)* is widespread, and notable for its conspicuous migrations.

One of the most characteristic and noticeable beetles (Coleoptera) of Mendip downland is the large bloody-nosed beetle *(Timarcha laevigata)* which exudes a red fluid from its mouth and joints when handled.

Birds

Ecological changes on Mendip in the last century and a half have resulted from developments in agriculture, involving enclosure of open areas and their reclamation, the planting of hedges and afforestation. These changes have much affected the bird life. For example, afforestation has introduced a variety of habitat types ranging from low scrub, where nightjars breed occasionally, and grasshopper warblers frequently, to dense forest providing breeding sites for birds of prey; in 1974 one pair of long-eared owls bred on Mendip—the first for nearly fifty years. In contrast, in other areas, human disturbance has led to the reduction or cessation of breeding, and the entire loss of some birds. Formerly, for example, there were ravens and peregrines in Cheddar Gorge and black grouse were present on Black Down. The wood lark and the red-backed shrike have also decreased, but their decline on Mendip is mainly because of a general recession of these species in NW Europe. Now these birds are not seen, although a pair of ravens usually breed on Brean Down.

In a fairly recent survey of birds of the Cheddar Gorge, which because of human disturbance is of rather limited ornithological interest, sixty species were recorded. Jackdaws are numerous. Of general distribution, but particularly common in the wooded areas, are the wood pigeon (estimates were made of a breeding population of about two pairs per acre in mixed scrub woodland), carrion crows, magpies and jays and great and blue tits. Coal tits, although less numerous, are well distributed. Wrens nest on ivy-covered rock faces throughout the Gorge. The bullfinch occurs in thick woodland, the chaffinch being equally common; the greenfinch and goldfinch are generally distributed in scrub and form fairly widely ranging flocks in winter. Of somewhat more restricted distribution are the kestrel (a few pairs hunt over the plateau), the red-legged partridge, and the pheasant (present where arable land adjoins woodland). Green and great spotted woodpeckers are found in wooded sites only, and the stock dove is by no means as common as formerly. On the grassy plateau the skylark, meadow pipit and linnet are to be found, and in areas of scrub the long-tailed tit; however, like the marsh tit, it is not frequent in the Cheddar Gorge area. The goldcrest is to be found in conifers here; development of woodland elsewhere on Mendip may foster this bird, as well as tits. Among the common summer migrants are the willow warbler, chiffchaff, whitethroat (now less frequent than formerly), blackcap, tree pipit and cuckoo, and winter visitors include the redwing and fieldfare. However, redwings are in smaller numbers than at the large winter roost which has developed in recent years at Rowberrow Warren.

The skylark and meadow pipit are characteristic birds of the Mendip area generally. Of more restricted distribution, in the vicinity of Charterhouse and Priddy, are groups of corn buntings. The cirl bunting is present on low southern slopes where there are hedgerows with trees (perhaps particularly elms), whereas the yellowhammer may be found locally on higher ground and is often associated with hawthorn scrub. The tree sparrow is commoner on eastern Mendip than to the west. Rough and rushy fields on the east of the area may attract breeding curlew occasionally. Birds not often seen on Mendip include the barn owl, of which one or two still reside on the plateau, and the great grey shrike, of which one, and sometimes two, may winter occasionally. The hawfinch is local, and has been reported from Chewton Mendip.

Wheatears still bred regularly on Wavering Down two decades ago, but in very small numbers; with the disappearance of the rabbit (the birds seemed to use the warrens for breeding rather than walls) breeding here is now sporadic only. Stonechats were at one time far more plentiful than at present, and now breed only on Brean Down. Increasing disturbance could adversely affect them. Large quarries being actively worked, as at Asham Wood, discourage birds, but exhausted and abandoned smaller quarries attract kestrels and numerous jackdaws.

Sparrow hawks and a few pairs of buzzards breed in the woodlands, and one or two pairs of hobbies—part of the tiny Somerset population of this graceful migrant falcon—nest in outlying copses.

Mendip is of note in that the first arrival of wintering thrushes and finches is nearly always here. Large parties of these, numbering over 1,000 birds at a time, occur.

Bodies of water attract a variety of water birds, a few wintering duck using Emborough Pond. The construction of the Chew Valley Lake quickly led to large autumn and winter roosts of black-headed, common, herring and lesser black-backed gulls. Large numbers of waterfowl of many species also winter there, and many pairs breed.

Mammals

In reporting on the land mammals of the Bristol district in 1941, Tetley referred to over thirty species which were known from Mendip. One of the most striking changes in the mammals since that time is the complete disappearance of the red squirrel—which Tetley noted as becoming less plentiful than formerly—and its replacement, as elsewhere in Britain, by the grey squirrel. The latter was first recorded for Somerset from Old Draycott Wood, near Cheddar, in 1935 and has spread rapidly since, becoming common and widely distributed. Another change is the apparent loss of the polecat, always very rare, but seen in a fair number of Mendip localities in the last hundred years.

One group of mammals well represented on Mendip are the bats (Chiroptera), of which several species are abundant in the caves, notably at Cheddar and Wookey Hole. The Mendip caves are a major headquarters in Britain for the greater horseshoe bat which has a characteristic nose-leaf on its face. This bat is quite widespread in the Bristol area, but is not as numerous in Wookey Hole as formerly, probably because of the illumination of the caves for visitors. Other fairly common bats of Mendip caves are the pipistrelle and the whiskered bat, while also known from a number of localities are the natterer's bat, the long-eared bat and the lesser horseshoe bat. Most of these bats have been reported from Wells Cathedral, as well as the almost black barbastelle, rare in the Bristol district, but recorded also from Cheddar and Wookey Hole.

Mammals which are abundant or widespread on Mendip include the hedgehog, the mole, the brown rat (although this is less frequent than formerly), the weasel, the stoat and the fox. The badger is locally com-

6 Westbury-sub-Mendip quarry, showing the fissure where evidence has been found to prove that Palaeolithic man walked on Mendip nearly half a million years ago

7 Priddy Circles looking towards the Roman road and the Castle of Comfort Inn *(top right)*

8 The Roman town at Charterhouse, showing the irregular grid pattern: amphitheatre in middle distance *(left)*

9 Brean Down and Steep Holm: between the beach and the limestone rock face is the 'sand cliff', one of Mendip's most remarkable archaeological sites

mon; a new locality from which it has been reported recently is Bleadon Hill. The rabbit suffered a severe reduction in numbers because of myxomatosis in the mid-1950s, but has made substantial recoveries from this, and is now widespread again. The hare, unlike the rabbit, does not appear to be subject to epidemics and is of general distribution both on low ground and at higher elevations. The common shrew is abundant; the suggestion has been made that it is the commonest mammal of the Bristol district. The pigmy shrew is much more local, known for example from Cheddar and Bleadon, as is the water shrew, recorded also from these sites and from Chewton Mendip. While the dormouse may once have been locally common in hazel woods, there are relatively few records of this in the Mammal Survey reports given in recent years in the *Proceedings of the Bristol Naturalists' Society*. The field mouse is common and an early record indicates that it made up about 6 per cent of the food of a pair of barn owls at Chewton Mendip. In contrast, the harvest mouse is rare and local (reported from near Wells), and there are not many records of the yellow-necked field mouse, known from Wavering Down, and from woodlands at Rodney Stoke and Cheddar. Of common occurrence are the bank vole, water vole and the field vole. Deer are occasionally seen. Although not numerous, both roe deer and less commonly red deer have been reported in the new Forestry plantations.

The natural historian, whatever his specialism, is likely to recognise Mendip as an exceptionally attractive stretch of country, the intrinsic richness of its limestone flora and its fauna being further enhanced by its proximity to the Somerset Levels. Furthermore the extensive cave system supports a range of specialised animals, plants and micro-organisms. Wookey Hole has interestingly yielded a unique filamentous organism of uncertain affinity which shows characters of both fungi and algae. Collembolans (springtails) are frequent in Read's Cavern, and some have been reported as feeding on the fungus *Penicillium* growing on candle-wax left by cavers. Such a situation is but one illustration of the interdependence of organisms of which numerous examples are to be found in the diverse Mendip communities.

Notes to this chapter are on pages 264-6.

3

Early Mendip

P. J. Fowler

THE MENDIP HILLS and the surrounding landscape contain evidence for man's activities from some half a million years ago up to the present. Archaeologically, it is both a 'classic' and a typical area: 'classic' in that it possesses sites of far more than local interest which have stimulated a tradition of scholarship over the last two centuries, and typical in that on its complex geology and generally thin soils can be studied the vicissitudes of human communities trying to establish at different times a working relationship with their environment.

The archaeology of its caves is without doubt Mendip's distinctive and major contribution to knowledge of early Britain. Brean Down, Dolebury, Charterhouse and the Priddy area are also important, and many other sites, both on the hilltops and along the lower ground to north and south, contribute to what can be pieced together as a story, however fragmentary, of a relationship, changing through time, between men and their habitat. Because men have many needs, it is doubtful if satisfaction was often achieved within the Mendip environment alone (c 9000 BC was possibly one exception), and so in this brief account we shall also be looking north across the Vale of Wrington, east towards the Chalk country and south across the Somerset Levels. If we could but discern it in early times, as in the documented past, we would probably see a constant interaction between the high lands of Mendip's summit and the low lands alongside. Man needed both: to hunt, to farm, to manufacture, to bury and to worship.

The First Men

The first men on Mendip came into an area looking totally different from now. The appearance of today's landscape is a relatively recent creation. The whole of the time covered by the sections in the rest of this chapter, and by all the succeeding chapters in the book, is but the passing of a few seconds compared to the period summarised in these first few paragraphs.

WESTBURY-SUB-MENDIP FISSURE

Mendip always has been important scientifically for its evidence of early man, principally from its caves. Now that status is dramatically enhanced with recent evidence from a fissure sliced by an active quarry at Westbury-sub-Mendip. Ever since its discovery in 1969, it has been clear that this particular fissure was especially significant since it not only contained a large faunal assemblage but one beginning nearly half a million years ago. It appears to belong to the interglacial period called the 'Cromerian', that is *before* the third last glaciation. Important though this is, with the presence of bones of the Etruscan rhinoceros *(Dicererorhinus etruscus* Falconer) and the scimitar cat *(Homotherium* sp), the interest would be primarily for palaeonotologists; the interest is increased enormously by the discovery of struck flints and charcoal associated with this material. Man, or more strictly and more probably, *Homo erectus,* walked on Mendip nearly half a million years ago, and was perhaps the earliest in Britain. It is nevertheless salutary to remember that, early though this is in relation to the bulk of Mendip's Palaeolithic evidence, it is but a quarter, on some accounts but an eighth, of the time from today back to the origins of man-like creatures in Africa.

CAVES AND THEIR DEPOSITS

Caves, fissures and rock shelters provide the rest of Mendip's early evidence. Here it is important to understand one of the basics of archaeology, stratification, that is the accumulation of one layer on top of another in a succession representing the passage of time. The earliest layers therefore occur at the bottom of the stratification. The processes causing such layers in caves and fissures are the changing climate and the occupation debris left by men and animals. A very cold period, for example, will cause angular fragments of rock to fall off a cliff face or a cave entrance through frost action, creating a characteristic layer of shattered flakes in the stratification; a high water table and flooding can deposit a layer of silt; the continuous process of water filtering through the Carboniferous Limestone creates the stalactites and stalagmites, so beloved of the show-cave proprietors, which can seal early layers in the caves with a concrete-like cover. While, however, the principles of stratification, and of its study, stratigraphy, are fundamental, in prac-

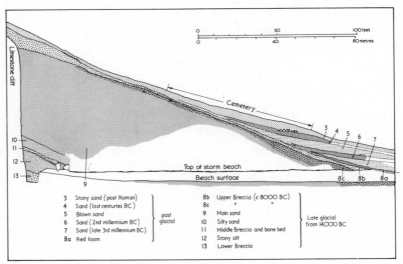

Fig 7   Brean Down sand cliff—section.

tice observing the evidence of early Mendip is complicated by various factors, some natural such as the redeposition of materials through water action or disturbance by burrowing animals, some artificial such as the disturbance by early man and the diggings of cavers and archaeologists over the last century.

One of the best examples of early stratification comes from Picken's Hole on the south side of Crook Peak. There the earlier of two bone-bearing layers, a red cave earth between layers of limestone fragments, contained bones of reindeer and red deer, wolf, fox, bear and voles, suggesting a contemporary forest environment in a climate rather cooler than today. Probably this layer represents a warm phase about 40,000 years ago during the last (Weichselian) glaciation. Above the overlying breccia was a layer of cave earth containing human bones. The animals represented included hyena, arctic fox, bear, mammoth, woolly rhinoceros, hare, red deer and ground squirrel, indicating a cold climate and mainly open tundra conditions some 35,000 years ago.

A site called Badger Hole, at Wookey Hole, has a radio-carbon estimate of c 18,000 years ago for material including two human jaw fragments. Contemporary fauna included mammoth, woolly rhinoceros, horse, bison and four types of deer, plus hyena, lion, wolf, fox and bear, all doubtless preying on them. All lived in an open environment of mainly grass, sedge and fern with a few junipers, willows, crowberries, pine, sea-buckthorn and rockrose.

Broadly contemporary are the earliest layers at one of the most remarkable sites on the whole of Mendip: the 'sand cliff' on the south side of **Brean Down** in the angle between the beach and the limestone rock face (Fig 7). It is a great pity that so crucial a sequence of stratified deposits demonstrating climate, flora and fauna in the area since within the last glaciation, should annually be further eroded, mostly in ignorance, by holiday-makers. Thirteen layers have been identified, the lowest five dating to the millennia of the last glaciation. The earliest contains reindeer, arctic fox, aurochs and voles, and so does the next but without the fox; nevertheless both clearly indicate a cold climate, though equally clearly the area was not actually under ice. That probably lay to the north and west. The third layer up is known as the 'Bone Bed' from its richness of faunal remains which included reindeer and giant deer, mammoth, aurochs, horse, wolf, arctic fox and hare. There is no hyena or rhinoceros, so again a cold late glacial climate is deduced. Hunting in it was man, evidenced by his handiwork on the giant deer antler.

AFTER THE LAST GLACIATION

These three sites give an impression of the types of evidence available and how they can be used for a time which is bound to seem remote and, to some, uninteresting. In fact, however fitful man's appearance on this glacial stage and however daunting the set with its roaming auroch, wolf and mammoth, we are really glimpsing the prologue to today. For man was surviving, through his adaptability, flexibility and mobility, the seemingly endless period of cold so that when the interglacial in which we now live began he was still in the wings ready to make another, and this time explosive, entrance.

In fact, he may have left the area altogether during the periods of intense cold, migrating south beyond the glacial frontier which in the period up to c 11,000 BC lay not far north of Mendip. As the ice retreated, the climate warmed and the sea level rose, man moved back, presumably following his animal meat supply, and occupied the caves. Radio carbon 'dates' can again help us to fix this phase in time: at Sun Hole, one of the several sites with human remains, a bear bone provided a 'date' of c 10,400 BC, and 'Cheddar Man' himself, a skeleton fully displayed at Gough's Cave Museum and once thought to be of a very early man, is 'dated' c 7,100 BC.

Gough's Cave itself has produced a great deal of evidence for this postglacial period: again we have the four types of deer (red, large red, giant Irish and reindeer), with horse and bison and the meat-eaters bear, wolf, fox and lynx; but gone are hyena and lion, mammoth and woolly rhinoceros. The vegetation, whatever extremes it had undergone in the preceding 10,000 years, was remarkably similar to that at Badger Hole: mainly grass and sedge with a little fern, and relatively sparse tree and shrub cover of birch, willow, pine, juniper, crowberry and sea-buckthorn. Gough's Cave is famous too for its 'art objects' made by Late (or Upper) Palaeolithic man, in particular two 'batons-de-commandement' which were probably actually used to straighten the shafts of spears or arrows, and a bone awl, made from a tibia of an arctic hare. This is incised with lines convincingly argued to form numerical groupings in a pattern suitable for making arithmetical calculations.

The 'human' aspect of these cave-living hunters, so difficult to appreciate when we gaze only at their superficially crude (but actually sophisticated) flint tools, is again illuminated by the ammonites with a burial in Aveline's Hole, Burrington Combe, another site which, like Gough's, it is easy to see from the roadside (though, unlike Gough's, it is not a show cave). Many other caves and rock shelters have produced evidence of use in this period about 11,000–7,000 BC but lack of space here prevents even their mention. The important fact is that, as Britain emerged from the long freeze of the last Ice Age, Mendip supported some of the most thriving and inventive communities among the small, scattered population of Europe.

The Later Food-Gatherers

It is normal in British prehistory to think of a 'Mesolithic' period (Middle Stone Age) intervening between the Upper Palaeolithic (Old Stone Age) and the beginnings of the Neolithic (New Stone Age: below pp 56–62). Such a period, usually envisaged as up to c 5,000 years long (c 9,000/8,000–4,000/3,000 BC), can now be seen to have been of crucial importance in the development of both the southern British landscape and the communities living in it, although archaeologically these millennia remain undramatic and difficult to identify. This has been true of Mendip from which, until recently, Mesolithic man seemed to be largely absent; and even now, the evidence remains relatively scant and certainly unimpressive compared to the preceding 'cave period' in immediately postglacial times.

One question is why the practice of living in caves apparently ceased. What happened to our thriving Late Palaeolithic communities? Did they move away, or did they literally die out? Whatever the reason, the archaeological record in caves by and large shows little human use between the immediate postglacial millennia and the last few centuries BC (but see below, pp 60 and 61 for exceptions in the fourth, third and second millennia). The claimed absence of Mesolithic material from

Mendip's caves, taken to indicate the absence of Mesolithic man from
Mendip as a whole, can be countered by showing that Mesolithic flints
are present in some caves; examples are Rowberrow, Haywood and
'Totty Pot' above Cheddar Gorge. Nevertheless, although the use of
caves was not intense during the several thousand years before the
appearance of Neolithic communities, does the relative absence of
evidence from the 'obvious' sites indicate man's absence only from the
caves or from the whole of the Mendip? Or is he to be looked for outside
the caves but still on Mendip? Or off Mendip but somewhere else in the
general region?

In fact, Mesolithic man's activities appear to have been much more
widespread over southern England than has been appreciated. This was
probably due to a rising population in what was, after all, a long period.
We can point with fair certainty to where some of the local evidence has
gone: on the shores of the Bristol Channel/Severn estuary, below what is
now high water mark. There is little doubt that a much more extensive
land-surface than now existed in the postglacial period. Finds of submerged forests and Mesolithic sites along the coasts of South Wales and
the east side of the Channel show that it was here that at least some of the
communities were living. Presumably food supplies of fish and birds
were the attraction.

In such circumstances, the presumably well-wooded valleys and
flanks of Mendip could easily have been enviable hunting grounds for
meat and raw materials such as hide and bone. It has been customary
therefore to explain away the undoubted Mesolithic flints on Mendip as
merely the debris of hunting parties, at best representing temporary
camping sites. But the size of some of the 'flint-scatter' sites and the fact
that their material contains large amounts of waste flakes, indicating the
working of flint on the spot, suggests more than mere temporary camps.
Surely it can at least be argued that, as the climate improved, the higher
ground of Mendip became habitable without the need for a cave; and
indeed that the gradual submergence of the coastal plains, a process
probably largely completed by c 5,000 BC, drove the fishing communities inland.

Nevertheless, the Mesolithic period of Mendip is as yet at a very early
stage of study; but at least it is now recognised to exist through the
collections from sites such as Wright's Piece near the Castle of Comfort
Inn, those above Ebbor Gorge near Westbury-sub-Mendip, one now
being excavated near Priddy, and accidental finds made in excavating
Gorsey Bigbury (below, p 59) and the Tyning's Barrows (below, p 64).
The tools themselves are of normal Mesolithic types including blades,
burins and many small worked pieces called microliths. Axes are absent,

apart from one example from Green Ore, and pebble flint is very rare as raw material. When it is appreciated that every single piece of flint on Mendip was imported, almost certainly from the chalk country 25 miles and more to the east, these communities can be seen as something more than self-sufficient hunters. The point is emphasised by several Mendip sites which have also produced artefacts of Portland Chert, a clear hint of social organisation beyond that of the simple, independent nomadic family unit. Greensand Chert, probably from the Blackdown Hills in south Somerset, also occurs, so the impression of a nexus of 'trade' contacts across a wet and forested landscape is fortified. Actually, the landscape can only be inferred since, in stark contrast to Palaeolithic studies, there is a complete lack of environmental evidence for these thousands of years on Mendip: it might in fact be questioned whether the Mendip summits were forested at all in these millennia, though it is fair to assume that such vegetation existed on the lower ground round about.

Mendip's First Monuments

Perhaps surprisingly, the dearth of good archaeological and environmental evidence continues on Mendip long after the arrival of Neolithic colonists in Britain and specifically in the south-western peninsula of Britain. Mendip itself seems to have been bypassed as, in the fifth and fourth millennia BC, a new relationship between man and his surroundings developed. This is understandable, yet is probably not the full story. Nevertheless, at the moment there is no evidence of early (ie before c 3,000 BC) Neolithic communities on Mendip. Such evidence as there is belongs to the third millennium BC.

Yet, just a few miles to the south in the raised peat bog of the Brue valley, some of the most dramatic evidence of early farmers in Western Europe is almost daily being recorded. It consists of timber trackways, marvellously preserved in the peat, forming a system of communication between the 'islands' in the Levels and between them and the Polden Hills to the south. The present pattern accurately reflects the incidence of modern peat extraction, now on a huge commercial scale, which has mainly worked south of a line due west from Glastonbury; it would be no surprise if future work were to reveal a corresponding pattern running north to the Isle of Wedmore and the southern shore of Mendip. In any case, the existing pattern and nature of the trackways strongly suggests that farming communities in the fourth millennium BC were living and grazing their stock, perhaps cultivating their fields, on the low-lying islands of the broad valley between Mendip and Polden and on the

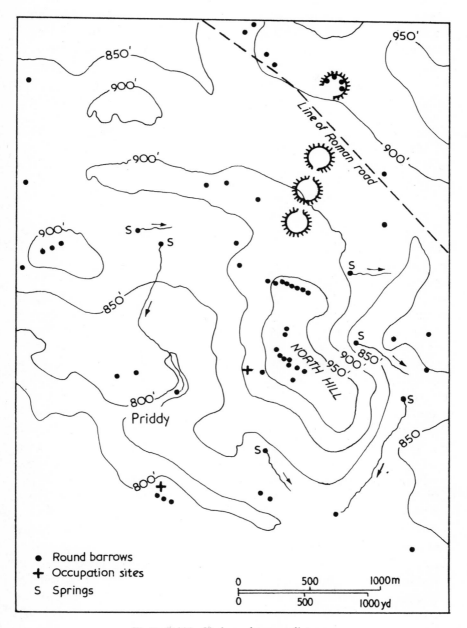

Fig 8   Priddy Circles and surrounding area.

flanks of the Poldens themselves. At this stage it is only inference, but it seems legitimate to envisage the southern skirts of Mendip and the knolls lying just 'offshore' to the south being utilised in a similar manner. Conversely, the more exposed summits were probably not settled, though their use for summer grazing seems likely.

PRIDDY CIRCLES

The single item of environmental evidence from the Neolithic period on Mendip indicates that the area around the Priddy Circles (see Fig 8) was open grassland when Circle No 1 was constructed. Woodland probably existed within a few miles, but we can wonder whether the summit plateau ever had been wooded, or whether its state sometime about the middle centuries of the third millennium BC was the creation of 1,000 years of grazing or, possibly, cultivation. The evidence is yet to come. The Circles themselves, although they exist as the most remarkable of Mendip's early field monuments, are equally ambiguous. Four circles exist, one only partly surviving north of the Castle of Comfort Inn, the other three in the fields to the south. They form a nearly straight line, with a gap between those three and the fourth large enough to have taken a fifth circle. The Roman road to Charterhouse (below, p 69) passes through this gap, and one wonders whether the military engineers have not dealt even more ruthlessly with a prehistoric monument than they dealt with two disc barrows on Oakley Down, Dorset. Circle 1 has a diameter of 157.5m with an entrance to the north and is slightly flattened in plan on the west. Circle 2 is a true circle, with diameter and entrance similar to No 1. Circle 3 is flattened in plan on west and east, being 157.5m in diameter north–south and 148.5m west–east. Its entrance faces that of No 2. Circle 4 is 169.5m in diameter, probably with an entrance facing south-south-west, west of which the bank and ditch seem not to have been built. Four round barrows are in the interior.

Strictly speaking, the purpose and date of the Priddy Circles are unknown. It is only recently that they have been firmly recognised as being, in archaeological terms, 'henge monuments', that is a type of structure defined by superficial characteristics such as circularity of plan, a ditch usually *inside* an enclosing bank, and a single entrance or two opposed entrances. The name 'henge' is derived from Stonehenge, illogically because the Old English root referred to the 'hanging' stones there, ie the trilithon and lintelled arrangements, a unique occurrence for which there is certainly no evidence at Priddy. Internal features of standing stones and timber structures, possibly lintelled, are, however, known from other henges such as Avebury and Durrington Walls, Wilts, and the negative evidence from the Priddy Circles is certainly no proof that the areas bounded by the banks and ditches were always empty. In fact, archaeological excavation of the Circles has so far been limited to one small area of one Circle, the southernmost. It was, however, revealing, and sufficient to point to the potential of the sites as sources of information in, one hopes, the distant future. There is certainly no case for further excavation at the moment.

The small-scale excavation of the southern circle, mainly around its entrance, showed that some upright stones had formed the first feature on the site. It was displaced by the construction of the bank, basically two concentric rings of posts, stakes and hurdles. Between them, first, two low dry stone walls were built, then more stones were piled between the walls, and finally the material from the digging of the ditch was heaped on the stones, the whole structure originally being about 1½m high with a ditch some 1m deep in front of it. At the entrance, the ends of the bank were also revetted in wood to make a slightly funnel-shaped passageway in from the causeway of undisturbed ground between the ends of the ditch.

Such detail does not, however, help much in telling us the use and date of the sites. The most likely interpretation is that the circles represent some sort of ceremonial centre. The most likely date, pressing the similarity of the Circles' form to that of Phase I at Stonehenge (circular enclosure with single entrance and *outer* ditch), is c 2,500 BC. Lest that give an impression of too great an exactness, perhaps it should simply be said that the Priddy Circles were probably built and used sometime in the second half of the third millennium BC.

Remarkable though it is for there to be four henge monuments so close together, the Priddy Circles are in fact part of a large group on western Mendip consisting altogether of six sites. One, known as Gorsey Bigbury, lies just 4 miles to the north-west; the other, near the Hunters Lodge Inn, lies 1½ miles to the south-south-east. There are no other known examples of this type of site nearer than Salisbury Plain, though it is tempting to envisage the stone circles at Stanton Drew as having a related ceremonial function, perhaps at a slightly later date. Excavations at Gorsey Bigbury showed that the site was built earlier than the use of Beaker pottery (see below, p 61) on the site, though this evidence itself indicated that people had lived on or beside the site during this secondary phase.

Little is known about the living sites of the Neolithic period. They are not represented by visible structures on Mendip, but some at least are presumably indicated by the surface scatters of flints common on the high ground and the relatively rare occurrences of Neolithic artefacts in caves. Tom Tivey's rock shelter near Leighton, from which came a complete bowl, is one such example; Sun Hole near Cheddar with its pottery ladle is another. That men were living and working on Mendip in the period c 4,000–2,000 BC is also indicated by the many flint and polished stone axe-blades found in the area. The flint came from the chalk country, some of it imported as large lumps of raw material subsequently worked into shape on Mendip. The axe-blades form part of a well-attested 'trade' in hard stones from various parts of western to southern Britain. Many Mendip examples came from West Cornwall, others from North Wales, the Lake District and even Brittany.

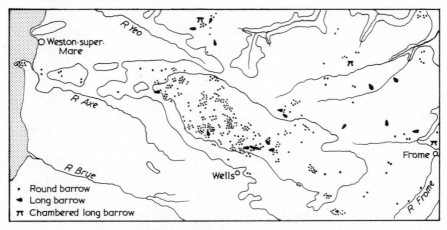

Fig 9   Distribution of long and round barrows on Mendip.

Long Barrows

In contrast to the slight evidence for living sites, the places of the dead are monumental. Long barrows, as they are called, are nevertheless not very common on Mendip, the distribution seeming to be peripheral to the main concentrations in Wessex and on the Cotswolds. Only five, plus a possible bank barrow, occur on the high ground of Mendip proper, with a cluster lying on Broadfield Down to the north and a scatter of ten or so between Mendip and the Bath/Frome area (see Fig 9). Undoubtedly the best-known and most visitable is that at Stoney Littleton between Radstock and Wellow which, although heavily restored, clearly illustrates the main characteristics of the 'megalithic', chambered type of long barrow: a long mound, trapezoidal in plan and almost triangular in elevation, with the highest part towards the wider end where an inturned entrance gives access to a central passage with side-chambers and a terminal chamber. This is the 'Cotswold-Severn' variety, but by no means all of Mendip's long barrows are similar, despite external appearances. One at Priddy, for example, was apparently a stone cairn surrounded by a low revetment but with no chambers; others in St Cuthbert Out parish appear to be simply long mounds. On Pen Hill one of them with side-ditches is, quite exceptionally, 227m long and looks like the bank barrows at either end of the Ridgeway Barrow Group in south Dorset (below, p 62). Though the records of the Neolithic barrows in the Mendip area are now conveniently and exhaustively assembled, the quality of excavation and the amount of destruction is such that we have tantalisingly inadequate information about even burial itself in the two millennia to c 2,000 BC.

The Second Millennium BC

With the evidence again being mainly sepulchral, and with similar caveats about its quality, the period between c 2,000 and 1,000 BC is difficult to write about historically. At the beginning Mendip, in common with many other parts of eastern and southern Britain, saw the arrival of new people, the first clearly evidenced in the archaeological record for some 2,000 years. These we call the Beaker people, simply because of their characteristic pottery, one form of which we call a beaker. In fact the pottery was made in several forms and with a variety of decoration; but it is generally distinctive, not least because of its high level of technical competence compared to its insular predecessors and successors. On Mendip it has been found at Gorsey Bigbury, and amongst debris in a swallet hole nearby (above, p 59) where it seems to indicate an occupation site, though probably the people there towards the middle of the millennium were not the earliest of the Beaker immigrants. Their pottery has been found on the foreshore and in the sand cliff at Brean Down and in the Chew Valley. Nevertheless, the Gorsey Bigbury material is most important. About 100 different pots were represented, one of the largest assemblages of Beaker pottery in southern England, and with them a big collection of animal bones indicated that cattle, pigs and some sheep were all being kept. In addition, the impression of a single grain of naked barley could hint at the arable side of the economy although, more soberly, it really serves to underline the crippling paucity of environmental evidence from later prehistoric Mendip. For the rest of the millennium, such evidence as there is, apart from the barrows, reflects the changes in metal technology and typology better documented farther south in Somerset and elsewhere in Britain.

Round Barrows

Mendip's chief claim to notice in the Bronze Age rests on its round barrows, the circular mounds of varying structure below and within which part of the population was buried during the second millennium. Some 460 round barrows have been identified in 'old' north Somerset from Mendip to the Bristol Avon, of which more than 300 occur on Mendip itself (see Fig 9). The densest overall concentration is from above Croscombe west right across the Mendip plateau to the combe between Cheddar and Shipham, a distance of only 16km (10 miles). This concentration can be compared with the three other great round barrow cemetery areas in southern Britain: in the area centred on the South Dorset Ridgeway, there is an average density of ten barrows per square mile over some 45 square miles, rising to forty per square mile if a 1 mile wide strip along the Ridgeway itself is taken alone; around Stonehenge, the barrow concentration in 12 square miles gives an average density of about twenty-five per square mile; the concentration around Avebury covers 9 square miles averaging ten barrows per square mile. On Mendip, the area defined above covers some 30 square miles and contains almost exactly 300 barrows. The average density is therefore also some ten per square mile—a remarkable consistency with Avebury and south Dorset, which nevertheless underlines the primacy of the Stonehenge complex.

Within this Mendip focal area, and on eastern Mendip, where another fifty or so round barrows have been recorded, the barrows occur singly, in pairs, in small clusters and in major groups. The groups—cemeteries is surely a permissible word in the context—are themselves arranged in deliberate patterns: in lines as on Beacon Hill and on Small Down, and south of the Priddy Circles on Ashen and North Hills; or in clusters around some focal point or feature as on Stock Hill, Chewton Mendip, and near Barrow Rake Farm, St Cuthbert Out. In only a very few cases, compared to south Dorset and the Cotswolds, is there a direct relationship between a round and a long barrow: one example lies beside the main road just north of Chewton Mendip. On the other hand, we seem to see on Mendip, even if we cannot appreciate its significance, as striking a correlation between the earlier henge monuments and round barrows as has been noted at Stonehenge, at Avebury and in south Dorset. It would not be surprising therefore if future work on Mendip produced, perhaps beneath one of the hill-forts (see below, p 65), a Neolithic causewayed enclosure similar to those already discovered in each of those other three areas.

Excavation of Mendip's round barrows has been going on since Roman times but those with adequate records are few. The best-excavated examples, now all destroyed, lay on Chewton Plain. Their details, briefly summarised, give an indication of the structure and contents of these funerary sites. In one was a primary cremation in a pit; in a second was a primary cremation in a collared urn covered by a flat slab, with a secondary cremation in a pit and three intrusive crouched Roman inhumations near the edge of the mound, which consisted of an earthen core capped by non-local stones. Two other barrows covered primary cremations, one with a flint arrowhead. Another covered a primary inhumation associated with bits of Beaker pottery and had been opened in the Roman period. A sixth barrow also contained a primary inhumation, this time flexed in a crouched position on its side in a slab-lined grave; but this was replaced, some 1,700 years later, by another crouched inhumation, one of three Roman burials inserted into the barrow, which consisted of a heap of earth over the original grave, on top of which was a walled cairn, in its turn covered by soil. These excavations further produced a few more precious scraps of that environmental evidence so scarce on Mendip: three of the barrows contained oak charcoal, one of them ash too, suggesting that the trees in the locality in the later centuries of the millennium may well have been similar to those of today.

The excavated Chewton Mendip barrows are probably typical of the majority on Mendip, though others have produced more elaborate structures and, rarely, more exotic finds. A barrow on Black Down, Burrington, covered a stone grave containing a complete Beaker of 'classic' proportions, possibly the earliest of our period so far found on Mendip, and was built as two ring cairns against which a later (c 1,400 BC) cremation cemetery had developed. Beneath a round barrow at Pool Farm, north-west of the Castle of Comfort Inn, was another stone-lined grave. The stone forming the south side is probably the most important single 'find' from Mendip in this period, for it is covered with incised decorations in the form of ten small hollows and six feet—a remarkable object, difficult to parallel in Britain and best compared to rock-carvings in southern Scandinavia. It is now safely in Bristol City Museum. At Tyning's Farm, only a mile or so west of Gorsey Bigbury, five barrows were excavated, the most elaborate containing a central ring-cairn of Old Red Sandstone blocks faced with upright limestone slabs. It and another, consisting of stone cairns retained by outer kerbs, were surrounded by penannular ditches, while the other three in the group were basically earthen mounds with complex structural histories. In a primary burial pit beneath one of these barrows was an inverted urn containing the cremated bones of a woman and child, a bronze awl, jet beads and green segmented faience beads.

The bronze awl reminds us that, technologically, the significant development of this millennium was the appearance of metal, first copper and then bronze. Quantitatively, the early metal on Mendip is not impressive, the main example being a bronze dagger from a barrow in Old Down Field, West Cranmore. It was not until after c 1,500 BC that bronze objects became more common. Tools like palstaves and sickles appeared but, although south Somerset is characterised by many ex-amples of Middle Bronze Age technology, few of these products reached Mendip. Indeed, on present evidence it seems that after a *floruit* in the centuries after c 2,000 BC as a burial and cult centre, surely for a con-siderable area round about, Mendip declined into relative in-significance until its own mineral resources, notably lead, iron and then silver, were demanded by the next stages of technological development.

The First Millennium BC

The metal technology of the prehistoric communities in southern Britain changed significantly twice in the last thousand years BC. In the later stages of the Bronze Age after 1000 BC, lead was added consistently to the products of the bronze-smith and, later still, iron was increasingly used instead of bronze/lead as the preferred material for a widening range of artefacts. Not that bronze ceased to be used: it persisted right through the millennium and beyond as the metal for a wide range of decorative objects such as broochesg in any case, it was only in the last centuries before the Roman Conquest and then during the Roman period that iron came into common use for daily purposes in, for exam-ple, farming.

Evidence for these important developments is present on Mendip but the significant role that the area must surely have played in them has largely to be inferred. Lead of course was present in quantity in the Mendips and much iron ore is available in various forms in the surroun-ding landscape. Although direct evidence of exploitation in the first millennium BC is hard to come by, it is most unlikely, particularly in view of the general scarcity of metalliferous deposits in southern Britain, that the mineral resources of Mendip were not worked by later prehistoric man. It is tempting, for example, to see the relative concen-tration of bronze hoards and artefacts of later prehistoric times in Somerset as reflecting the availability of lead on Mendip just as the large amount of later ironwork reflects the local availability of iron ores. On the other hand, there is no physical evidence yet identified on Mendip

10 From Wavering Down a Saxon estate (and modern parish and county) boundary stretches east over Callow Hill: open hilltop country contrasts with early hedged fields and later walled enclosures and modern afforestation on distant Black Down

11 The overall medieval field-pattern survives at Little Keyford, south of Frome: the open-field strips, fossilised by later hedges, are clearly seen from the air

12 Four primitive Norman carvings at Blagdon which have survived three rebuildings of the parish church

13 'The goodly new high tourrid steple' observed by Leland at Chewton Mendip *c* 1540, symbolising the later medieval prosperity deriving from wool and cloth

14 Medieval townscape at Axbridge: long narrow strips of building and garden radiating from the market place (*see* Gazetteer, p 215)

itself for prehistoric mining—has it really all been destroyed by medieval and nineteenth-century workings?—and the evidence for bronze and iron smelting is not common. Indeed, no bronze-smith's workshop is known before the Iron Age, though both bronze and iron working sites are known in the last centuries BC and into our era, evidenced mainly by 'smelting hearths' and slag. Three caves, for example, Read's Cavern, Rowberrow Cavern and in Chelms Combe, Cheddar, have produced such evidence.

HILL-FORTS

This supposed importance of the area in technological terms is not reflected in the superficial field record which is typical of much of southern Britain. No field monuments can confidently be ascribed to the earlier part of the millennium; thereafter the hill-forts dominate the Mendip archaeological landscape. There are between seventeen and twenty hill-forts on Mendip proper, depending on the definition of a hill-fort, with important outliers at Worlebury, Cadbury Congresbury and Brent Knoll. Generally, if superficially, they appear as empty areas enclosed by one or more banks and ditches broken by one or more entrances. Sometimes they are visually impressive, like Dolebury, Maesbury and Tedbury; mostly, however, they are surrounded by low banks and slight ditches, and many are in a poor state of preservation. One indeed, Dinghurst overlooking the Churchill gap, has been completely destroyed; another, at the north-east corner of Brean Down, has its military aspects accentuated by installations of World War II (themselves now very much part of the site's archaeology). In size these sites range from the roughly 65 acres of Tedbury to 1 acre at Dinies Camp, Downhead, half a mile north of Cranmore Tower, so almost certainly a whole range of functions, and different combinations of functions, is being masked by bracketing them all together under the umbrella title of 'hill-forts'.

In the first place, even if any are truly military, a significant difference of intention by the builders must be represented by the contrasts between, for example, the areas enclosed, the positions of the sites, and the size and complexity of the enclosing structures. It is difficult to believe that Dolebury is the same phenomenon as Burledge, overlooking the south-east corner of Chew Valley Lake above Sutton Wick, or that either is the same as Dinies Camp. It seems likely that, in looking at Mendip's so-called hill-forts, we are in fact looking at a range of settlement type from homestead to incipient town, and a range of function from farm to fortress.

A major difficulty here, again, is lack of evidence. We can see these sites and it is improbable that their number will be significantly increased; but in the absence of good excavated information, it is impossible to move confidently from description to sequence or from listing to social, political and economic prehistory. No major excavations have taken place on any of the hill-forts, so there is no local basis, only general analogy, for a discussion of function; several small-scale excavations of varying competence—Brean Down, Banwell, Dolebury, Burrington, Burledge, Small Down, Tedbury, Kingsdown and Dinies Camp—have taken place and provide some information, particularly about the enclosing banks and ditches, without indicating whether the sample examined is representative or otherwise. Nevertheless, on the available evidence it appears that some sites were in use earlier than others—Burledge, Pitcher's enclosure, Banwell—that some were in use during the middle and later pre-Roman Iron Age (c 400 BC onwards)—Dolebury, Tedbury—and that at least one, Kingsdown, belongs specifically to the first/second centuries AD.

This scrappy information could well hint at an interpretation postulated for Wessex: an early phase of relatively numerous small enclosed settlements, a middle phase of consolidation into fewer, larger units, and a final phase of local 'imperialism' focused on two major centres, in this case Tedbury and Dolebury, with Worlebury a third claimant to the west. If the seventeen to twenty 'hill-forts', in addition to their multifarious functions, also represent a sequence in a socio-political process, then their overall distribution on the ground cannot be regarded as a pattern of settlement existing at any one time. Nevertheless, the overall distribution can be interpreted as supporting some such sequence, for it is notable how the hill-forts tend in any case to cluster towards the western and eastern ends of Mendip where the two major sites lie. The same observation can be expressed differently: the relative absence of hill-forts on central Mendip, and the possibility that those there are early anyway, suggest a consolidation to east and west politically and, in addition, might hint at an increasing abandonment of the central area with a deteriorating climate perhaps helping to create an appearance not dissimilar from today's. All, however, is supposition in default of good evidence.

OTHER SETTLEMENTS

Though the hill-forts dominate the archaeology of the period, they by no means represent the whole picture. Other types of settlement existed and have been briefly glimpsed in archaeological contexts. The earliest

settlement evidence in the area came in the form of a ditch coinciden-
tally beneath the Roman temple at Pagan's Hill, Chew Stoke, while
other later evidence, including the foundations of circular, timber
houses, was excavated on low-lying ground nearby now filled by Chew
Valley Lake. Another settlement, so far the sole example of its type on
Mendip, was partly excavated when the M5 motorway cut through into
the Lox Yeo valley near Christon. Significantly, the site, though firmly
in the Mendip hills, lay on a relatively sheltered knoll just above the
valley floor. Traces of one round timber building were recorded to one
side of an area containing fifteen pits, in eleven of which were thirteen
skeletons. Most of the burials were flexed, though often placed without
much care in pits already containing rubbish. Two burials shared pits
with a dead dog and although all, except one wearing an iron bracelet,
were unaccompanied by grave-goods, the pits produced a large amount
of occupation debris ranging in date from early to late in the pre-Roman
Iron Age. Probably the site was a type of unenclosed farmstead of which
many other examples await discovery in the area. Another, again with a
round, timber house, lies under a Roman farmstead at Row of Ashes
Farm, Butcombe.

We can guess that the farmers were cultivating small, squarish fields
with wheat and barley, and were keeping cattle, horses, sheep and goats;
but of direct evidence there is very little. Some of the best comes, once
again, from caves, for communities were certainly living there—and
burying there too. Wookey Hole, Read's Cavern (with its notable iron
shackles), Gough's Old Cave and Hay Wood Cave are some of the caves
with evidence for activity in the last centuries BC and the early decades of
the first century AD. Whether these people were of the Dobunnic or
Durotrigan tribes we do not know. Mendip just before the Roman
Conquest seems very much to have been a frontier territory, a no-man's-
land in which, as coins appear for the first time in the local
archaeological record, coin hoards like that from Nunney were buried
for safety, and not recovered.

Roman Conquest to Saxon Settlement

Mendip is one of the places in Britain where AD 43–4 really made a
difference. Conquest came and with it a Roman military presence.
Nothing is known, unfortunately, of the events of the Conquest nor
indeed exactly when and how the army took over; but certainly imperial
lead was being produced by AD 49 and it seems probable that Mendip
became a centre of Roman activity very soon after the landings of 43.
Indeed, since the mineral resources of Britain, somewhat exaggerated in

reports circulating in Gaul before the invasion, were probably as attractive in Roman eyes as the grain which Britain had been exporting to Gaul, it could well be that Mendip was one of the prime targets. If so, this could explain Vespasian's urgency to pacify the Durotriges since hostile forces to the south could hardly provide a satisfactory background to state investment in industry. The actual course of the Conquest of Wessex is generally now seen as being heavily dependent on sea-transport but, from whichever direction Mendip was taken, a route march to Charterhouse would have been required. The thought raises, however, the possibility that Sea Mills in Bristol was used as a base in this initial phase. Otherwise, a long walk north from Dorset or north-west from Salisbury Plain would have been necessary.

Lead Mining

A small military fort, probably of more than one phase, shows clearly on air photographs, and is just visible on the ground, on a small spur overlooking the Blackmoor Valley near Charterhouse. It has not, however, been excavated, so its occupants and dates(s) are unknown. It is of course tempting to see it as the base for a military detachment supervising the takeover, organising the native labour and directing the construction of the first roads. Certainly this sort of activity must have been taking place in the first five years after 43–4 since early post-Conquest inscribed lead pigs give us the vital information. Lead pigs, or ingots, are simply oblong blocks, trapezoidal in cross-section, in a form suitable for transport, and they have in fact been found in numerous places in southern Britain and on the Continent. One from Wookey Hole (see above, p 67) was inscribed:

TI . CLAVD . CAESAR AVG . P.M. TRIB. P. VIIII. IPM XVI DE BRITAN (product) of Tiberius Claudius Caesar Augustus, Pontifex Maximus, in the ninth year of his Tribunician power, and sixteen times acclaimed Imperator, from the British (lead-silver works).

From internal evidence this stamp can be dated 49; another pig, this time from Blagdon on the north side of Mendip, can be similarly dated. Several of the later Mendip pigs have an inscription moulded on the front:

BRIT.EX.ARG.VEB
British (lead) from the Veb . . . lead-silver works.

If we correctly identify the Charterhouse area as the centre of the lead-silver works, was its Roman name 'Veb'-something? And does this place-name element by any chance survive still at Ubley—'V(e)b' with the element 'leah' appended? Unfortunately, a duller but sounder explanation is that the 'Ub' is derived from a Saxon personal name such as 'Ubba' (see below, p 254).

The early and successful imperial exploitation of the lead-silver deposits must have had numerous social consequences. If, for example, British communities were concentrated in a few of the hill-forts, would they not have been dispersed? A hint that this may have been so is that several settlements in the area apparently begin in the mid-first century. The Row of Ashes settlement at Butcombe is a case in point, with a rectangular wooden house apparently marking the start of life anew on a pre-Roman Iron Age settlement; and there too, associated with all the contemporary evidence for metal working in bronze, iron and lead, were fragments of Roman military chain mail, otherwise something of an odd item on a small peasant farm. The idea of a deliberate planting out of the population in the countryside round Mendip is at least a possibility. Alternatively, if central Mendip was marginal to the centres of pre-Conquest activity as suggested above (p 66), then it may have been necessary to draft workers into the new mining centre at Charterhouse. Certainly the direction of labour must be envisaged, not only for the mines but also to build roads.

ROMAN ROADS

The early export of lead implies that at least the main roads were soon under construction. Mendip is linked eastwards across Salisbury Plain, via Sorviodunum to Winchester (Venta Belgarum) and the port at Clausentum (near Southampton) from which lead was probably shipped across the English Channel. It has been suggested that the road continued west from Charterhouse to Uphill, providing a more obvious outlet from the River Axe to the Bristol Channel; but the ground evidence is unconvincing. Another road led north-east from Charterhouse down across the Chew Valley towards Bitton, from which there was easy access westwards to Sea Mills (Abonae) on the River Avon, again with access to the Bristol Channel. Pigs have been found at Bristol and Bath in or beside the Avon, but they have likewise been found beside the eastward road to Southampton Water.

Four of them were found together at Green Ore by Rookery Farm. Here was one of the large settlements from the first century onwards, its activities indicated by plentiful evidence of smelting. What is probably a similar settlement, as yet unexcavated, lies south of the road and east of

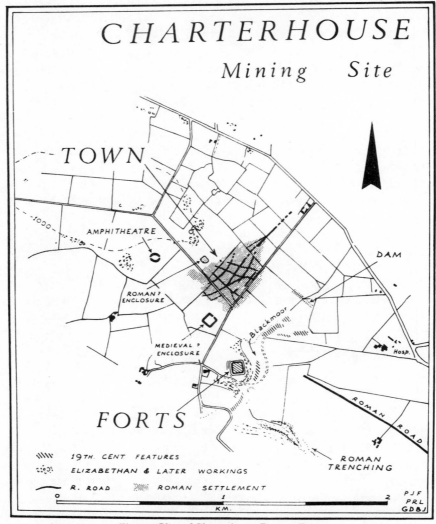

Fig 10   Plan of Charterhouse Roman Town.

Priddy village, stretching some distance into an area of nineteenth-
century re-smelting. On Beacon Hill, $4\frac{1}{2}$ miles farther east, the eastward
road crosses or is crossed by—it is not known which is the earlier—one of
the main roads of Roman Britain, the Fosse Way, coming up in textbook
straightness from Exeter to Bath (Aquae Sulis) and beyond to
Cirencester (Corinium), Leicester (Ratae) and Lincoln (Lindum). It
may originally have been intended to mark the rear of a frontier zone,
serving bases and establishments like Charterhouse pushed out in front,

but as soon as the frontier itself was moved to the Severn and beyond into Wales it ceased to have any strategic importance. Its enduring civilian importance as a line of communication roughly along the interface of highland and lowland Britain is demonstrated by its service today as everything from trunk road to footpath. The shortest, and quickest, way from Mendip to Leicester is still basically to drive along the Fosse Way, while the road to Southampton Water was lost long ago.

SETTLEMENTS

A small planned town with dubious amphitheatre and complex waterworks developed at Charterhouse (see Fig 10) but, minerals apart, Mendip proper did not apparently develop into a thriving part of the Roman province, probably because it remained under imperial control. A modest prosperity developed along the valleys to north and south, especially on the north where a string of villas, possibly planted by Gaulish capitalists in the late third century, are spaced out along the Yeo and Chew Valleys, with 'native' settlements, known on the hillsides, as at Row of Ashes Farm, Butcombe, north of Blagdon Lake, and suspected beneath existing villages like Congresbury, Wrington and Blagdon (see below, p 74). On Mendip itself, a villa site at Star, Shipham, was first occupied as a non-villa settlement in the mid-first century, acquiring a range of stone-footed buildings by c AD 100 which lasted through several modifications for some two centuries. About 300, the whole was demolished and replaced by a range of rooms with a corridor, again enlarged and modified before apparently also being demolished some time after c 350. People, however, continued to live on the site, now using hand-made pottery, a striking similarity with the evidence at the Row of Ashes farmstead, 5 miles away north-east across the Yeo valley in Butcombe parish. Star villa, together with what is undoubtedly a much larger villa settlement with a cemetery on Winthill, Banwell, are isolated examples in western Mendip. The latter has produced one of the few intrinsically beautiful—and valuable—archaeological finds from Mendip: a decorated late-Roman glass bowl, now in the Ashmolean Museum, Oxford. No villas are known on the central highlands (cf the pre-Roman Iron Age situation, above, p 66, and the situation in the Second millennium BC, above, p 61). Indeed, rather remarkably, the characteristic cluster of villas around Bath hardly extends south on to eastern Mendip: beyond those at Paulton, Wellow and Hinton Charterhouse, the Whatley villa (actually in Nunney parish) alone qualifies as of Mendip. Even the small town on the Fosse at Camerton and another Fosse-side settlement at Charlton, just east of Shepton Mallet, are not truly on Mendip.

It seems that the Roman administration was solely interested in minerals as far as Mendip was concerned, and that the great bulk of the hills was only of marginal interest to the farming communities basically settled on the lower ground to north and south. There are some fields of probable Roman date, notably at Bradley Cross east of Cheddar, north of Bleadon, above Christon, and on Brean Down, but probably these are the surviving outer margins of lower-lying agricultural systems. Some people were living in caves, particularly in the third and fourth centuries, their main interests seeming to be herding and metal working, including counterfeiting coins. In the later period, pewter production became an important local industry using Mendip lead, Camerton being the nearest known manufactory, so presumably miners continued to be the bulk of Mendip's small, and relatively impoverished, population.

Religion and Burial

The third and fourth centuries also saw the development of local pagan religious centres, Romano-Celtic temple sites. Outside Bath, the largest so far located in the area was on Pagan's Hill, Chew Stoke, with another u miles to the west at Henley Wood beside Cadbury Congresbury hill-fort. Both sites are visible from a temple on Brean Down, a temple characterised by an unusual plan with projecting wings in addition to the normal central *cella* and ambulatory. An almost exact replica of this plan appeared in 1972 when another temple site, this time already badly damaged, was excavated on Creech Hill, Lamyatt, just off the south-eastern corner of Mendip. Both temple sites were in use in the fourth century; indeed, at Brean Down the temple was not built until after 367 and certainly continued in use into the fifth century. The last phase of its life was marked by a small rectangular building built just to the south of the temple proper beside a large mound, probably a prehistoric barrown still visible above the cliff edge today.

Over the cliff and slightly inland lies the great Brean section already referred to (above, p 53). In one of the higher layers inhumation burials indicate a cemetery which stratigraphically lies between Roman and medieval. It seems extremely likely that this is an early Christian cemetery, dating from sometime between the fourth and eighth centuries AD. Little is known about this particular cemetery but the type is represented elsewhere in the area, notably at the two Romano-British temple sites on Henley Wood and Creech Hill, Lamyatt. It seems possibly significant that all three temple/cemetery complexes occur just outside a hill-fort. That on Brean Down, east of the temple, has produced evidence from a very small excavation that it may have been re-used in Roman times or later, while the Cadbury Congresbury site has shown conclusive evidence of occupation and construction, probably in part at least for religious purposes, from the fourth to the sixth centuries. One of the indicators is the presence of imported Mediterranean pottery, plausibly with Christian associations, of types now well known in western Britain and Ireland. Other material at Cadbury Congresbury indicates links with Western Europe and pagan Anglo-Saxon eastern England, the whole showing in many ways a remarkable range of contacts with the remnants both of the civilised, classical world and of the barbarian Europe replacing it.

The Last New Settlers

It is, however, not surprising that this evidence—and there is surely more to come—should be concentrated at the moment at Mendip's western end and its adjacent Bristol Channel approaches, for it was the sea rather than the land which was the main medium of movement and communication in these seminal centuries. It is difficult to perceive what was happening along Mendip's length, paralleled to the north by the frontier earthwork now called West Wansdyke, though the Brean and Cadbury Congresbury results at least indicate some of the archaeological evidence that can now be sought. It would be no surprise, for example, to find Dolebury re-emerging as an important centre of local life in the fifth century, though probably much of Mendip lay rather as it did until the Enclosures of the later eighteenth and nineteenth centuries (above, p 66 and below p 105) and as Black Down is today. On the other hand, on however reduced a scale, possibly lead mining continued and metal working persisted; certainly there is plentiful evidence, if not from Mendip itself, of a continuing tradition of bronze and iron craftsmanship in the Severn Basin well into the early medieval period.

Hill-forts and temples apart, it is nevertheless unlikely that there was much settlement on Mendip, or indeed that Mendip as such was very important, as the area generally adjusted to the collapse of an urban-based administration and a capitalistic, monetary economy. The changes were taking place amongst the communities and on the lands spread along the river valleys, around the edges of the marshy alluvium, along the main roads and around Bath. These changes, in where people were living, in how they made a livelihood and in how they were grouping themselves, had been developing at least from the 360s when a fairly severe shock seems to have been administered locally to the established order. It was just over two centuries from then to the Battle of Dyrham (577) when, according to the 'official' account in *The Anglo-Saxon Chronicle*, pagan West Saxons took over the Cotswolds and, by implication, Bath (was West Wansdyke built by Britons about now? Or was it already old?). Nearly another century was to pass, again according to the same source, before the West Saxons burst through the physical constraint of Penselwood (658) and absorbed politically the British lands to the west.

Conventionally, it is from the mid-seventh century onwards that the basic rural settlement pattern of today was established by West Saxon newcomers, giving us our nucleated settlements, the Horringtons and Whatleys of eastern Mendip. There are obvious exceptions, however, like the eloquent Stratton-on-the-Fosse, where a continuity of actual settlement site from Roman times is suggested. We can also surmise that some of the present villages only took root in their existing places in later Saxon times. Is it not also likely that many a Saxon farmer, moving into a populated landscape already with 300 years of readjustment behind it since the heyday of the villa estate economy, in fact settled into an existing framework? Priddy village is at the western end of a large Roman settlement (above, p 70); Cheddar developed north of a villa, immediately west of which a royal palace grew up in late Saxon times. Camerton village is just downhill from and north of a late Roman/possibly early Christian cemetery lying between it and a small roadside town on the Fosse; Shepton Mallet, so awkwardly situated just off the Fosse, may well owe its chronic traffic problem to a shift in settlement focus from Charlton beside the Fosse, now its eastern suburb, in the centuries between 366 and 658. Mendip's early history is written not only in its dead archaeological monuments but also in its living landscape, many elements of which existed before the arrival of the last major folk movement into the area thirteen centuries ago.

Notes to this chapter are on pages 266-9.

4

Saxon and Medieval Landscapes

Frances Neale

Saxon Settlement

THE MENDIP LANDSCAPE which the Saxons found in the 650s survives today in many of the names still used for places and features along its length. In three ways the place-name evidence supports the suggestion, made at the end of the previous chapter, of some elements of continuity between British and Saxon settlement.

Some names which the newcomers found in use on their arrival, they continued to use themselves: names in the British language used by the Iron Age inhabitants of Mendip, and preserved in this way to the present day. Such names include the rivers Axe and Frome, two of the main natural boundaries of Mendip; Mendip itself, probably connected with the British *mynydd*, 'hill'; Priddy (*pridd*, 'earth'), its British name evidence of its long pre-Saxon mining associations; and the chain of natural landmarks along the spine of Mendip: Pen, Crook and Brean, to which the Saxons, adopting the names presumably without understanding their meaning, added their own tautological descriptions: Pen Hill, Crook Peak, and Brean Down. The British *crŭc*, 'peak' or 'hillock', occurs several times along Mendip: Crook Peak and nearby Christon, Churchill, Church Hill south of Croscombe (called Crichull in 702), Evercreech from Creech Hill nearby, and the isolated Critchill Farm south-west of Frome. The continued use and preservation of these names implies contact between newcomers and older inhabitants, and an element of continuity enhanced rather than diminished by the uncomprehending addition of 'hill' to the existing name.

Apart from these few earlier survivals, a blanket of Saxon place-names marks their progress in taking possession of the newly acquired territory. Many are purely descriptive: Black Down and Blagdon; Hale (Winscombe): the hollow; Callow: the bare hill; Wells; and the expressive Cheddar, from *ceodor*, the deep, dark cavity or 'pouch'. Others record man-made features, old by the seventh century: the barrows of Elborough, Emborough, Rowberrow; the Iron Age ramparts (*burh*) labelled Tedbury, Maes-(or Marks-)bury, and Dolebury; or the Roman roads which gave their names to Stratton-on-the-Fosse, and perhaps also to Street (st672502), Newman Street (st651447) and Stoney Stratton (st655394). Fords were vital to communications, especially across the more broken land at the east end of Mendip, and so needed identification: Coleford, Cloford, Keyford, Egford, Edford, or simply plain Ford (st591537). A number of minor Saxon names have remained in local use, remarkably unaltered. The distinctive watershed of Shute Shelve perpetuates Saxon *la Scyte*. The road still called The Lynch is a mini-ridgeway (Saxon *hlinc*: ridge) joining two parts of the Winscombe valley settlements. Hylsbroke, the name of Langford Brook in 904, survives as a house-name. Perhaps most mysteriously evocative of all is Murder Combe, the deep, overgrown cleft where the Frome–Mells road crosses Whatley Bottom. This name is no relic of a nineteenth-century colliers' riot or eighteenth-century highwayman: but memory of some unknown local tragedy, recorded as *Mordrancombe* in 942 and preserved as part of our place-name heritage ever since. The great majority, however, are possessive place-names: Locc's family (Locking), Locc's settlement (Loxton) and Locc's river (Lox Yeo); Bana's well and Wine's valley (Banwell and Winscombe); Waendel's tree and Truttoc's hill (Wanstrow, Trudoxhill). Saxon-owned *tons* or settlements are scattered the length of Mendip, often in clusters: such as Hutton, Loxton, Christon, Webbington, Compton (Bishop), Bourton at one end; and Shepton (Mallet), Charlton, Pilton, East and West Compton, North Wootton at the other. Yet these possessive Saxon names do not necessarily imply the creation of settlements where none previously existed. They could equally well represent the takeover by a Saxon newcomer of an existing British settlement, emphasising the new owner by attaching a 'personal label' to the place. The frequency with which recent archaeological work is producing Romano-British finds, and occasionally buildings, from sites now occupied by Saxon-named villages, would seem to support this facet of British-Saxon continuity.

New Saxon creations might seem more definitely implied by the few names which suggest primary and subsequent stages of settlement: names such as Ston Easton, which is east of, and by implication later than, the principal village of Chewton Mendip; or similarly Weston Town, west of Wanstrow. Westbury-sub-Mendip lies west of Wells, with Easton in turn lying east of Westbury: a triple relationship. Slightly different, the Charltons near Shepton Mallet and Kilmersdon, and Chilcompton set at the head of a side valley above Midsomer Norton, imply secondary settlements on the outskirts of estates by the surplus 'churls' and younger members of an overpopulated community.

A third element in place-names suggests a degree of continuity.

Remarkably few Saxon names on Mendip imply pioneer farming and its associated landscape changes. A meagre four names—not necessarily all Saxon in date—suggesting early farmsteads are discussed below (p 97). Shipham, Shiplate and Shepton (Mallet) take the roots of the medieval wool and cloth industry back at least to Saxon times, but sheep farming involves minimal alteration of the landscape. There is a conspicuous lack of the -*ley* names denoting the woodland clearance usually associated with the Saxons: only Leigh-upon-Mendip, Coley, Whatley and Ubley. When so much of the Saxon charter evidence (see below, p 81) suggests a cleared, farmed landscape, the implication follows that the Saxons were utilising and developing settlement and landscape patterns that were basically already in existence; pioneer farming had ceased to be a major feature meriting record as a place-name.

A fourth element of continuity which, like the place-name evidence, hinges on the long-delayed Saxon advance beyond Selwood, derived from the influence of Christianity. By the time the Saxons reached Mendip, they were no longer pagan but Christian, and respected the traces of British Christianity which they found. These include the tenuous, much-debated evidence of dedications: St Vigor at Stratton-on-the-Fosse, St Bridget at Brean, St Nectan at Cheddar, and the association of Lantokai with Leigh-on-Mendip. More solid is the archaeological evidence of apparently Christian burial grounds associated with Roman and post-Roman sites, from Brean and Winthill in the west, to Camerton in the east.

The Saxon settlement of Mendip under Cenwalh, and the missionary work of his kinsman St Aldhelm, took place almost simultaneously. In the last decades of the seventh century, Aldhelm founded a religious community at Frome, as well as at Bradford-on-Avon to the north, and Bruton to the south. He and King Ine are reasonably associated with the origins of Wells. He died in 709, in the little wooden church at Doulting. Fragments of carved Saxon crosses have been found around the same area, at Frome, Nunney and Shepton Mallet; while another fragment at Rowberrow suggests the spread of the Saxon church westwards. By the time of King Alfred, in the late ninth century, 'minsters' existed at Banwell and Cheddar: probably only two out of an organised system of minster or missionary churches covering the area. The 'community at Cheddar' merited special mention in King Alfred's will; and by the tenth century there was a second Saxon church in Cheddar: the little private royal chapel dedicated to St Columbanus, erected over the earlier Saxon hall within the palace compound (see p 90-1). Wells became the cathedral church of the diocese in 909. By the middle of the tenth century, the minsters serving large areas were being replaced by

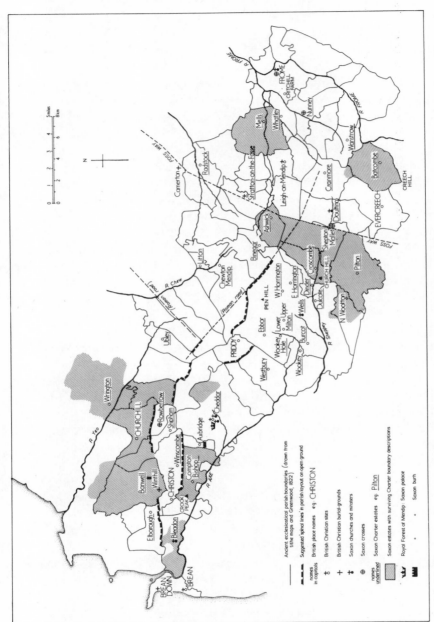

Fig 11   Saxon Mendip—showing parish/estate layouts; British place-names; British and Saxon
Christian sites and Saxon estates.

more local parish churches. Bleadon church is mentioned in 956, and is doubtless typical of many other modest, rural and undocumented Mendip churches.

Mendip Estates

To this same late Saxon period may also be assigned the development of the parishes themselves, on the one hand centred around the parish churches, but on the other an equally intrinsic part of the early secular estates that were often their *raison d'être*. The parishes of east and west Mendip are distinctively different shapes, reflecting the way in which the differing terrain has conditioned landscape history (see Fig 11). Those at the west end tend to be narrow and angular in shape. Many are laid off from a continuous spine of high ground, to form classic layouts extending from hilltop through hillslope to valley, with the settlements lying at the foot of the hill near spring line or river, and on the chief routes around the bottom of the hill. Such layouts suggest open hilltops, where a parish/estate could be planned with some degree of systematisation. In east Mendip, the parishes are more rounded and less deliberate in shape, utilising the valleys penetrating the hills and forming an erratic jigsaw over the higher ground between. This pattern suggests an absence of open ground and systematic planning; instead, a parish/estate started in the valley and, piecemeal, gradually pushed back the tree-cover, up either side and towards the head of the valley. Settlements tend to be situated centrally within these more circular parishes.

The four parishes of Ubley, Compton Martin, West and East Harptree form a classic block of the western 'strip' layout (see Fig 13, p 89). Of similar size and alignment, they span the range of available land (see also p 89) from hill to valley, with the four villages lying at the foot of the hill and linked by the principal road. Four of the five parish boundaries down the hillside utilise stream-gullies on the lower hillslopes; the westernmost is a dry gully significantly named Merecombe, the 'boundary valley', and so called at least by the early twelfth century. The fifth boundary, symmetrically (and perhaps deliberately) the central one of the group, is based upon the old Roman road from Chew up to Charterhouse. The hilltop head ends of the parishes utilise prehistoric barrows as boundary markers, but it is possible to discern an attempt to keep to a line through Blagdon to Ubley and Compton Martin. The protruding hammerhead of West Harptree parish would appear to break this pattern; but in fact the apparent anomaly provides valuable clues to the extent of two formerly separate medieval hilltop estates:

Temple Hydon and Chancellor's Farm. Excluding these estates, the original West Harptree would have finished more or less in line with Compton Martin. This particularly fine example of Saxon and medieval estate planning seems worth recording as it was unfortunately destroyed by the reorganisation of local government boundaries in 1974 (see p 13).

The layout of parish and estate went hand in hand, and ecclesiastical parish boundaries are a valuable aid to a study of the surviving Saxon charters of Mendip. The estates mentioned in these charters cannot be taken as a representative sample, since the charters only survive where—and because—the recipients were literate, record-keeping ecclesiastical bodies. Nonetheless, the coverage by both surviving and lost but recorded charters is sufficient to show that the parish/estate layout which was to form the basis of Norman and medieval Mendip was in existence by the tenth century. A sweep of charters, mostly of the 940s and 950s, shows that the eastern flank of the hills was effectively parcelled up, even though only two of the charters, for Mells and Batcombe, survive in any detail. The great Pilton charter of 702, neighbouring North Wootton of 946 and the list of Wells estates c 1065 establish the pattern of pre-Conquest estates in central southern Mendip. To the north, chance records of Saxon Litton, Chewton, Binegar, Stratton and Radstock (Welwestock) presuppose the existence, also, of the intervening estates. Similarly, the Saxon estate of Blagdon is implied by a charter (lost) for Ubley on one side, and another (surviving) for Wrington/Burrington on the other. To the west, the conjunction of several ecclesiastical landowners, all literate and tenacious of their rights, has preserved a block of documentation for the layout of Saxon estates at this end of Mendip.

Occasionally, traces of the physical boundaries of these Saxon estates survive on the ground. One of the most striking is the die-straight Saxon boundary between Compton Bishop and Winscombe, running from Crook Peak along the natural boundary of the Wavering Down skyline, past 'Ealmes fold' (the only sheltered spot for stock keeping being now occupied by Hill Farm) to the remarkable land-bridge watershed of 'la Scyte' (Shute Shelve). 'The path uphill', continuing straight to 'Callow', is marked by the remains of a bank and ditch and—a particularly remarkable alignment as seen from Wavering Down—by a dense, wide no-man's-land strip of undergrowth, where the twentieth-century parishes and farms on either side still respect this example of Saxon estate planning.

Where these Saxon charters survive with a boundary survey, which acts instead of a map to define the area of the grant, the landmarks

15 Hill edge and hilltop: between Ubley and Blagdon the erratic shapes of fields cleared piecemeal from medieval woodland give way to the mathematical enclosures resulting from Acts of 1771 and 1784

16 Hilltop enclosures following Acts of 1792 for the parishes of St Cuthbert Out, Dinder and Croscombe. The faint line of the Roman road from Charterhouse crosses the line of the Somerset & Dorset Railway in the centre of the picture below the hill-fort of Maesbury

17 John Billingsley of Ashwick (1747–1811) who was largely responsible for the enclosure and improvement of the Mendip plateau

18 Warren Farm, one of the new hilltop farmsteads established in Ubley parish following the Enclosure Act of 1771

chosen along the boundary can provide information about the Saxon landscape. Trees are frequently used as boundary markers, especially at the eastern end of Mendip: implying a wooded landscape, but one sufficiently cleared to make specific trees definable. Prehistoric barrows and hill-forts were utilised wherever available, as reliably permanent and prominent landmarks; so, too, was the Roman 'Old Fosse' road on the boundaries of the Pilton and Radstock estates. Many other roads were clearly extant in Saxon times: La Drove at Bleadon, Combisberghewei or Copplesbury Lane and the 'Old Way' at Batcombe, the Milkway above Cheddar and many other named and unnamed 'weies'. Evidence of farming appears: ploughland is mentioned at Batcombe and Pilton, fields at Batcombe and Cheddar, farmsteads at North Wootton and Cheddar, 'folds' for stock at Compton Bishop and Bleadon. Hedges feature at Pilton, Burrington, Mells and North Wootton; a wall at Pilton; and dykes at Bleadon and Batcombe. Sheep are mentioned at Mells and probably at Burrington, and wolves (awareness of which implies stock-keeping farmers) at Mells, Batcombe and Wrington. Such details can be multiplied many times. In themselves small and, because the surveys are essentially linear, selective, they do add up to the first shadowy written record of a settled, farming landscape.

Mendip was royal territory—all the surviving Saxon charters originated as grants from the king—and the south-west generally was a stronghold of the Godwin family. The impact of the Norman Conquest in 1066 upon the established Saxon order might therefore be expected to be drastic. In personal terms, the takeover of the new order as summarised 20 years later in Domesday Book was certainly thorough. Apart from King William himself, Norman lords such as Roger de Corcelle, the Bishop of Coutances, Serlo de Burci and major tenants such as Azelin de Perceval, nicknamed The Wolf, all appear holding long lists of lands that must, it would seem, have upset the former status quo. The very occasional surviving English tenant, for example Brungar the Englishman at Havyatt, or Godwin an Englishman at Draycott, are identified by this badge of rarity. Yet when the distribution of land tenure on Mendip is analysed (see Fig 12) the impact of the Norman, like the Saxon, Conquest would appear to have been less marked than at first thought. Along the length of Mendip, the distribution and balance of the royal and ecclesiastical estates survived the Conquest unchanged, and formed a strong element of continuity which stabilised and contained the changes that did take place. Moreover, the distribution of these unchanging estates prevented the build-up of any great power blocks among the new secular Norman landlords, whose holdings were all scattered and intermixed. A careful balance, it seems, prevented any

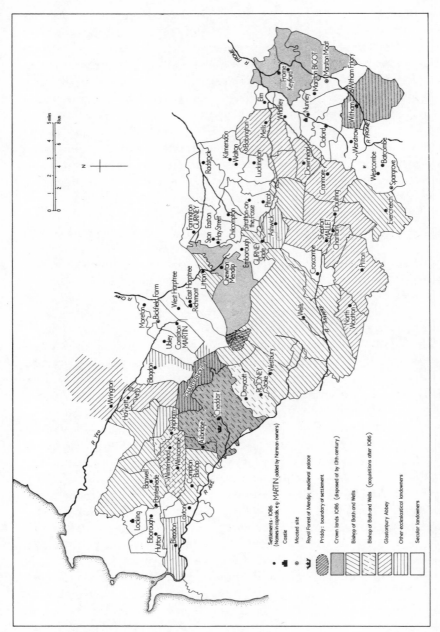

Fig 12   Norman and medieval Mendip—showing settlement pattern and distribution of landownership from 1066 onwards.

Settlements - 1086
(Names in capitals e.g. MARTIN added by Norman owners)

Castle

Moated site

Royal Forest of Mendip: medieval palace

Priory : boundary of settlement

Crown lands 1086

Bishop of Bath and Wells

Bishop of Bath and Wells (acquisitions after 1086)

Glastonbury Abbey

Other ecclesiastical landowners

Secular landowners

one landholder achieving complete dominance—and preserved in the process the older Saxon patterns of settlement and estate. There are very few topographical Norman-French place-names on Mendip: Richmont (fine hill), the former castle at East Harptree; Vallis (from *falaise*, a cliff) near Frome; and the former Play Street, Cheddar, a corruption of *palais* and a clue to the site of the Norman royal palace, which is now called Station Road: more prosaic but equally useful in commemorating another defunct and fast-vanishing man-made structure.

The changes that did take place were personal rather than topographical. The Bishopric and Abbey continued: but Bishop Giso of Wells and Abbot Turstin of Glastonbury were Normans. The Norman Conquest, as a process of personal self-assertion, is demonstrated on Mendip in three ways. Some of the new Norman-French families emphasised their authority during the generations after the Conquest by attaching their names to the (Saxon) places they had acquired: Rodney Stoke, Shepton Mallet, Compton Martin, Gurney Slade, Farrington Gurney and Marston Bigot. Others built castles to demonstrate their power: at Richmont in East Harptree (see p 87) and at Locking. Many more expressed their ownership as dominantly but less aggressively by building or rebuilding their local parish church. A few of these Norman churches are mentioned in 1086, but many more survive on the ground. Sometimes the whole church still stands: the elaborate Compton Martin, or the simple field church at Christon. More or less extensive traces of a Norman church often survive subsequent rebuilding, as at Kilmersdon. Even when the whole church has been completely rebuilt, the Norman font (such as the remarkable decorated example at Locking) may be kept as proof of antiquity. One of the most curious survivals is at Blagdon, where the body of the church has been completely rebuilt three times, in 1317, 1823 and again in 1909, out of which survives one single stone from the earliest known church, carved with four powerfully primitive early Norman heads, staring pop-eyed at their twentieth-century surrounding (see Plate 12).

While the Saxon and Norman Conquests brought fewer changes than might have been expected, change did nonetheless come: but later, and as a result of three national political events unconnected with Mendip itself. The first two, the capture and ransom of crusading King Richard I and the problems of rewarding the Bishop of Bath and Wells, one of the negotiators for his release, and the pecuniary difficulties of King John which led to the sale of much of his land in this area, radically altered the balance of power on Mendip. The power of the Crown as a local land-owner was gone; and the territories of the Bishop henceforth formed one solid, dominant mass of land along the south side of Mendip. His estates were flanked by sizeable areas under the control of other ecclesiastical bodies: not only the ancient Glastonbury and Bath Abbeys, but smaller estates of Witham, Winchester, St Augustine's Abbey and St John's Hospital in Bristol, the Knights Templar, Stanley Abbey in Wiltshire and many others. The ecclesiastical dominance of Mendip was by the thirteenth century fully formed. It not only conditioned much of the medieval history of Mendip, but also holds the key to its decisive end in the sixteenth century with the third national event, the Reformation and the dissolution of the monasteries.

Village and Town

Domesday Book gives the first overall picture of Mendip settlement and landscape. It shows that by 1086 Mendip was already not one landscape but two: a duality which forms a central theme of its medieval history. The distribution of places listed in Domesday Book shows the villages of 1086 lying at the foot on the hills, with their associated landscape of streams, woods, roads and fields. They form a tightly-enclosing ring around upland Mendip, which is by contrast a blank area: a distinct landscape with a separate and equally distinct history. Only at the eastern end, with its different topography and estate pattern, are villages scattered evenly over the map. This ring pattern of settlement was a feature strongly emphasised in the earliest seventeenth-century picture-maps of Mendip, where a ring of village churches forms a surrounding border. It is a pattern still evident on the eve of the Enclosure era (see Chapter 5).

Almost all the Mendip villages forming this pattern have a compact, nucleated layout; but within this framework they offer a great diversity of shape, development and underlying history. Some, such as Batcombe and Croscombe, are linear villages by force of geography, cramped within a narrow, steep-sided valley. Others, superficially similar in layout, but without the same natural compulsion, are street-villages which have deliberately taken a length of the road as a focus, as at Compton Martin, with a back lane running symmetrically behind. A deliberately 'planned layout', never completed, can be seen at Mells, owned by Glastonbury Abbey. Here Abbot John de Selwood (1457–93) intended to rebuild the village in the shape of a cross; but he only completed one arm of his new plan: the significantly named New Street, a fifteenth-century terraced street linking the church and the main road.

Another group of villages has grown in a more circular fashion, around one central focal point. At West Harptree, a particularly fine example, the focal point is the meeting of six roads, with the parish church standing close alongside. The manor houses (two of them) take up a comparatively less important position, on the outskirts of the village. At Nunney, commerce dictated the focus of the village, with all the incoming roads funnelled into the small, triangular market place; it was granted a market in 1260. The church is set back on the edge of the village, while the castle (normally an early and focal feature of a village) is in this case a latecomer on the scene and occupies a position designed more for scenic than military effect.

Some villages have shrunk, like Christon where the earthworks of a formerly larger village extend up the hill. Others have disappeared altogether, like the village at Babington wiped out to make the Park, and the deserted settlement observed recently at Upper Milton. Others, again, have shifted or split in the course of their long history; this often makes for a particularly complex and interesting topographical patternm At Holcombe, the village migrated up the hill, leaving behind it the old Norman parish church and the slight earthworks of the original settlement. A recent examination of Bleadon has shown it to be a three-part village: the main settlement and field-system around the parish church; a second settlement centred on the manor house, and with its own medieval fields, which is probably the separate Manor of Oldmixon; and a third, abandoned settlement on South Hill. Blagdon is another three-part village, stemming from 1154 when Robert fitzMartin gave Blagdon church and its temporalities to the Cistercian Abbey of Stanley in Wiltshire. The church and nucleus of houses clustering around it, known as East End, occupies a bluff projecting from the steep northern slope of Mendip. The fitzMartins, however, continued to own the secular manor until the fourteenth century, and needed a headquarters. Space on the East End bluff was limited. Their manor house, farm, pound and associated buildings were sited on the adjoining bluff, and named West End: a full quarter-mile from the church. The third element is Street End, on the uphill border of the village, and this has the characteristic cellular pattern of lanes, paths and building plots as ociated with post-medieval mining settlements and seen most clearly at Shipham. It developed, probably between the sixteenth and eighteenth centuries, on the common land fringing the village on the side nearest the mines.

The towns that ring Mendip are as diverse as the villages. Wells is a tenth-century cathedral city, Axbridge a tenth-century fortified town. Frome was a flourishing market town in 1086 and probably before. Shepton Mallet, Midsomer Norton and Radstock, on the other hand, were medieval villages that only became towns under the impetus of local industry in the seventeenth to nineteenth centuries. One intended town that failed altogether was Rackley, near Compton Bishop, set up under papal and royal charters 1179–89 as a port and borough on the navigable River Axe. All that now remain are the farm preserving the place-name, and traces of two wharves in the bank of the much-altered river.

A curious common denominator between several of the older Mendip towns is the way in which they have shifted their sites over the centuries. Frome moved from the river-crossing at Spring Gardens to the site of the Saxon St John's Church. The town centre of Wells, where the street plan is aligned not upon the present but upon an earlier cathedral church, has gradually migrated from around St Cuthbert's towards the cathedral and the 'wells' themselves. Recent research has now suggested a shift of site at Axbridge, at first appearance one of the least altered medieval towns in the area. Sited on the edge of the royal Cheddar estate, the original function of Axbridge was to collect the supplies needed for the royal household when it was in residence at Cheddar, or to sell them and forward the proceeds when it was not. From this developed in turn a market and, to provide the necessary currency, a Saxon mint. In the Burghal Hidage of c 911, Axbridge was listed as one of the fortified towns of southern England, with a wall some 550 yards in length. The position of this *burh* wall has long been a mystery. It is now suggested that the original Saxon *burh* in fact lay immediately to the south of the present Square. With more peaceful late Saxon/Norman times, and the increasing marketing required by the royal household at Cheddar, the market square with its parish church grew up immediately outside the cramped *burh*, on the main road and the spring line. By 1086 it already had some urban organisation, with its thirty-two burgesses. As the fortified *burh* fell altogether into disuse, and the market flourished, the medieval town grew up entirely focused upon the Square, leaving the Saxon site to decline into a quiet back street. The present town is thus the second Axbridge: a medieval town with street plan, building layouts and many actual buildings in a remarkable state of preservation.

Axbridge retains intact a group of small, timber-framed medieval houses of a kind that were widespread in the fifteenth century but have, in this area, almost completely disappeared with the era of stone rebuilding in the seventeenth century. Stone medieval houses survive occasionally, as at Mells and Vicars' Close, Wells. Elsewhere, medieval houses do survive, but are almost always more or less hidden or incorporated into sixteenth or seventeenth century rebuildings. Nonetheless, medieval roofs, fireplaces, doors and windows have remarkable powers of survival, and many more examples are coming to light with the growing interest in vernacular architecture. Buildings survive for almost all levels of medieval society except the lowest and least substantial peasant cottages, from the great beamed halls such as the Old Baptist Chapel at Croscombe and Old Court, Upper Langford, or the smaller stone court room of the Manor House at Shipham with its fine windows, down to substantial farmhouses such as Vallis, plainer farmsteads like Pool Farm, Sandford, and the occasional surviving yeoman's cottage such as Orchard Cottage, Sandford. A few medieval moated houses survive on the lower ground fringing the Mendip area: Bickfield Farm, still with its house; impressive, abandoned Marston Moat; and remote Spargrove, near Batcombe. Of the three medieval castles of Mendip, Locking motte-and-bailey appears to have no known history. Richmont at East Harptree and Nunney Castle, however, form a neatly complementary pair. Richmont was a Norman keep on what is still a spectacular and evocative site. It had its moment of dubious fame in 1138 when a ruse enabled King Stephen to take it by storm. Nunney Castle, on the other hand, was not built until 1373 and provides the startling spectacle of what was once a fashionable French-style château-castle set down in a Somerset village.

For all the ecclesiastical domination of Mendip, there was apart from the canons of Wells only one religious house in the area. This was the Carthusian Priory at Witham, founded by Henry II in 1179 as part of his penance for the murder of Thomas à Becket, and the first Carthusian house in England. The religious house was established in a remote corner of Selwood Forest, on the south-eastern tip of Mendip. A corruption of its name was given to a farmstead on central Mendip, part of the foundation's original endowment, which became known as Charterhouse. The priory at Witham disappeared so completely after the dissolution that its correct site has only recently been rediscovered (ST758416) and the church, great cloister and associated buildings identified. Such complete disappearance of an ecclesiastical building is, however, unusual. Indeed, the most universal survivals of medieval Mendip are its churches, the subject of much detailed study. The great majority were more or less completely rebuilt in the fifteenth century. Their style, their famous towers—many now identified as the work of a single group of travelling masons—and, in some cases, their fine interior fittings are not, as the Norman churches were, simply an assertion of ownership, but a reflection of the economic prosperity of Mendip in the fifteenth century. Mendip produced wool, cloth, lead and stone (see Chapter 7); some of these products and much of their profits were put back into church buildings, by ecclesiastical landowners and prosperous lay tenants alike.

Two Landscapes: (1) Hillside and Valley

Immediately around these villages and towns of Mendip extended the intensively farmed medieval landscape of fields, meadows and woodland that served their needs: concentrated at the downhill end of the western strip-parishes, and centrally in the more circular valley-parishes of the east. Domesday Book provides the first overall picture of this landscape. There is more meadowland on the north side of Mendip, where estates run gently down into fertile river valleys, than on the south, where many descend abruptly into waterlogged marshes; and more woodland on the milder south and west flanks than on the north. Every estate has some ploughland; but only a few, where the topography provides a larger area of fairly level land above the marshes, as at Wells and Chewton Mendip, support more than ten ploughteams. Proportions of pastureland and numbers of demesne sheep on each manor tally closely with the extent of hilltop falling within its boundaries: moderate in Ubley, Compton Martin and the Harptrees, and very large in Cheddar and Wells. The east end, in keeping with its more broken terrain and more scattered villages, reveals a pattern of intermixed small and medium tracts of meadow, ploughland, woodland and pasture.

Many traces of this medieval farming landscape survive on the ground today, or can be picked out from maps and air photographs. In particular, medieval open fields have been 'fossilised' by sixteenth- to seventeenth-century hedges put around groups of strips which, though amalgamated into rectangular blocks, nonetheless manage to give an overall impression of the layout of open fields. Where medieval ploughing was, in times of land-hunger, extended up the hillslopes, traces sometimes survive in the terrace-like lynchets formed between the ploughed strips. Particularly fine expanses of such field-patterns are to be seen south of Frome, and around Chewton Mendip; while good flights of lynchets survive at Litton, Christon and Bleadon. Farther up the hillsides were the woods. Mendip woodland needs to be treated with caution, since it can undergo disconcerting changes. Original woodland in the areas on the south side, emphasised in Domesday Book, survives only in patches, mostly between Cheddar and Croscombe; and more extensively on the north side above Ubley and Compton Martin. All Banwell Hill, Sandford Hill, Dolebury and Mendip Lodge Wood, however, is nineteenth-century plantation. At Shute Shelve, Kings Wood on one side, with its name and its wild yew trees, is almost certainly ancient, while Rose Wood on the other is open ground in nineteenth-century prints. Ancient woodland at Rowberrow had disappeared by the late eighteenth century, but has since re-grown. Fields

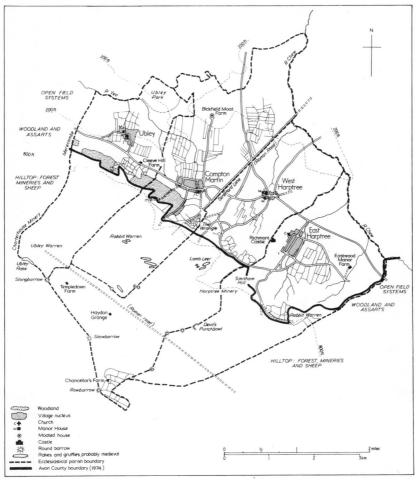

Fig 13   Ubley, Compton Martin, East and West Harptree—parish layout, settlement and
medieval field-patterns, indicating bands of land-usage.

were often carved out of the woodland on an individual piecemeal basis.
These 'assarts' form a characteristic jigsaw pattern of small fields along
the higher hillslopes, forerunners of the 'sidelings' of the Cheddar area.
A reference to crofts at Frome in 1218 which were free from common
rights suggests such assarts on the fringes of Selwood. On three occasions
in the thirteenth century, the bishop obtained licence to assart a total of
120 acres in the woods of Cheddar; the fields thus brought into cultivation were to be enclosed with a small ditch and a low hedge. Sometime prior to 1362, fields separated by boundary stones had been
enclosed near the woods of East Harptree. The Harptree area offers a particularly fine example of medieval field-patterns. The fossilised open
field-pattern of the valley around the villages changes abruptly to the

small, irregular assarts of the hillside, which in turn halt suddenly at the brow of the hill, beyond which are only the mathematical patterns of nineteenth-century fields (see Fig 13).

Because so many Mendip estates were owned by ecclesiastics, who were both able and literate estate managers, many detailed records of medieval estate management survive to complement the evidence on the ground. The abbots of Glastonbury compiled custumals of their estates in 1189 and 1238. The bishop did the same for his lands in 1290. These custumals, laying down the services due from each villager in return for their lands, provide not only the names of the ordinary inhabitants, but a virtual calendar of the farming year. Surveys, particularly those made for new owners in the sixteenth century, provide more details about the landscape as it stood at the very end of the medieval period. Kilmersdon, surveyed in 1571, still had its great open fields functioning, with the tenants holding unfenced strips and turning all their animals into the fields after harvest.

Two Landscapes: (2) The Hilltop

Above and behind this intensively developed landscape of the settlements was a second landscape, totally different in appearance and history. The demarcation between the two is not only a matter of contours, still less a creation of the enclosure era (see Chapter 5). It can be picked out, as at Westbury-sub-Mendip, in the continuous hedgeline formed by early fields along the edge of the hill; below the line are older, varied field-names and above are nothing but unnamed 'Allotments'. A name such as Street End, Blagdon, can emphasise the difference between the settlement area and the hilltop beyond. At intervals there occur the 'Lipyatt' and 'Rhodyate' names, still not wholly understood, but all on roads up on to Mendip and all implying the existence of barriers between the two landscapes. Lypiatts have been noted so far at Shipham, Cheddar, Churchill and near Holcombe. A *lepegeate* appears in the Ashwick Saxon charter, and *hlypcumbe* in that of Radstock. The English equivalent, 'Deerleap', is above Wookey Hole (ST51 7489); and Rhodyates occur at Blagdon and Banwell.

The hilltop above this demarcation line served three roles which conditioned not only its medieval appearance, but also in consequence its modern one, producing the landscape which characterises Mendip for most people today.

Firstly, it was the Royal Forest of Mendip. This role extended back to the Saxon kings of Wessex, if not beyond. The king himself owned Cheddar, which formed the core of the Forest. Here was his palace:

a series of royal hunting-lodges, built and rebuilt for successive visits, from the time of King Alfred on to the thirteenth and fourteenth centuries. The site of the palace was rediscovered in 1960, and a massive excavation exposed what is probably the most complete picture of a palace compound of such early date yet found in England. Some of the royal halls can be dated very precisely, from dated documents issued by the king and addressed from Cheddar. Similar documents issued from Frome, and reference to the 'gate of the king's hall' on the boundary of Selwood Forest in the thirteenth century, suggest a similar Saxon and medieval palace at the eastern end of Mendip, possibly on the site of the present Brewham Lodge.

Mendip Forest was a royal game reserve, with its own administration and jurisdiction which extended not only over the king's own estates but over those of other people where his forest rights were deemed to extend. Thus the forest jurisdiction continued even after King John had sold Cheddar itself. At its peak, the Forest of Mendip extended the whole length of Mendip, from Black Rock at the mouth of the River Axe to Cottle's Ash (now transmuted into Cottle's Oak) on the western boundary of Frome, so that it adjoined the Forest of Selwood. Between 1219 and 1300, however, the boundaries of both forests were redefined and limited to the original royal estates.

Although the 'Royal Forest', as a term, meant a game reserve not necessarily heavily wooded, there was sufficient woodland on the royal estate at Cheddar to make royal grants of timber a feature of Forest records. Large trees were sought after not only for timber building, but as scaffolding on stone church buildings; while occasionally woodland was granted to be cut for fuel for the furnaces of the local mine workings. Timber was sufficiently important, indeed, for it to become a source of friction when the manor of Cheddar had passed to the bishop and he claimed the trees as part of his manorial property and no longer a royal forest right. Trouble came to a head with open quarrels between manorial servants and royal foresters, and led rapidly to the disafforestation of Cheddar, and the effective end of the Royal Forest of Mendip in 1338.

The game preserved in the Royal Forest is known from licences, court and other records. King Edmund hunted the 'flying stag' with hounds (p 183). So, illicitly, did Richard Marshal of Congresbury in 1261, and was caught doing so with his three mastiffs. Still more reprehensible, the Rector and Clerk of Shipham were jointly accused of poaching in 1265, while in 1260 a virtual deer-trapping scheme had been uncovered, organised by Brother William and other Carthusians of Witham, presumably working from their base at Charterhouse. In 1283 Thomas de Berkeley obtained licence to hunt not deer, but foxes, polecats, hares and badgers in the Forest; but he was to keep out of the King's Warren. Numerous rabbit warrens, royal and private, were situated around the edge of the hill. Most only now survive as place-names: Rowberrow Warren, Warren Farm and Lodge in Ubley, Stoberry Warren above Wells and Warren Hill at Cheddar; but a few of the long banks called 'pillow-mounds', built to encourage the rabbits to burrow and stay in the locality, also survive, at Dolebury Warren within the prehistoric hill-fort, and on Shute Shelve Hill. On the outer fringe of Mendip, safely separate from royal territory, were private deerparks, ranging from the great parks of Glastonbury and the bishop at Pilton and Evercreech respectively, to smaller private parks such as those at Chilcompton and Ubley. Ubley deerpark, at the northern extremity of the parish, was extant in 1280 when Richard de Aumari was allowed to take five live bucks from Mendip, to replace five that had escaped from his park and presumably made their way back on to the hill. Grants of live deer from the Forest to stock such parks were not infrequent. In 1231 five does and a buck from Cheddar Forest were granted to the bishop for his deer park, and in 1225 ten does and two bucks had even been sent from Cheddar to stock a deerpark on Lundy Island.

The second role of hilltop Mendip was as a source of lead and other metals, stone and, at the eastern end, coal. The industrial activity of the seventeenth century onwards, described in Chapter 7, grew out of the medieval exploitation of Mendip, in its turn the successor to the prehistoric and Roman mining industries (Chapter 3). While the tradition of mining on Mendip is thus probably continuous from prehistoric times until the closure of the last coal mine in 1973, it would however seem that medieval mining was on a small scale compared with the Roman industry or the seventeenth-century revival. Documentation is extremely slight, and physical evidence has, by the nature of the occupation, been overlaid and destroyed by later exploitation of the same mineral-bearing strata. It is difficult, if not impossible, to distinguish medieval gruffies and tips from later ones, without excavation. Nonetheless, the scraps of written evidence suggest that medieval mining was as widespread, if on a smaller scale, as the later mining that pockmarks the hilltop today. In 1189 the bishop obtained a licence to mine for lead on his Mendip lands, and in 1235 he was also licensed to dig for 'iron and every other kind of mine' at Hydon. At the same time he was also given 40 acres of timber at Cheddar, for use as fuel 'so long as the timber shall last': suggesting an attempt at controlled use of woodland, not often recorded in the medieval period. In 1287 the monks of Witham acquired a similar licence to work 'all mines of lead' on their own estate at

Cheddar Gorge

Visitor Information

SOMERSET BY THE SEA.

WELCOME TO CHEDDAR GORGE

Cheddar Gorge is Britain's largest gorge and probably the country's best-known limestone feature. This immense cleft splitting the Mendip Hills from top to bottom is about 2 kilometres (1¼ miles) long.

How was the Gorge formed?

It used to be thought that the Gorge originated as a huge cavern whose roof collapsed. But experts now believe that the Gorge was largely cut by summer meltwater during the various "Ice Age" periods over the past two million years.

The area was never directly affected by Ice Age glaciation but would have experienced arctic conditions in which the underground drainage system was blocked with ice. Every summer when the winter snow melted there would have been an enormous flow of water which gradually cut the gorge deeper and deeper.

The carboniferous limestone, into which the Gorge is cut, was formed 280 – 345 million years ago. The horizontal bedding planes and vertical joints of the limestone divide the rock into natural blocks. Movements of the earth's crust since the limestone was formed mean that the rock at Cheddar Gorge now has a southerly dip of about 20 degrees. This dip is clearly evident at various places in the Gorge and accounts for why the cliffs on the south side of the Gorge generally have steeper and longer drops.

The spectacular cliffs on the south side of the Gorge are close to vertical and are over 100 metres (330 feet) high. In some places their height is nearer 150 metres (500 feet).

Spectacular viewpoints

For many visitors their first impression of the towering cliffs of Cheddar Gorge is from a drive along the road which runs through the Gorge. The best time to appreciate this drama on foot is when the road is quiet (try early morning or evening in summer or anytime out of peak season). When the road is busy it can be more rewarding to get away from the traffic and enjoy the views from the cliff tops.

Cheddar Gorge has an unusually large number of rare plants, including the Cheddar Pink and Cheddar Bedstraw which are found only in the Cheddar area, together with seventeen other plants which are nationally scarce.

The site's rich wildlife includes twenty-nine resident species of butterfly – over half the British list. Bats and dormice, both threatened groups, are also well represented.

The geology of the area is also an important part of the scientific interest. The two million year history of the Gorge and associated caves has been traced and study of the sequence of stalagmite deposits has provided important evidence of alternating warm and cold periods during the past 350,000 years. The bones of a caveman and ice age animals including mammoth, bison, cave lion and hyena have also been found in the caves.

Follow the Country Code

- Enjoy the countryside and respect its life and work
- Guard against all risk of fire
- Fasten all gates
- Keep your dogs under close control
- Keep to public paths across farmland
- Use gates and stiles to cross fences, hedges and walls
- Leave livestock, crops and machinery alone
- Take your litter home
- Help to keep all water clean
- Protect wildlife, plants and trees
- Take special care on country roads
- Make no unnecessary noise

Park and Ride

At busy times of year you may find the Gorge area very congested because of the sheer number of visitors. In the school summer holidays, a park and ride service is usually operated by Cheddar Showcaves from a car park on the western outskirts of Cheddar in an effort to reduce this problem. Tell your friends - it can take the frustration out of trying to park.

KEY

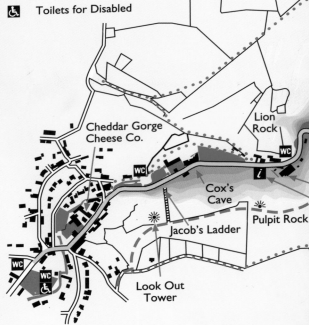

- Cliffs
- Gorge Road
- Parking Area
- River and Ponds
- Buildings
- **· · · ·** National Trust Permissive Path
- **- - -** Permissive Path
- **· · · ·** Public Footpath
- **— —** Bridleway
- **> > >** Very Steep
- Viewpoint
- **WC** Toilets
- Toilets for Disabled

Cheddar Gorge Cheese Co.

Lion Rock

Cox's Cave

Pulpit Rock

Jacob's Ladder

Look Out Tower

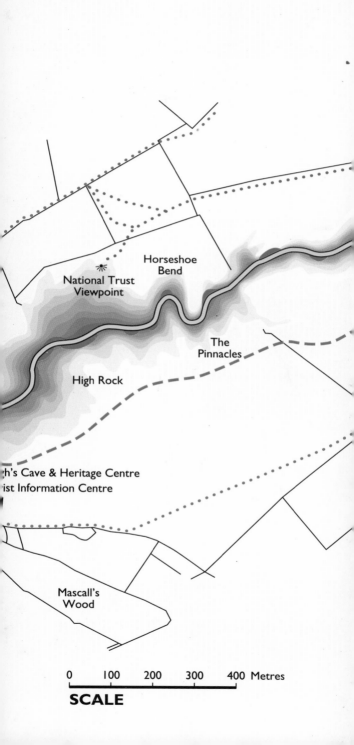

Horseshoe
Bend

National Trust
Viewpoint

The
Pinnacles

High Rock

h's Cave & Heritage Centre
ist Information Centre

Mascall's
Wood

0   100   200   300   400 Metres

SCALE

The River and Ponds

At the lower end of the Gorge one of the largest underground rivers in Britain emerges into daylight through eighteen separate springs.

This river, known as the Cheddar Yeo once powered seven water mills and this explains the origin of some of the ponds in the area. Other ponds were constructed by Bristol Waterworks Company in the 1920s. Water is abstracted from the river here and piped to Cheddar Reservoir for storage before becoming the drinking water of thousands of people in the surrounding areas.

Other attractions and facilities

A whole range of other visitor attractions and facilities are available in the lower gorge area including a wide selection of cafes, tea rooms, restaurants, public houses and shops. The Cheddar Gorge Cheese Company provides an opportunity to watch Cheddar cheese made in the traditional manner and a variety of other local crafts. The Parish Council's Garden of Fragrance offers a quiet riverside refuge.

Public Toilets are available at several locations. Facilities for disabled visitors are located in the Cliff Street car park and a Parent and Baby Room is provided for visitors to Cheddar Showcaves.

The **Tourist Information Centre** provides a full range of services to help the visitor, including an accommodation booking service. An out-of-hours display will give information on attractions and accommodation when the office is closed.
Tel : 01934 744071
Fax : 01934 744614

Site of Special Scientific Interest

An area of over 1090 acres (441.3 hectares) of the Cheddar Gorge, including the adjoining uplands and associated dry valleys at the head of the gorge, is a designated Site of Special Scientific Interest.

The area contains a wide range of semi-natural habitats including unimproved grassland, heathland, broad-leaved woodland and scrub.

Footpaths around the Gorge

There is a National Trust permissive path and several public footpath and bridleway routes which give access to the Mendip Plateau above the cliffs. You can use these routes to reach popular viewpoints (see map overleaf).

For the more adventurous walker the paths provide the opportunity of circular walks. A circular route 4 miles (6.5 km) long can take you above both sides of the Gorge. Alternatively you could complete your circuit by walking through the Gorge along the road. Maps and guides are available at local shops and the Tourist Information Centre.

Safety :

The cliffs on both sides of the Gorge are potentially dangerous.

- Take care near cliff tops
- Do not attempt to scramble up/down the sides of the Gorge – a rock fall could endanger lives
- Do not throw down or dislodge stones or rocks

Wear appropriate footwear and clothing to suit the weather conditions.

Cheddar Showcaves

The Mendip area contains numerous cave systems which are a typical feature of a limestone region.

Near the lower end of the Gorge there are two impressive showcaves – **Gough's Cave** and **Cox's Cave** – which are open to the public. Here you can penetrate deep into the ancient limestone and see a spectacular series of stalagmites, stalactites and other colourful rock formations which have taken over half a million years to form.

Cheddar Showcaves offer an inclusive ticket giving entry not only to Gough's Cave and Cox's Cave but also to their **Heritage Centre** and the opportunity to climb the 274 steps of **Jacob's Ladder** to enjoy the dramatic cliff-top views, particularly from the Look Out Tower.

You should allow yourself plenty of time to fully appreciate these attractions.

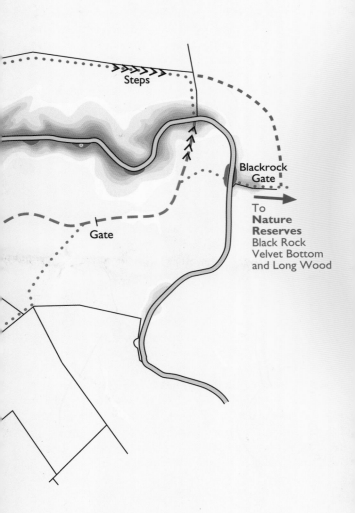

N

Steps

Blackrock
Gate

To
**Nature
Reserves**
Black Rock
Velvet Bottom
and Long Wood

Gate

**MAP OF
CHEDDAR GORGE**

Charterhouse. The framework of the principal landowners establishing their 'mining liberties' was thus starting to take shape in the thirteenth century, although the fully-formed organisation of the four Lords Royal and their Liberties of Chewton, Harptree, Priddy and West or Charterhouse only became apparent from the 16th century onwards (see p 146). Other landowners exploited small mines on their estates. An otherwise unrecorded lead mine on Glastonbury's estate at Burrington is only known because, in 1489, the churchwardens of Yatton purchased a ton of lead for their church roof from it, at a cost of £4 13s 4d. The individual, elusive miners themselves only start to appear with the increasing number of wills and surveys made in the sixteenth century. Typical miners were Walter White, William Oldland and John Page of Blagdon who worked two pits for lead at Hazel Down, above Ubley and Compton Martin; Walter White had half a hundredweight of lead in hand. William Reynes of Chew, making his will in 1543, described himself as a husbandman; but apart from leaving a cow to his servant, his main bequests were of a hundredweight of lead apiece to the churches of Blagdon and Compton Martin.

Orpitts Lane, mentioned in the Kilmersdon survey of 1571, acts as a reminder that mining was not restricted to central Mendip; although in east Mendip it has always been more concerned with coal. Small coal mines were exploited in the Kilmersdon area from at least the fourteenth century onwards, and several 'colepytts' were being worked by individual tenants in 1571. Quarries were similarly exploited on a private, local and small-scale basis, usually only for local building (see p 155). Occasionally, however, demand for the fine building stone produced by Glastonbury's quarries at Doulting, or the decorative Draycott 'marble' from the bishop's quarries there, both much used in local church-building, stimulated larger-scale quarrying development. Permits such as that of 1362/3 by which Glastonbury allowed Bath Abbey to quarry stone at Doulting from where the men of Whatley left off, southwards to the place where the Wells workmen had been quarrying, suggests an active and businesslike organisation.

Both quarries and coalmines, however, were essentially private, manorial concerns, whereas the lead mines, like the Forest, transcended property boundaries. The Mineries organisation as first written down in the sixteenth century (see p 146) was almost certainly the codification of long-established medieval customs. The four Lords Royal and their mineries, the ancient, simple methods of staking a claim, and the independent jurisdiction, even in cases of sudden death in mining accidents, are all products of this separate role of Mendip, totally distinct from the close-knit network of manorial controls that covered the surrounding hillsides and valleys.

Thirdly, the Mendip hilltop was common pastureland, on which all the surrounding settlements turned out their animals, and in particular their sheep. From references noted above (p 81), sheep farming had been a feature of Saxon Mendip; and by 1086 the pattern of pastureland and flocks was (see p 88) already established. For the great ecclesiastical landowners, sheep farming was the most profitable and labour-saving way of utilising their hilltop land, which was usually (especially in central and western Mendip) a long distance from the villages. Henry II's inclusion of the hilltop estate at Charterhouse in his original endowment of Witham Priory suggests that such sheepwalks were desirable as early as 1180, since this totally isolated foothold in central Mendip can have had little other use beyond its mining and pasture rights. Each settlement had its share of the hilltop pasture, on which all the villagers were free to turn out their stock. This right was jealously guarded. A famous dispute (by a later quirk of the surviving documents always associated with the Mineries Code, but in fact a completely separate event) over common rights brought Lord Chief Justice Choke himself to Mendip in 1461, to supervise the settlement of the case by the Lords Royal. The rights of all Mendip tenants to turn out in summer as many animals as they could feed through the winter was upheld.

Over and above the commoners' rights, special grazing rights were sometimes granted. William fitzMartin of Blagdon granted St Augustine's Abbey, Bristol, common of pasture for fifty sheep and thirty mares with their issue of two years, on the north side of the road called Raganachereswei: probably near the little farmstead of Ellick, which the abbey also held. In 1233, the Knights Templar acquired 20 acres of land (the 'extension' of West Harptree known as Temple Hydon, around the present Templedown Farm: see p 79-80) with which went the much more important right to common of pasture for 1,000 sheep and 60 other animals. Because the sheepwalks were open and unfenced, intercommoning arrangements were made between adjoining land owners. Burrington and Blagdon, Blagdon and Ubley intercommoned as neighbours: but on the open hilltop such arrangements might be much more far-reaching. Glastonbury, in a survey of Wrington and Burrington in 1517, claimed common of pasture over the hills from Burrington all the way east to their lands at Downhead and Doulting. Much earlier, in 1235, Bleadon at the western extremity of Mendip complained about obstruction of their common rights which extended to Priddy and Harptree.

Sheep on the great ecclesiastical estates, such as the Manor of

Wrington, with Burrington, were organised on a large scale. Manorial accounts of Wrington in the fourteenth to fifteenth centuries show the size of flocks, and gains, losses and sales of animals and wool through the year. The shepherd in 1491–2 received the remarkably high annual stipend of 26s 8d. He had on occasion one or two assistants, who helped to fold the sheep (with much expense on hurdles, tar and paint) near the village for the winter, and drive them up on to Mendip for the summer. Sheep were driven from Glastonbury to Wrington, and from Mendip to Glastonbury, and the shepherd received an additional 3s 4d for his stay on Mendip. A typical smaller-scale sheep farm kept by a more distant monastic landowner was that at Rowberrow, which belonged to St Augustine's Abbey in Bristol. In 1407 the abbot leased the farm to Walter Bevice of Wrington and Alice his wife. The abbey retained the sheephouse, and was to provide timber and carpentry for its repair, while the tenant-farming couple were responsible for all the other buildings. The Bevices, on the spot, were to make half the haycrop from the farm available for the abbot's sheep, and were to provide straw for thatching the sheephouse. The abbot was to organise the washing and shearing of sheep, but the Bevices had to find the shepherd's salary of 5s p.a. and provide hurdles for the folds. At the bottom end of the scale was the individual small village sheep farmer utilising his common rights: such as John Meryfield of Downhead, who died 1481/2 and whose principal bequests in his simple will consisted entirely of sheep: one to each of his godsons and twelve to his daughter Isota. The medieval flocks, large and small, that grazed on Mendip together made up the flourishing medieval wool and cloth industry described in Chapter 7, the chief monuments of which are the fifteenth-century churches in the surrounding villages and towns, all rebuilt when the medieval industry was at its height.

These three facets of hilltop Mendip, the Forest, the Mineries and the sheepwalks, have one important feature in common. All depended on open terrain, extending over the hilltop unimpeded by finite boundaries. It is this common feature that characterises the medieval, and has produced the modern, landscape of the hilltop. The Forest and the sheepwalks left virtually no evidence upon the ground beyond a few pillow-mounds and place-names; the mines and quarries leave plenty, scattered overall; but all three, the unobstructed game reserve, the gruffies following geological strata and the flocks on the hill for the summer, required freedom from the constraints of lanes, hedges, walls and fences that delineated the hillslopes and valleys. This open terrain, the great blank of Domesday Book, is, however, far from being a blank landscape. So many different interests were involved in hilltop Mendip—landowners and their commons, Lords Royal and their Mineries, and above all the king and his Forest—that they were in fact all the more anxious to define their territorial rights. The process of defining notional boundaries across open ground, without creating obstacles such as the boundary walls, hedges and banks that served elsewhere, produced a number of boundary surveys which carried the methods used in Saxon charters on through the twelfth and thirteenth, and into the sixteenth, seventeenth and eighteenth centuries. Boundaries were defined by describing natural features or man-made landmarks; and such boundary descriptions can be combined to build up an overall picture of the landscape.

The landscape they describe is essentially that caught, just prior to enclosure, by the map of Day & Masters in 1782, which in turn has much in common with the seventeenth-century picture-maps of Mendip. They all show an open hilltop, laced with unfenced tracks and drove-roads that curve, merge and divide again without any of the angular order and restraint imposed by fields and property boundaries. Many of these tracks had uncouth, ancient-sounding names: Raganachereswei, the Wyarepathe. Broad Way was doubtless a well-used drove-road, while Stanrode, Stanamlane and Foss Road may well be remains of the Roman road-system near Charterhouse. At the junctions of tracks there were often crosses or marker stones, which were probably particularly valuable in snow. Several such crosses are shown on the seventeenth-century Hobhouse map of Mendip, and more detailed sixteenth- and eighteenth-century drawings suggest they were true crosses, raised on pedestals. Meleweie Cross mentioned in 1181 may be associated with the Saxon Milkway above Cheddar, Hopwells Cross and Boultings Cross marked road junctions above Compton Martin, Meer Oak Cross stood at the head of Longbottom and Smetcombs Cross near Gorsey Bigbury, while Nedge Cross and Tor Cross marked the edge of the open hill above Chewton Mendip.

Prominent then as now on the open ground, round barrows formed landmarks which were frequently used as boundary-points for Forest, Mineries and manorial estates, as they still are for parishes. Nowadays they are largely anonymous; but their importance in the medieval landscape is emphasised by the individual names given to them: names which, it is obviously implied, were widely and generally recognised by all users of the hilltop: Stobarrow and Stangbarrow, Knightbarrow and Deadmansbury, Nigheberewes and Stondenestones, and many others. Mine workings scatter the landscape: a 'hollow duct', Harechine, Ubley Rake and Culverpitt Rake all suggest linear gruffies, while Snedelesputte, Selverputte and Scholdeputte were perhaps more or-

19 Gothick toll-house at Old Down on the Wells-Bath road built by the Wells Turnpike Trust

20 The first motor-bus to reach Mendip: the Bath-Midsomer Norton service at Radstock *c* 1906

21 The M5 (opened in 1973) cutting through the Lox Yeo valley with Crook Peak in the background

22 Cheddar station, 3 August 1869: the opening of the broad gauge branch from Yatton on the Bristol & Exeter Railway

dinary diggings. Water was all-important on the top of Mendip, both for stock and for mining processes, so that ponds and springs were valuable landmarks. Lynleghespulle (Lillypool Farm, near Shipham), Hoppewelle, Horsewelle, Hyndwell and Bikwelle were all used to mark boundaries of the Royal Forest and of the Witham Charterhouse estate. Where nothing else was available, special boundary stones were set up, to mark a boundary line without preventing the passage of sheep and huntsmen. Some were anonymous, but many had their own names: Sliperstone, Broadstone, Harestone and the *petra perforata*, the stone with a hole in it. Some names have a trace of hobgoblin: the stone called the Witch, another called Hob-in-the-Moss, Morgan's Stone and the stone called the Long Man. Most of these stones have disappeared; a few have been replaced by neat nineteenth-century boundary stones. One medieval survivor is the Donstone, on Callow Hill, mentioned as part of the boundary of the Borough of Axbridge in its royal charter of 1559. The Donstone is not particularly large, and some of the landmarks used on Mendip are tiny. Fair Well is a minute spring still to be found near St Cuthbert's, Priddy, where it is quite overshadowed by nineteenth-century mining reservoirs. Fair Well, however, was one of the boundary markers between Priddy and Chewton settled by the Bishop of Bath and Wells and Lady Joan de Vyvona of Chewton in 1296, and still marks the parish boundary between the two.

Uncouth and 'faery' names, tracks and crosses, prehistoric barrows, mine workings and a few scattered springs and pools, supplemented by boundary stones: all add up to an open, bleak, undeveloped landscape. Its unchanging appearance is emphasised by the perpetuation of these simple descriptions, with their limited range of features, from the tenth right into the eighteenth century. At the same time, the often small size of the landmarks, and their individual names, are evidence of the intimate local knowledge which Mendip people had of this open medieval landscape. While these descriptions emphasise its open, empty nature, it would be wrong to regard the top of Mendip as altogether uninhabited. Hilltop settlements, tiny and piecemeal, existed in greater numbers than is usually realised. Two names to which age and distortion have given an artificially primitive ring are Ebbor and Green Ore. Both in fact are derived from the same Saxon word: Ebba's-worth and Green-worth, two Saxon 'worths' or farmsteads. These are the only two 'worth' place-names in this area, and suggest some rather specialised local meaning as a hilltop farmstead. 'Aebbewyrth' appears as early as 1065, and several small twelfth- to thirteenth-century deserted settlements have recently been found there. Green Ore was an isolated hilltop sheep farm belonging to Hinton Charterhouse. A plan of c 1700 shows it as a couple of sturdy stone buildings set amid three small stone-walled enclosures, in a sea of open ground. It was probably typical of other detached farmsteads, such as the Witham sheep farm at Charterhouse. Another early farmstead was Ellick, above Blagdon, which was extant at least by the early fifteenth century. The 'Ill-wick' or 'hill-farm', with its fields clustered in a fold of the hills between the still open expanses of Black Down and Burrington Ham, retains something of what must have been its medieval appearance. The name of Tyning's, too, implies early enclosure on this otherwise typical nineteenth-century farm site. Chancellor's Farm, bordering Priddy but forming its own niche as an extension of West Harptree parish, was extant before the end of the sixteenth century.

Unique as the only proper village on this part of the hilltop, however, is Priddy. It appears briefly as the subject of a lost Saxon charter of c 688-726, is absent from Domesday Book and only reappears intermittently as part of the bishop's estates in the medieval period: enough, however, to show that it did exist as a village, with its twelfth- to thirteenth-century church, and enhanced by its fourteenth-century fair. On the map and on the ground, the nucleus of ancient Priddy, with its small, close-knit fields, its trees and hedgerows, and its deep-cut, curving lanes, is immediately distinct from the nineteenth-century landscape of straight lines, large fields, level roads and stone walls around it. That these were true village fields, for corn and hay, as early as 1235 is shown by an agreement that they could be enclosed, but that the Mendip commoners, who had been complaining, might turn their animals into them after harvest. The four mineries must also have presented the appearance of considerable settlements, to judge from the seventeenth- and eighteenth-century maps on which they appear: clusters of buildings, mine shafts with winding-gear, furnaces and kilns, tips and reservoirs centred on Charterhouse, Priddy and Smitham Hill. Finally, the hilltop must have been scattered with the folds and 'bothies' of sheep-farmers, living out on the hill all summer and rounding up their flocks from time to time. Increasingly, archaeological investigations are showing that earthworks, often hitherto dubbed prehistoric or Roman, are in fact medieval stock enclosures and isolated buildings.

Politics and Pioneers

The medieval hill-landscape was, therefore, far from unoccupied; but the settlements that did exist were, like the surrounding landscape, totally different, in their isolation and remoteness, from the nucleated villages of the valleys. This is the nub of the character of medieval

Mendip. The hilltop was not particularly wild, nor particularly extensive, nor remotely unknown. It looms above and behind every village of
the settlement-ring. It is always there—and yet always separate, contributing to the fabric and prosperity of the villages, yet remaining
distinct from them. Medieval people of Mendip lived in the one
landscape, and used the other.

The end of medieval Mendip is the end of this separation of the two
landscapes. It was abruptly marked by the national upheavals of the
Reformation and the dissolution of the monasteries, and the consequences of the minority of Edward VI. Between 1539 and 1548 these two
basically political developments broke, for the first time since the Saxon
period, the continuity and power of the great ecclesiastical landowners.
First all the monastic landowners, Glastonbury, Bath, Winchester,
Witham and others, disappeared altogether. Then the Bishop of Bath
and Wells was forced to sell many of his lands to the Duke of Somerset,
Regent of Edward VI. Some were subsequently recovered, but the
break had by then been made.

In their place came new owners: men who bought their estates for
cash, often piecemeal, breaking up the ancient territories. They were
farming for more immediate personal profit, and prepared to try new
methods of doing so. Perhaps most important of all, they lived on the
spot to manage their new estates. The mood of change was evident even
in estates that had previously been in secular hands. Many landowners
commissioned surveys, from which to assess the potential of their often
newly-acquired estates. At Kilmersdon in 1571 the old Manor and
Court House in the village was merely a 'site', while a stable there had
been newly converted into a dwelling house. Similarly, the former
Botreaux mansion a little way outside the main village, at Walton, had
fallen into ruin and was let as an acre of walled pasture: except for the
sheephouse which, stone-walled and tiled, was a cottage leased to Joan
Board, widow. At the same time, plans were afoot by which another
tenant was clearing land and building a new mansion at Bullock's Hill.
The centres of medieval authority were being abandoned or converted,
and a fresh start made. Similarly, about 1540 Sir John Newton of East
Harptree used Richmont Castle as a quarry from which to build himself
a more up-to-date residence at what is now Eastwood Farm, formerly
the castle grange. Another survey made at Ubley about twenty years
earlier than that of Kilmersdon, shows that in 1553 many of the villagers
had 'closes', paddocks and orchards around their houses, and many of
their holdings in the old open fields are also called 'closes', implying that
they were already being hedged, to give the fossilised field-pattern that
to some extent still survives today. The principal tenant, John Roynon

of Cleve Hill Farm, held fields 'which lyethe in severall [ie separately] togethers one close after thother'. The cumbersome effort to describe the small enclosed fields, still to be seen above the farm and under the woods, suggests how novel was the idea of such fields, all clustered around one farm. A descendant ventured further; in 1611 a John Roynon was brought before the manorial court at Ubley for making encroachments upon the common of Mendip with fences and ditches: perhaps higher up above Cleve Hill Farm. The group of fields around the significantly-named Newlands Lane above Blagdon are of similar appearance and situation to those of Cleve Hill, and may be of much the same date. The valley farmers were gradually encroaching on to the hilltop with their fields and fences.

On the hilltop itself, the classic example of the secular takeover is that of the May family at Charterhouse. Robert May purchased this part of the Witham estate in 1544, and the family settled there for several generations. Robert May having made this initial outlay, his son Robert May junior appears to have carried developments a stage farther. He provoked great unpopularity among the commoners by excluding them from Charterhouse Down—an action which led, as part of the effort to secure restitution of common rights, to the drawing of the earliest complete map of Mendip, the Hobhouse map with its ring of churches and lists of commoners. The only development that would effectively deny common access in this way was the creation of enclosed fields on the Down, around the Charterhouse farmstead. This, it would seem, was Robert May junior's contribution to the new estate, in the time of Queen Mary or Queen Elizabeth. The next stage, in the early seventeenth century, was the building of the present Manor Farm, Charterhouse (it had never aspired to be a manor in the medieval period): one typical example of the great rebuilding which, in the second or third generation after this great upheaval of ownership, gave Mendip most of the fine 'old' buildings distributed over both hill and valley today. Where the Roynons and the enclosures of 'Newlands', still based on the villages around the foot of Mendip, nibbled at the edge of the hill landscape, pioneers like the May family started to establish farms right on the hilltop, centralised among their own fields—the first hilltop fields since the remarkable settlement of Priddy.

Together, the two processes of gradual encroachment and pioneer farming marked the beginning of the end of the distinction between the two landscapes of Mendip. They paved the way for the final creation of the present hilltop landscape, described in Chapter 5. While these sixteenth- to seventeenth-century changes were of great importance for those living on or near Mendip, it was, however, a much longer time before they were sufficient to make any overall impact on the hilltop landscape. Seventeenth- and eighteenth-century descriptions (see p 102) make it clear that the hilltop as seen by outsiders was still a bleak wilderness. This slow, late change, however, only serves to emphasise that the landscape of the eighteenth- to nineteenth-century enclosure era is new compared with that of the centuries which preceded it. It lies correspondingly thinly upon the older open terrain of medieval, Roman and prehistoric Mendip, which shows all the more clearly through this topmost layer of the landscape palimpsest. An essential part of the character of the Mendip landscape is the awareness of this older and very different past lying just under the surface of present appearances.

Notes to this chapter are on pages 270-1.

5

Mendip Farming: the last three centuries

Michael Williams

THE PERSON WHO TRAVELS through the ordered and relatively prosperous landscape of the Mendip Hills at the present time could be excused if he or she thought that the mature scene on either hand had existed for ever. But on the contrary the present scenery is relatively recent. The preceding chapter has shown how very different the landscape appeared before about 1770.

To appreciate the changes in, and character of, what we see in the rural landscape, we need to know something about the history of farming during the last 300 years, during which time successive generations of farmers have struggled to win a living from a part of Somerset not generally considered to be the most productive. The story of that struggle is, perhaps, best looked at in three parts. Firstly, there was Mendip as it was during the century before 1770; secondly, Mendip as it was transformed by enclosures and reclamation; and thirdly, Mendip as it has evolved during the last 100 years.

Mendip before 1770

To write about Mendip farming before 1770 is very difficult because the sources of information are slight. Most travellers had their eyes focused more intently on other parts of Somerset; to them, Mendip was a waterless waste, a void, a vacuum, that was worth only a token statement for the sake of the completeness of their account, or, at best, a short description because they really could not avoid seeing the upland mass. Typical was Leland in 1543 whose sole comment was: 'The lengthe of Mendepe from este to weste by estimation is 20 myles and where it is brodeste a 6 myles, in many placis lesse', which was accurate but inadequate. The sheep farming on the high plateau was ignored; if there were any descriptions of the region they were concerned more with two local curiosities: Cheddar cheese, and Wookey Hole. Cheddar cheese always, and rightly, got a mention. In 1568 it was said to be 'excellent and prodigious', in 1662 the 'Best and Biggest', and in 1724 Daniel Defoe thought it 'the greatest and best of the kind in England'. With the cattle fattened on the Levels, the woollen manufactures of the western parts of the county, and the stocking knitting of Wells and Shepton Mallet, together with the broadcloths of the eastern Mendips, both based on Mendip wool, Defoe thought the cheeses were one of the most important products of the county.

Wookey Hole attracted attention as a curiosity but, surprisingly, Cheddar Gorge was ignored. The love of The Picturesque, particularly of wild mountainous scenery, so encouraged by the poetry of Wordsworth and the paintings of Salvator Rosa, had not yet affected early eighteenth-century British aesthetic tastes. Craggy scenes denoted barrenness and a lack of productivity, and their description was not worth the printer's ink. Perhaps a hint of what was to come lay in Celia Fiennes's account of her *Journeys* through Somerset in 1698, for after crossing Mendip her sole comment was that there were 'high ridges of hills which does discover a vast prospect all wayes' — it was simply a good vantage point for the rest of Somerset. William Gilpin, the prophet of The Picturesque and author of *Observations on the Western Parts of England* and of many other books on travel through England and Wales, went to Wookey Hole but bypassed Cheddar and Ebbor Gorges. For him Mendip was a mere 'background' to the grander view of Wells Cathedral and Glastonbury Tor with their associations of antiquity, although he did say of the cliffs around Wookey Hole: 'A recess of this kind appears of little value to those who are acquainted with mountainous counties, but in the south of England it is a novel scene.'

The age of The Picturesque, when the elements of the landscape were looked at as if they were parts of a painting, was also the age of scientific inquiry and careful observation, which showed its first flowerings in Somerset in the parish by parish accounts by Collinson in his three-volume *History and Antiquities of Somerset ...*, in 1791, by Locke in his *Survey*, compiled sometime between 1794 and 1798, and by Billingsley in his *General View of the Agriculture of the County of Somerset*, in 1795, which was printed in a second and enlarged edition in 1798. Although they did not eschew the picturesque or antiquarian, these authors were more concerned with the systematic collection and accurate first-hand observation of what the land looked like and how it was used. For example, in 1791 Collinson said of Mendip:

In many parts there is very little depth of earth, the rocks rising above the turf, which, however, affords good pasture for sheep and grazing cattle. The surface in other parts is covered with heath, fern and furze. The air, especially in the winter, is moist, thick and foggy, and so very cold that frost and snow inhabit these heights longer than they do almost any other parts of the county; and the few remaining trees, their leaves blasted and discoloured by the severe winds from the Channel, never attain to any considerable size.

He proceeds to emphasise the still-apparent distinction between the two landscapes described in the last chapter, contrasting the bleak upland with the 'fine vales' which surrounded it—intensely cultivated and grazed, and densely settled, with dozens of self-contained village communities. Apart from a few scattered houses such as those around Priddy and Charterhouse, only at the extreme eastern end of Mendip where the plateau was lower and less exposed was this settlement pattern broken (see p 88). Locke's account was substantially the same.

The pre-Enclosure landscape and farming pattern on the plateau, with its emphasis on common grazing, has been discussed in the preceding chapter (p 100). By the eighteenth century the common grazing was a useful and profitable addition to the economy of the villages, but it did not make them very prosperous compared to other settlements in Somerset. A hint of their prosperity relative to other parts of the county is given by the *Proportion Roll* of 1742, which confirms the evidence of the Hearth Tax of 1644/5. The *Proportion Roll* allocated the proportion that each parish should contribute to the raising of a county tax of £100. The average for every 1,000 acres (404.68ha) of ten Mendip parishes was 1s 5d (7½p); for ten parishes in the vales to the north, 2s 3d (11p); and for ten parishes in the Levels to the south, 3s 1d (15p), which made the Mendip parishes half as wealthy as their more prosperous neighbours to the south. The real wealth of Mendip at this time lay not in the farming but in the woollen manufacturing in Frome and its surrounding villages. Daniel Defoe described Frome as

> so prodigiously increased within these last twenty or thirty years that they have built a new church and so many new streets of houses, and those houses so full of inhabitants, that Frome is now reckoned to have more people in it than the city of Bath, and some say, than even Salisbury itself, and if their trade continues to increase for a few years more, as it has done for the past, it is very likely to be one of the greatest and wealthiest inland towns in England.

Mendip Transformed: 1770-1870

Because such a great proportion of the arable fields of Somerset had been enclosed from an early date, much of the effort in 'improving'

agriculture during the late eighteenth century went into the reclamation of the hitherto common grazing grounds of the lowland Levels, the
western hills near Exmoor, and the Mendip Hills. Agricultural improvement was spurred on by a rising demand for food from the rapidly
increasing industrial population of the country and by the stimulus of
high prices, inflation and scarcity during the Revolutionary and
Napoleonic Wars when overseas supplies of wheat were curtailed. These
pushed the price of wheat on the Windsor market from 52s 3d (£2.61p)
per Winchester quarter in 1794, to 144s 7d (£7.22½p) in 1801. These
trends, which had been evident for years before, put a premium on land
that could be converted to agricultural purposes. Attention in Somerset
was directed first at the Levels, and although there were experiments in
cultivation, their uncertain drainage conditions made them far more
suitable for grazing. At almost the same time the Mendip Hills were
'attacked', a potent factor in this early attention being that John
Billingsley, one-time wool manufacturer and later author of *A General
View of the Agriculture of the County of Somerset* and many articles on
agriculture, had devoted his time to farming at Ashwick Grove, near
Oakhill. Billingsley knew his local region intimately, and he was a major
goad in the effort to transform the old common grazing land and disused
mining areas of the plateau into 'productive farms' through enclosure,
and to rationalise the old commonage rights.

In 1770, East and West Cranmore acquired an Act to enclose their
part of Mendip at the extreme eastern end of the plateau, but as no
Award exists of the enclosure, there is no way of knowing the actual area
affected. They were followed by Ubley in 1771, and Doulting and Stoke
St Michael in 1775. During the years from 1782 to 1797 most of the other
settlements did the same: Shepton Mallet and Wookey in 1782, Blagdon
in 1784, West Harptree in 1787, Westbury, Compton Martin and the
Mendip portion of Bleadon in 1788, Croscombe and Dinder, and Wells
(St Cuthbert Out) in 1792, and again in 1793, East Harptree in 1794,
Banwell and Cheddar in 1795, and Shipham and Winscombe, and
Chewton Mendip in 1797. After 1797, only the enclosures of Cheddar,
Priddy and Rodney Stoke (1811) and, 100 years later, Burrington (1911)
were concerned with the main body of Mendip, and the remainder of
the enclosures were on the outliers of Carboniferous Limestone to the
north, at Wrington and Long Ashton Downs between 1807 and 1813.
There were, in addition, some private enclosures between Shipham and
Priddy.

To understand fully the impact of this transformation it is best to look
at the ways in which the soil was changed, the land use was changed, and
how the fields, fences and farms came into being.

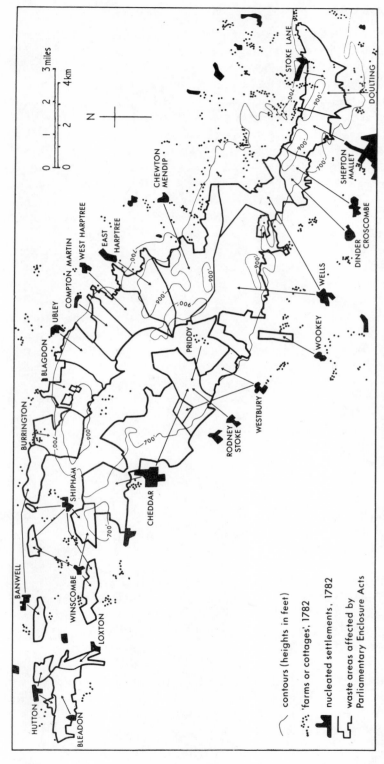

Fig 14 The Mendip Hills: based on enclosure maps and awards at the Somerset Record Office, Taunton, and on Day & Masters' map of 1782.

CHANGING THE SOIL

Fig 14 shows the areas affected by Enclosure, and the distribution of settlements, both individual farmhouses and villages, which are taken from Day & Masters' map of *The County of Somerset* printed in 1782. Most of the land affected by the Enclosure Acts was above 700ft (213.36m), on the exposed plateau top, although in the west, towards Brean Down, the 'waste' was located at a much lower altitude because of the greater exposure to the sea winds, and because of the shallow rocky soils which had developed on these steep slopes.

The high plateau had a distinctive soil cover, and it is important to know something about its character if we are to appreciate the way in which the bulk of enclosure went ahead and farming evolved, because the first and crucial task in the transformation of Mendip was to change that soil. Almost all the area enclosed, with the exception of the thin stony soils on the hill above Cheddar and in the vicinity of Bleadon and Loxton, is covered by a variety of soil types, which all have a similar character in that they are silty, free-draining, easily worked, but moderately to very acid. Interspersed amongst these soils are patches of poorly drained peaty soils. These are spongy, black and underlain by a rust-coloured layer of iron-enriched clay. These soils are hard to cultivate because of their surface wetness, the hard iron-pan and their great acidity. They are most prevalent on the southern sides of the Burrington and Blagdon enclosures, and throughout the Wells and Dinder and Croscombe enclosures (Fig 14).

Writing in 1795, Billingsley accurately distinguished between the two main soils of the plateau which he described as 'for the most part deep, loamy and of a good consistence' and elsewhere as 'a fine yellow mould', although occasionally there were to be found 'spots of land less valuable, being of a light spongy nature, black in colour and totally unproductive of corn on the first cultivation'.

Both soils presented problems, and a great deal of preparatory labour and capital investment were needed before they would be cultivated successfully. The paring and burning of turf was a long standing West Country technique for the colonisation of new land, and although it had never been practised in the Mendips, it became a widely advocated answer to the problem of preparing the loams and the black moulds for cultivation. But paring and burning was not the best answer; their acidity could be counteracted only by liming. By extensive and laborious experiments, accompanied by careful accounting, Billingsley was able to demonstrate as early as 1788, in his paper on 'Thoughts on burn-baiting on Mendip-Hills', that liming was superior to paring and

burning on his own land. The various stages suggested and carried out
by Billingsley in preparing the loamy soils for cultivation and for improved pasture are best summarised in tabular form, together with his
estimate of the cost of each operation on each acre (.405ha) of average
land. The details are taken from his extensive 'Essay on waste lands'
which appeared in the *Letters to the Bath and West of England Agricultural
Society* in 1807.

	£	s	d	p
Removing rocks, clearing stones, levelling, burning furze		15	0	75
First ploughing	1	1	0	105
Second cross-ploughing		18	0	90
Dragging		8	0	40
First harrowing		3	0	15
Liming at 160 bushels per acre	2	12	0	260
Spreading lime		2	0	10
Second harrowing		1	6	7½
Rolling		1	0	5
Third ploughing		5	0	25
Third harrowing		1	6	7½
Rolling		1	0	5
Fourth ploughing		5	0	25
	£6 14s 0d			£6.70p

If the above thorough scheme of reclamation was carried out by
Billingsley, then there was every justification for the claim to be made for
him that he had ploughed and reploughed his 3,000 or 4,000 acres
(1,214' or 1,619ha) of land four or five times, and that he had spread
500,000 bushels of lime on it.

These methods of improvement were tedious, expensive and, above
all, ineffectual on the badly drained soils. On these soils, paring and
burning were a useful beginning, and with the spreading of lime some
improvement was possible. But the hard iron-pan below the black
humus still impeded drainage and had to be broken up. One method
used widely before deep ploughing became common was to shallow
plough and harrow the land, then throw it into a series of mounds and
gutters to expose the rust-coloured iron-pan. The land could then be
either planted to potatoes or let out to potato growers; the clay was
pulverised by pick-axe or mattock and thrown up on to the mounds of
black silt thereby giving them some tenacity. The total operation was

calculated to cost £15 an acre, but this did not take into account the return from the potatoes, which could equal or exceed the costs of improvement. The next season the alternative areas were selected for gutters or mounds, so that over the course of a few years the whole of the pan was broken, and the soil turned and mixed.

Changing the Farming

With these changes the old common grazing system of farming declined and an attempt was made to introduce a more diversified mixed farming system. Billingsley's advice was 'to provide all necessary buildings for shelter in the winter, and for the purposes of making mountains of dung', and to the farmer, 'to grow but little corn and that little in the highest perfection; to have breadth of turnips, cabbages, potatoes, vetches, artificial grasses' and consequently 'to maintain a great stock' of sheep, cattle, pigs and poultry. Unfortunately the course taken was the reverse of these wise suggestions; allotments were assigned to farms in the vales and the Levels, and farmers took six or seven crops of grain in succession, a 'rotation' of wheat, oats, oats, oats, fallow, wheat, oats, being common. One farmer in 1851, after taking three crops of oats in succession from one field, was still saying that he would 'take as many oat crops as the land would bear first . . . then lime it, and take only two crops, as he wished to lay it down to grass in good heart!' It was sheer exploitation, which beggared the plateau soils to such an extent that some landlords restricted ploughing, even going so far as to limit tenants to grazing alone.

Some indication of cropping in the parishes in the vicinity of the Mendips is given in Table 2. It is based on the manuscript Agricultural Returns of 1801 which are kept in the Public Record Office. Not all parishes were covered by the Returns, and in the Mendips those for Priddy, Charterhouse, Westbury and Ashwick, in particular, are missing. Nor were all the crops grown at the time recorded in the Returns. Nevertheless, provided one does not place too much emphasis on the absolute amounts (especially as 1801 was considered to be an above-average harvest in Somerset), but considers more the proportion of any parish under particular crops and their ranking one against another, then the Returns can be regarded fairly safely as a sample of the true conditions.

Wheat was important enough to account for more than 50 per cent of the crop land in Blagdon, Ubley, Wookey and Cheddar, and there was not one parish which did not return some wheat. But oats was in an even more commanding position, being grown in all parishes and accounting

Table 2

PERCENTAGE OF LAND IN CROPS, 1801

(100 acres=40.479ha)

Parish	Total Acreage	Wheat	Barley	Oats	Potatoes	Peas	Beans	Turnips and Rape
Blagdon	1,240	64.8	0.4	27.4	4.8	0.3	0.5	1.6
Bleadon	272	56.3	16.8	5.2	9.7	4.5	7.8	
Cheddar	305	59.3	2.9	11.9	15.2	1.0	9.6	
Chewton Mendip	467	33.4	4.3	49.0	8.0	4.4	0.4	0.4
Compton Martin	449	34.7	17.2	25.3	5.6	1.0	0.5	15.7
Dinder	183	26.0	1.0	63.0	7.0	1.3		1.0
East Harptree	368	19.6	4.0	64.8	11.5			
Rowberrow	41	32.5		55.0	12.5			
Shepton Mallet	101	21.8	6.9	61.3	4.9	4.9		
Ubley	199	55.6	11.6	19.1	10.6	1.0	2.0	
Wells	1,533	33.9	5.7	48.7	9.4	2.0	2.6	0.4
West Harptree	267	18.7	2.2	56.2	14.9	0.3		7.4
Wookey	213	50.3	10.2	18.7	7.0	7.0	4.6	2.4
TOTAL	5,638	41.5	5.7	38.0	8.6	1.8	2.1	2.2

Source: PRO, HO 62/2

for over 50 per cent of the crop land in Bleadon, Rowberrow, Shepton Mallet, West and East Harptree, Chewton and Dinder, and over 48 per cent in Wells and Chewton. Barley hardly entered into the Returns for the Mendips. The outstanding preference for oats lay in its suitability to the harsh climate and thin soils of the plateau, conditions which also accounted, in part, for the abundance of potatoes, which was over 10 per cent of the crop land in five of the thirteen parishes. All in all, the evidence of the Returns supports independently the evidence from other sources.

After the period of exploitive grain farming died down in the 1820s and 1830s, grazing became important again. It was said, however, that the changes in farming had produced a sheep with a coarser fleece which was not suitable for the woollen industry. In any case, the rise of the woollen industry in the West Riding of Yorkshire, the reluctance of the local manufacturers to mechanise their processes, and the competition of cotton and Australian wools, all tended to diminish the importance of sheep for wool, and to increase their importance for meat. During these years there was also a great expansion of potato growing, the potato crop being used to break up new ground and being sown alternately with oats. Over 2,000 acres (809ha) of 'gruffy ground' (land disturbed by lead mining) in the vicinity of Priddy alone were either planted by local farmers or let out to potato 'jobbers', who came up to the plateau for a short season. Eventually, falling prices and the potato blight in 1845 put an end to this system.

By the middle of the nineteenth century the Mendips were used in the summer mostly for the grazing of cattle from the Levels and for the grazing of sheep throughout the year. There were also substantial patches of land being cultivated intelligently by the farmers who had come up on to the plateau to establish their farmsteads. But much still needed to be done, and it was the view of Sir Thomas Dyke Acland in 1851, in his prize-winning essay on 'The Farming of Somersetshire', that 'assuredly, a large part of the Hill must be reclaimed again before it can be properly farmed', a view which was echoed by Joseph Darby in 1870 in his account to the Bath and West of England Society on 'The Farming of Somerset'.

Hedges, Fences and Fields

Enclosure meant the hedging and fencing of the new fields created on Mendip. Between 1771 and 1813 some 27,500 acres (11,129ha) of land were enclosed on Mendip and it required probably about 1,650 miles (2,655km) of partitions, a length which would have been considerably

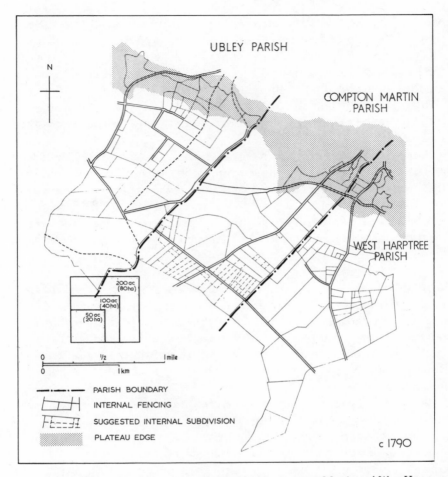

Fig 15   The Mendip enclosures in the parishes of Ubley, Compton Martin and West Harptree
c 1790. The shaped plateau edge lies between the 800ft and 400ft contours.

greater had the fields not been well over 10 acres (4.04ha) in size, some of
them being in excess of 30 acres (12.14ha). A sample of the initial sub-
division of the once open landscape in the adjoining parishes of Ubley,
Compton Martin and West Harptree is shown in Fig 15. It is based on
the Enclosure Awards for those parishes. What subsequently happened
is shown in Fig 16, which suggests that many of the original subdivisions
suggested by the Commissioners of Enclosure were too large or inappropriate.

An exception to the generalisation that enclosure meant large fields
was the provision of 'potato gardens', presumably for displaced commoners, in an area known as The Wrangle in Compton Martin. Here

23 Mells Road: 2–6–2T No 5542 on a typical GWR branch line train from Frome to Bristol

24 *Gamecock c* 1910 (driver Bob Baker, fireman Joe Bryant) worked the narrow gauge line from Downhead quarry to Waterlip

25 Maesbury summit on the Somerset & Dorset line: a northbound express hauled by ex-LMS 4–4–0 No 40697 and 2–8–0 No 53807 (ex-SDJR No 87)

26 New Rock Colliery, Chilcompton (1819–1968) in its rural setting

27 St Cuthbert's Leadworks, Priddy, shortly before closure in 1908

certain earlier enclosures were subdivided into half acre (.202ha) blocks on which houses were erected.

Because of the abundance of Carboniferous Limestone which either outcropped or was lying near the surface of the shallow soils, dry walls were most common, although they gave 'a farm a very cold and naked appearance', and gave very little shelter to stock. Yet the enclosers often preferred the hawthorn quickset. The quickset grew rapidly and soon became close, thick and impenetrable, such as those hedges near Shepton Mallet which by 1806 were 8–10ft (2.4–3m) high, and so thick that Billingsley said 'that a bird can scarcely creep between them'.

Billingsley was the principal advocate of the quickset, and as he sat on at least seven of the Mendip Enclosure Commissions (East Harptree, Rodney Stoke, West Harptree, Croscombe and Dinder, Cheddar and both the Wells (St Cuthbert Out) Commissions), and had reserved substantial allotments in these and other enclosures, he had plenty of opportunity to put his preferences into practice. Billingsley was said to have enclosed between 3,000 and 4,000 acres (1,214 and 1,619ha) of his own land, creating nearly 100 miles (160.9km) of hedge and ditch fencing, and to have planted 1,500,000 thorn plants. At his own recommended planting of one every 3in (7.6cm) this gives approximately 95 miles (152.9km) of quickset fencing.

But the rigours of the exposed situation of the Mendips demanded that some sort of 'dead' fence, usually a dry stone wall, be erected as a temporary shelter, it being recommended that the wall be demolished later, the stones to be used for either lime burning, road building, or drain making, or, if they were of good quality, for farm buildings. The advantage of the dry wall as a rapidly erected shelter was enhanced by the cheapness of its construction, especially where the stones were abundant and had to be cleared from the fields anyway. A substantial dry wall, 2ft (0.6m) wide at the bottom and 5ft (1.5m) high, cost 10s (50p) or less per rope of 20ft (6mz in 110y which compared with 11s (5tpz for hedges with banks; 13s 6d (67½p) for quickset hedge with a low stone wall; 15s (75p) for a list wall (a combination of dry walling and turf) and 17s 6d (87½p) for a mortared stone wall.

Exposure to the weather was one problem in the establishment and growth of the live hedges, and stock was another. Some protection was afforded by the sheltering stone wall on one side, and often a ditch was dug on the other side. But these measures could have provided only a partial solution to the problem, for the need was to keep livestock out of the field for as long as possible after the hedges had been planted. This was stipulated in some Enclosure Awards, although how well the regulation was observed, is not known.

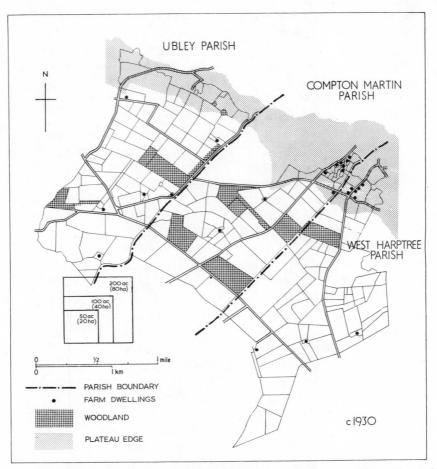

Fig 16   The Mendip enclosures in the parishes of Ubley, Compton Martin and West Harptree
c 1930—based on os 1:25,000 maps.

All in all, the dry limestone walls predominated and gave to the
Mendips one of the distinctive elements of its landscape. Writing in
1851, William Sturge said, 'the fences are generally stone walls, with a
few white thorn hedges', a description that one would not need to alter
at present. Yet, he added that although the low stone walls were inex-
pensive because of the abundance of stone, they were ill-adapted to 'this
bleak district'. The high Devonshire and west Somerset earth and stone
banks with beech on top would have served the stock better.

Closely associated with fences and hedges was the planting of trees.
Billingsley summed up the advantages well in his 'Essay on Waste
Lands':

Judicious and well-disposed belts and clumps of trees increase the beauty as well as the value of new inclosures. There are very few descriptions of soil or climate where trees of some kinds will not grow in clumps. They afford shelter and defence to the fields, are pleasant to the eye and ultimately profitable.

He recommended planting fir, larch, beech, ash, sycamore and birch at 1-perch intervals along the hedges, but his suggestions were rarely taken up in practice as relatively few hedges were established and trees were more usually planted in clumps or belts. Fig 16 shows the outcome of planting in the three typical parishes of Ubley, Compton Martin and West Harptree on the northern portion of Mendip. This pattern of woodland plantation, mainly for windbreaks rather than for timber, was the result of many haphazard individual landlords' and tenants' decisions; there was little method or plan in it compared with the almost circular plantation that enclosed about 400 acres (161.8ha) on Green Ore Farm in Chewton Mendip, which excited much comment and attention from the local agricultural writers such as Acland, Sturge and Darby in the latter half of the nineteenth century.

THE NEW FARMSTEADS

A great many new farmsteads were created on the newly enclosed land. The location of most of them is shown in Fig 17, but as few of them bear a date, their construction must be traced from map evidence. Certainly those farmsteads located within the enclosed areas were new; they did not appear on the enclosure awards, but they do on Greenwood's *Map of the County of Somerset* printed in 1822, and also on various editions of the Ordnance Survey maps throughout the nineteenth century. Farm names also help in dating the farms. Names like Upper Canada, Victoria, and Wellington, and Mendip, and Warren Farm, are indicative either of events of the age or of conditions on the plateau, such as rabbit warrens, where the new farms were being established. The majority of the new farms, however, did not appear until after the 1820s.

Most of the allotments on the plateau were assigned to homesteads in the villages of the surrounding vales and to individual farms on the plateau slopes. As Acland pointed out correctly, the attitude of these farmers was to exploit the new enclosures and they 'grew oats without manure as long as the land would bear it'. When the detrimental results of this method of land utilisation became apparent, more enlightened landlords built new farms on the plateau, and every opportunity was

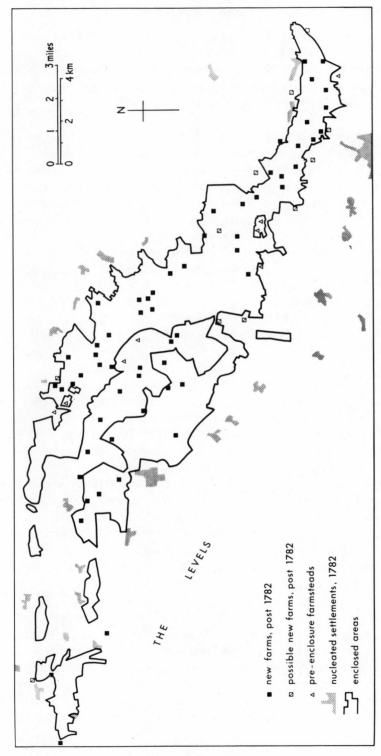

Key:
■ new farms, post 1782
▨ possible new farms, post 1782
△ pre-enclosure farmsteads
nucleated settlements, 1782
enclosed areas

THE LEVELS

Fig 17 New farmsteads in the Mendip enclosures after 1782.

taken to site them carefully and build them on convenient and spacious lines.

Many farmsteads were situated fairly centrally to their land and sited either in hollows or in the lee of slight eminences on the plateau, the farmhouse usually having an east or south-east aspect. Most were constructed of local creamy grey limestone with a slate or tile roof and, in plan, were adapted to the needs of wheat and sheep farming. The dwelling house was flanked on one side by a large barn and stalling for cattle, and on the other by a waggon house, often with a granary overhead. There was sometimes a pigsty and a poultry house. In 1802 it was calculated that a house and buildings for a 400–500 acre (161.8–202.3ha) farm could be built for £1,200, and we are fortunate in having the detailed costs of improvement (though not of land and interest charges) of Wigmore Farm in Chewton Mendip parish. The farm was 400 acres (178ha) and the total costs were as shown in Table 3.

Table 3
COSTS OF ESTABLISHING WIGMORE FARM, CHEWTON MENDIP

	£	s	d	Per cent of total cost
Reclamation costs				
Cutting furze, levelling, hauling off surface stores, draining	183	19	2	
Ploughing, dragging, and manuring 380 acres (153.7ha) at 160 bushels of lime per acre	2,090	0	0	
	£2,273	19	2	56.8
Establishment costs				
Stone and quickset fences	287	19	0	
Roads	100	16	4	
Limekilns	40	0	0	
Future fencing expenses	256	10	8	
	£685	6	0	17.1
Dwellings and farm buildings				
Cottage	44	14	10	
Main building (house, stable, barn, stalling)	846	0	0	
Wagon house and pigsty	150	0	0	
	£1,040	14	10	26.0
TOTAL	£4,000	0	0	99.9

Source: J. Billingsley, 'Essay on waste lands', 1807

There was one other item of expenditure that was not accounted for in this list of costs, and that was related to water supply. The new farms on the plateau lay at a great distance from the old sources of water and, to

meet the need for new supplies, springs were sometimes utilised, wells
sunk in favourable localities or, more usually, ponds dug; one was set
near the house and others in the fields, perhaps one at the intersection of
four fields.

Enclosure had transformed the landscape of the plateau. The open
sheepwalks disappeared, and were subdivided by hedges and fences into
rectangular fields. New farmsteads were established and new crops were
introduced. A good summary of the changed scene in many parts of
Mendip was that of W. Phelps in his *History and Antiquities of Somersetshire*
of 1839, who said that the enclosures had quite

> altered the aspect of the forest. Farm homes have been built and an
> increasing population is spreading itself, roads communicating with
> different towns and villages round its base intersect this once dreary
> mountain in various parts, affording an easy access to it. Arable
> husbandry predominates wherever the soil will admit the plough, and
> fine crops of barley, oats, and in more favoured spots, wheatn are
> grown. Turnips and other vegetables capable of resisting the ordinary
> winter frosts, thrive well.

After 1870

DECLINE AND DETERIORATION

The early hope of the widespread establishment of a system of
mixed farming on the plateau was clearly not fulfilled by the latter
half of the nineteenth century. In fact, much of the ground so pain-
stakingly reclaimed was lost to cultivation and replaced by natural
pastures, or at best by sown pastures. Whereas the 50 years after 1770
had been characterised by advance and improvement, the 70 years
after 1870 were characterised by retreat and deterioration.

Writing in 1870, Joseph Darby suggested that the deterioration,
already apparent, was largely the result of a widespread 'disregard of the
primary laws of agricultural production' with the exhaustive grain cropping by the farms on Mendip and around its edges. This 'scarifying
course of husbandry' had led to a 'general breakdown' of the soil structure and fertility so that when several successive crops of oats were taken,
and the soil could yield no more, it was sown down to pasture again. But
the grass was poor, and 'often in a filthy as well as impoverished condition', fit only to be grazed during the summer, as of old, by the stock
from the surrounding areas. But the distinctive fine-woolled Mendip
sheep had all but disappeared. There were model farms, to be sure, such

as that of Henry Davies of Oakhill whose 1,400 acres (566.5ha) were producing bountiful crops, but were also consuming 3cwt (208kg) of superphosphate and guano, and 20 bushels (454kg) of turf ashes per acre per annum, to say nothing of unspecified, but large, quantities of lime. Clearly some people had followed Billingsley's precepts and it paid them well, but the majority had not listened to his wise advice.

Around the plateau, on the other hand, farming was generally more successful. There were the smallholdings of 1–5 acres (0.4–2ha) on the south-facing sunny side of the Mendip slopes, between Axbridge and Rodney Stoke. The light, well-drained soils of the New Red Sandstone were used for the growing of peas, potatoes and a number of other early crops, particularly strawberries, and the land commanded prices ranging between £3 and £6 an acre, according to the depth of the soil and the aspect of the block. The 'jobbers', as they were called, were competing against the growers of early vegetables on the south coast of Cornwall in the supply of the London market, the success of these distant Cornish growers being largely attributed to the direct railway communication with the capital which the nearer Mendip growers did not have until some years later.

The hillslopes were really a mass of market gardens that produced 'early and heavy crops'. The dairying in the lowland clays around the southern foot of Mendip still flourished, of course, and Cheddar cheese still maintained its reputation. Medium-sized 100 acre (40.5ha) or slightly larger farms, letting at between £3 and £4 per acre, reflected the continued prosperity of this area and its farming. To a lesser extent the clay vales to the north of Mendip were also enjoying prosperity after judicious under-draining, the use of artificial fertilisers, and the removal of hedgerows in small fields had upgraded the farming. Pastures were almost universal and much milk, butter and inferior cheese were produced.

Only the farming on the plateau seemed to be in general state of decline. Admittedly conditions on Mendip were somewhat unusual because of the lack of farmsteads situated in the midst of the land they served. But the problem was more general than that: the years from 1870 to 1940 were years of general decline of cultivation in Somerset, and in Britain as a whole. In 1872 Somerset had 296,868 acres (120,232ha) of arable land (28.3 per cent of Somerset), but this amount declined, especially during the agricultural depression of the 1880s, to reach a low point of 158,218 acres (64,078ha) (15.3 per cent) in 1914, the total being lifted a little by ploughing up during the blockade of World War I, only to drop again to 129,707 acres (52,531ha) (12.5 per cent) in 1936. Imports of cheap overseas grain, meat and cheese undercut the producer on marginal land, which Mendip was, and the emphasis was put more on stock products such as milk, butter and meat. Consequently, the amount of permanent grass for hay and for grazing increased throughout these years, and much of the cultivated land was abandoned completely and reverted to rough grazing, as indeed did some of the improved pastures on the plateau, with a lack of stocking and manuring. In many ways it was a period of extended rural depression and distress; low wages, low returns and massive rural depopulation as people left the country areas for better-paid jobs in the towns were obvious manifestations of this rural change. But technical changes in the form of better and faster transport, and the concentration of former cottage- and villagedbased industries like cheese making, cider making and milk dairies became centralised in factories in the main towns surrounding the plateau, such as Frome, Shepton Mallet, Highbridge, and even as far away as Bristol. Blacksmiths, thatchers, timber workers and implement makers found less employment. The whole fabric of rural society was changing with the changing countryside as the number of rural craftsmen and rural workers declined. Sir Rider Haggard's *Rural England*, written in 1909, gives an intimate and colourful account of these changes.

These trends continued almost unabated, and by the time of Stuart-Menteath's report for the nation-wide *Land Utilisation Survey* of 1938, farming in the Mendips, as in Somerset as a whole, had reached about its lowest ebb. In seventeen parishes covering the southern half of the plateau and the adjacent lowland area, and in twenty-one parishes covering the northern half of the plateau and the adjacent areas, there was a total of only 1,494 acres (605ha) of land in cultivation, or less than 1.4 per cent of the land used for farming in this region (see Table 4). The decline in cultivation is highlighted when the amount of arable land is compared to that in thirteen core Mendip parishes 135 years before; it

Table 4

CULTIVATION IN NORTHERN AND SOUTHERN MENDIP REGIONS, 1938

| | Northern Slopes (21 parishes) | | Southern Slopes (17 parishes) | | |
	Acres	% Somerset production	Acres	% Somerset production	Total acreage (38 parishes)
Wheat and Barley	242	1.2	111	0.4	353
Oats	162	1.p	144	1.0	306
Beans and Peas	10	0.4	87	4.0	97
Potatoes	29	1.4	123	5.t	152
Fodder	232	1.p	297	1.0	529
Horticulture	13	1.4	44	5.0	57

Source: Based on Stuart-Menteath, pp 74-5

was approximately a quarter only (Table 1, above). Of the remaining 103,000 acres (41,683ha) farmed in the boarder Mendip region and surrounds in 1936, approximately half was in rough grazing and half in permanent grass.

The large 300 acre (121.4ha) or more farms on the plateau were valued at a mere 10s to 30s (50p to 150p) per acre, and, because there was almost no cropping, few, if any, workmen were employed. Only where mowing occurred every year did the permanent grasses improve. There were a few sheep, and the main enterprise was dairy cattle for milk. In contrast, the condition of the farms on the southern slopes around Cheddar and Rodney Stoke was a different story. The great variety of soils, drainage conditions and aspect gave the opportunity for a variety of crops which ranged from intensive dairying on the lowland clay flats in the summer, to strawberry culture and other early crops on the well-drained loams of the slopes, and to sheep farming on the plateau pastures. Pasture ground in lowland dairy farms was worth from £2 to £3 per acre; of the 65 smallholdings growing strawberries near Cheddar, the average rental was between £5 and £6 per acre, but sometimes it went as high as £12 per acre. Lowland dairy farms employed two or three workmen, which was a measure of their greater productivity and prosperity.

WAR AND IMPROVEMENT

The outbreak of war in 1939 had much the same effect on British farming as had the blockade of Napoleon during the opening years of the nineteenth century. The uncertainty and discontinuance of overseas food supplies led to a great effort to increase home food production, particularly crops. In 1939 the government offered £2 per acre to farmers who ploughed up pastures during the following summer, and this policy had the effect in England and Wales of lifting the amount of land in cultivation from 8.9 million acres (3,601,705ha) in 1939 to 14.5 million acres (5,867,947ha) in 1944. Nowhere was this change more evident than in the Mendips, where the ploughing-up campaign produced a reversal of previous trends, and the beginning of the pattern of farming that has persisted until the present, under the stimulus of financial incentives. There has probably been a greater change in the Mendips than in any other part of Somerset, although the productivity of the lowland Levels has increased enormously with the extensive land drainage schemes and pumping.

The new pattern of farming on Mendip can be gauged from looking at Table 5, which consists of detailed agricultural statistics for 1968 for a

Table 5

CROPS AND LIVESTOCK IN THIRTEEN MENDIP PARISHES, 1968

(Tr = Trace, eg under 0.5%)

CROPS	Ashwick	Blagdon	Cheddar	Chewton Mendip	Chil-compton	Compton Martin	East Harptree	Priddy	Ston Easton	Ubley	Wells	Westbury	West Harptree
Total acres, crops and grass	1,185	3,652	4,166	4,991	1,604	1,788	2,293	3,047	1,999	1,257	10,976	2,466	2,706
% Wheat	1		1	2	4	Tr	4	11	1	6	3	1	3
% Barley	2	12	9	19	7	10	7	1	19	2	7	1	6
% Oats		5		1	Tr	3	2		3	Tr	Tr		
% Potatoes			Tr	Tr	2		Tr			Tr	Tr		
% Roots and fodder	1	1	Tr	1	Tr	1	2	3	1		1	1	1
% Total Tillage	3	19	10	23	13	14	15	15	24	8	11	3	10
% Temporary grass	2	20	3	20	26	16	21	36	30	24	16	7	11
% Permanent grass	96	61	79	57	61	70	63	48	46	67	72	90	79
% Orchards			4		Tr		1	Tr		1	1	Tr	Tr
% Small Fruit and Vegetables			4				Tr		Tr		Tr	Tr	
LIVESTOCK													
Total stock (ex poultry)	2,016	6,737	4,740	5,350	2,749	1,948	2,086	3,011	1,548	936	10,078	1,809	2,647
% Dairy cattle	39	11	18	31	23	25	33	26	44	45	41	46	29
% Other cattle	26	14	16	22	13	20	29	26	31	37	23	30	31
% Sheep	8	59	53	17	10	52	19	37		12	13	21	37
% Pigs	27	16	13	30	54	3	19	11	25	6	23	3	3
POULTRY (nearest '000)	3	2	53	2	7	19	1	1	11	1	36	2	6

Source: Parish Summaries, Ministry of Agriculture

group of thirteen parishes in the central core of the Mendips, stretching from Blagdon and Cheddar in the west to Norton–Radstock and Shepton Mallet in the east. On the plateau top, with the exception of some large farms in Priddy, Chewton Mendip, Wells and Blagdon parishes, and on the lower plateau in Ston Easton and Chilcompton, which grow oats, and some wheat and barley, the ploughing-up campaign has resulted less in cereal growing than in cultivation for temporary leys. Whereas before World War II the temporary grasses amounted to usually less than 1 per cent of the land in crops and tillage, they now account for as much as 36 per cent in Priddy, but most commonly for about 20 per cent. The leys are planted for three or four seasons, the nutritious grass giving a better yield and a longer growing season than the permanent grass. Fertiliser is important in upgrading the quality of the pasture, with slightly less than 1cwt (52kg) of superphosphates being used for every acre but with up to 2 tons (1,814kg) of lime every 4 to 7 years—Billingsley's advice of two centuries ago is still valid. The hay yields are high, but much of the herbage goes into the making of silage on the farms, because the quality of the hay in the fields can be uncertain because of prolonged periods of rain and mist. Elsewhere, natural grasses have been improved with the rectification of minute copper deficiencies in the soil and with the rehabilitation of areas of lead and zinc toxicity from old mining. What arable there is, is mostly for growing kale, oats, and dredge wheat and barley for feeding stock on the farms.

All this has led to a massive increase in dairying on the plateau, and a move away from the traditional Shorthorn cattle for cheese production to the high-yielding British Friesian cattle for milk, and to some Ayrshires. In most parishes, between 25 and 50 per cent of all stock are dairy cattle, and if all other cattle for meat production are included with these, the proportion of cattle to other stock rarely falls below 50 per cent, and often exceeds 70 per cent as in Ston Easton, Ubley and Westbury. Only in Blagdon and Cheddar are there vestiges of the old economy, and sheep numbers exceed those of cattle; only in Chilcompton do pigs exceed both cattle and sheep. Poultry were always kept on Mendip as part of the farm economy, but now broiler chicken hatcheries are important at Cheddar (53,000) and Wells (36,000).

But improving the quality of the grazing has not been the only prerequisite for change and improvement. Modern dairying requires three other important services: piped water, mains electricity and good all-weather roads for milk collection, all of which have come to Mendip in the last few decades, and have led to an intensification of dairying. They have been accompanied by other changes, such as more convenient farm buildings both for the farmers and their families, and for the stock that need large barns for shelter during the winter months.

One other aspect of the farming of these parishes needs to be commented on, and that is the number and the size of the holdings. Since World War II the number of holdings has dropped, but at an ever-accelerating pace since the late 1950s, as economies of scale are achieved through farm enlargement, particularly with regard to the use of farm machinery. For example, in Cheddar there were 156 holdings in 1958, but only 130 in 1968; in Priddy, 32 but now only 22; and in Ston Easton, 22 and now only 17. In every case it is the smallest holdings that have been eliminated, six under 5 acres (2ha) in Priddy so that there are now none in that category, and twenty in Cheddar so that there are now only sixty-one holdings under 5 acres (2ha). All this has not meant a decline in production; in fact it has increased, and in Cheddar, for example, the tradition of intensive cultivation still continues with 160 acres (64.7ha) of strawberries and other fruits, and 26 acres (10.5ha) of flowers and vegetables. But a greater and greater proportion of holdings are in the 30 to 300 acres (12.1 to 121.4ha) category, and it is becoming increasingly difficult to say, as so many writers did in the past, that Somerset is a county of predominantly small farms. The breakdown of holding sizes for the sample parishes for 1968 is shown in Table 6.

Table 6
THE SIZE OF HOLDINGS IN THIRTEEN SELECTED PARISHES
IN THE MENDIP HILLS, 1968
(5 acres = 2.033hs)

	Total number of holdings	Acres					
		¼-4	5-14	15-29	30-99	100-299	300+
Ashwick	28	1	5	2	16	4	
Blagdon	32		3	5	10	11	3
Cheddar	130	61	33	4	18	13	1
Chewton Mendip	22	1	3	3	2	10	3
Chilcompton	18	4		1	6	7	
Compton Martin	25	1	5	4	8	6	1
East Harptree	22	1	4		9	7	1
Priddy	22		4	3	5	6	4
Ston Easton	17	3	3		4	6	1
Ubley	14		2	1	7	3	1
Wells	101	9	5	10	35	34	8
Westbury	29	4	3	4	10	8	
West Harptree	30	1	3	5	14	5	2
TOTAL	490	86	73	42	144	120	25
AS % OF TOTAL		17.6	14.9	8.6	29.4	24.5	5.1

Source: Parish Summaries, Ministry of Agriculture

The landscape is changing rapidly in detail, but some aspects of Mendip linger on. For example, despite the new prosperity some of the regional contrasts remain. In 1962 Findlay noted that land on Mendip sold for between £50 and £80 per acre, while land in the northern vales sold for between £120 and £150 per acre, that in the lowland Levels for about £180, and the choicest strawberry gardens for between £500 and £1,000 per acre. Prices today are certainly greater, but the relative differences remain.

The price of land is an intangible, unseen quality of the landscape, although a very important one for its inhabitants. Another intangible quality of Mendip, which is also important for its inhabitants but, one suspects, more so for its visitors, is its quiet country charm. Although much of the land is cut into fields, crossed by roads, and dotted with houses, in many parts one still gets that sense of what Francis Knight described earlier in this century as 'an air of extreme loneliness and desolation'. In our ever-crowding world such scenes will be valued even more than before, and it is becoming evident that what was once described as lonely and wild is fast being recognised as a national asset.

Notes to this chapter are on pages 272-3.

6

Transport and Communications

Robin Atthill

Roads

WALKING, RIDING OR MOTORING about Mendip, the curious traveller
must constantly become aware of the changing pattern of roads, and of
tantalising glimpses of earlier patterns of communications which involve
all sorts of historical problems. A particular line of road may have been
in continuous use for nearly 2,000 years, or for less than 200, for much of
the high plateau remained uncultivated and unenclosed until late in the
eighteenth century. Many roads up on to Mendip begin as narrow
winding lanes between high banks and hedges, and suddenly emerge
into daylight to become open roads with wide grass verges and stone
walls—the new roads of the Age of Enclosure.

The very name New Road immediately arouses suspicion. New Road
from Draycott to Priddy does not appear on the 1817 os, but the old road
can still be traced climbing out of Draycott, and thereafter it survives as
a footpath until it becomes a lane again some distance short of Townsend. New Road at Cheddar was made by the Wedmore Turnpike Trust
about 1830 as a through route to Bristol, bypassing Cheddar on the west.
Roads that one takes for granted, such as Stoberry Hill by which the
Bristol road reaches Wells, or the A371 between Croscombe and Shepton Mallet, did not exist until well into the nineteenth century; the
bypasses at Coley and Litton on B3114 were built in the early 1920s to
alleviate postwar unemployment, the road between Winscombe and
Banwell was straightened out about 1926 and the old deviations are still
visible, and the main road from Banwell to Weston, past Locking, still
later, and even then it was not classified as an A-road.

EARLY ROADS

Prehistoric man moved east and west along the Mendip ridge,
avoiding the valleys and the marshes on either side, on a trackway which

entered Somerset near Upton Noble, on the watershed of the Frome and the Brue: at Whitnell Corner this trackway met another from Bath and the North which had kept to the higher ground past Timsbury and Clutton and Hinton Blewett to circumnavigate the head waters of the Cam and the Chew, before climbing on to Chewton Plain and reaching the main Mendip plateau at Red Hill near Emborough.

These old routes were superseded in the middle of the first century AD by the Roman Fosse Way which drove straight across country from Bath to Ilchester, and by the Roman ridge road which served the Charterhouse lead mines. A number of minor Roman roads, as yet unauthenticated or explored, their existence sometimes merely hinted at by the word Street in place-names, served outlying villas and settlements. The only such road to figure on the Ordnance Survey left the road to Charterhouse near Haydon Grange and followed the present-day parish boundary between Compton Martin and West Harptree, eventually becoming Stratford Lane and crossing the Chew to reach the site of a villa now submerged by the lake.

How far the Roman roads remained in use after the withdrawal of the legions in 410 is uncertain. The Fosse Way at any rate would have been useful for troop movements in times of war, but the Saxons as often as not used them as parish boundaries and founded their settlements at a safe distance to either side: Stratton is the only Saxon village actually sited on the Fosse Way between Bath and Ilchester.

In Saxon and medieval times, movement was by horse rather than by wheeled vehicle. Only the Roman roads were likely to be fit for vehicles, and they were broken by centuries of neglect. The Fosse Way somehow survived as a through route: on Day & Masters' map of 1782 almost the whole course of the road across Mendip appears viable, although by then the Turnpike Trusts were already at work.

Medieval traders moved along unmetalled roads: salt carriers, pedlars, packmen—and drovers; packhorses carried away the staple products of Mendip, wool, cloth and coal; lead, however, must have been moved by wagons, though some of it travelled by water from Rackley on the Axe; so must stone, though it is interesting to observe that stone from the quarries at Doulting would have travelled to Wells along a road with almost entirely easy and favourable gradients.

There was a certain amount of through traffic over Mendip. Chaucer's Canterbury pilgrims were not the only group making their way to medieval shrines; pilgrims were converging on Glastonbury and in various Mendip villages—Mells and Leigh and Ashwick for instance—there is a tradition of hostels where the travellers spent the last night of their long journey. The only dry-shod approach to Glastonbury was from the east, through Pilton and West Pennard; even travellers from Wells would have had to make a detour through North Wootton and Steanbow, clinging to higher ground, for there was no direct route across Queen's Sedgemoor, at any rate in winter. Glastonbury's road to the east continued through East Compton and over Whitstone Hill to join the Shepton Mallet–Frome road beyond Cranmore. The original road from Wells to London struck up over Lyatt and past Crapnell to join the ridge road near Masbury.

Between Bath and Wells there must always have been ecclesiastical to-ing and fro-ing while the monks of Bath and the canons of Wells fought for the see: they could travel through Emborough to join the Fosse Way at White Post, or through Chewton Mendip and Farrington Gurney, crossing the Cam Brook at Radford. There was no uncertainty, however, about the route to Bristol, striking due north over Rookham and dropping down Harptree Hill on to the watershed between the Chew and the Yeo before storming over the Dundry Ridge. The only other 'trunk' route over Mendip was at the west end, where the Bristol–Bridgwater road cut through the hills at Churchill and Shute Shelve more or less on the line of the later turnpike road and the A38.

Medieval traffic over anything but the shortest distances was likely to be military or ecclesiastical. The vast majority of the population was tied to the land, there was little opportunity or inclination to travel, and social and commercial traffic was limited in scale and almost entirely local in character. It was to meet these needs that the system of local roads developed. Ninety-three per cent of the villages and hamlets marked on the modern Ordnance Survey were already in existence at the time of the Domesday Survey, and roads and tracks emerged, linking farm to farm and village to village and joining the villages to the market towns, serving mills and other industrial sites such as coal pits. By the time of the Black Death in the middle of the fourteenth century the basic pattern of roads which we know and use today all around Mendip was more or less complete—except on the high plateau.

The earliest maps of Mendip date from the late sixteenth century and are diagrammatic rather than accurate surveys. They represent Mendip as roughly oval and ringed by churches symbolising the parishes that were concerned with common rights within the forest or with the mining laws which are reproduced in the margin of some of the maps. Except for the mineries, and Priddy and Charterhouse and one or two other settlements, the only features on the high plateau are a series of roads criss-crossing in every direction. On the Ashwick map almost every road is marked with a cross, and these represent wayside crosses or sign-posts such as those that guided travellers on the Dartmoor crossings see p 96) From this period the name Long Cross survives on the ridge road above Stoke St Michael. Along these tracks the products of the lead mines must have been transported, and at the east end of the hill the products of the coal pits: as early as 1617 the people of Stoke St Michael were complaining about the state of the roads owing to the traffic to and from the pits.

Day & Masters' map of 1782 was surveyed immediately before the enclosures and shows the plateau very much as it was two centuries earlier, with a network of unfenced tracks which it is hardly possible to identify with modern roads. The uncertainties of travel under these conditions are revealed in the diary of Claver Morris, the Wells doctor, who rode over the hill to Compton Martin and missed his way beyond Priddy Minery (2 October 1720), and on another occasion as soon as he had got beyond the enclosures at Deer-Leap (above Wookey Hole) 'there being a very thick fogg on Mendip', he again missed his way (8 February 1723).

Only a single generation later than Day & Masters, the first edition of the Ordnance Survey, published in 1817, shows the enclosures finished and the pattern of roads complete, except that no distinction is made between what we now know as motoring roads and those that survive as occupation lanes such as Dursdon Drove between Ebbor and Rookham, or those that served outlying farms such as Wigmore Farm near Eaker Hill. Unfenced roads are marked over Black Down from Tyning's Farm to Ellick, to Burrington and across Rowberrow Warren to Upper Langford. These still survive as rough tracks, but on a Wrington map dated 1738–9 the track from Tyning's to the bottom of Burrington Combe is marked as the 'Bristol road to Cheddar', which was approachhed over Warrens Hill past the present-day Stock Car Racing Stadium.

THE TURNPIKE ROADS

Between 1738–9 and 1817, however, the Turnpike Trusts had almost completed their appointed task—to make the crooked straight and the rough places plain. The inhabitants of each parish were no longer responsible for maintaining the main roads that passed within their boundaries: through the system of tolls collected and administered by the different Trusts, the onus and the cost of maintenance was shifted to the users of the roadsm During the eighteenth century a road system grew up comparable to that created by the Romans, and this new system met the demands of industrial growth and greater social mobility that reflected the peace and prosperity of the period (see Fig 18).

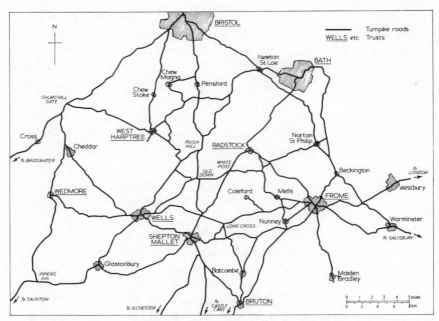

Fig 18 · Turnpike roads in the Mendip area, and the Trusts by which they were maintained.

The Bath and Bristol Trusts were established in 1707–8 and 1727 respectively, but as far as Mendip was concerned the real drive for road improvement came in the middle of the century with the establishment of the Wells and Shepton Mallet Trusts in 1753: Bruton and Frome followed in 1756 and 1757 and Buckland Dinham (later known as the Radstock Trust) in 1768. A small Trust was established at West Harptree in 1793 and, on the very eve of the Railway Age, two further Trusts on the south side of the hill, which obviously reflected a certain degree of prosperity brought about by the draining and enclosure of the moors in the basins of the Brue and the Axe. In 1827 the Wedmore Trust turnpiked the road to Cheddar and on through Callow Rocks to meet the Bristol–Bridgwater road near Rowberrow; in 1841 the Wells & Highbridge Trust took over the road from Wells to Cheddar.

The Bristol Trust reached Mendip by three roads: the modern A38 through Churchill, Sidcot and Cross; the Wells road over Dundry as far as 'the North Brow of Mendip'—appropriately enough the present boundary of the new county of Avon; and the easier Wells road, now A37, through Pensford and Clutton as far as Rush Hill, just south of Farrington Gurney. The Bath Trust reached Rush Hill and as far south as White Post on the Fosse ('10 miles & 4 furlongs from the Guildhall, Bath', as the boundary post proclaims).

Wells and Shepton Mallet were typical small town Trusts, maintaining 44 and 51 miles of road respectively, stretching out perhaps 8 or 10 miles in almost every direction. They both met the Bristol and Bath Trusts at Rush Hill and White Post; at the Beacon on the Mendip ridge the Wells and Frome Trusts met, and Wells also turnpiked the roads to Shepton (the Old Wells Road on the ridge above Croscombe) and through North Wootton to Steanbow between Pilton and West Pennard. Shepton Mallet maintained the roads leading south and west (towards Glastonbury, Ilchester, Castle Cary and Bruton), the Frome road as far as Leighton and the minor roads up to Long Cross and down to Batcombe.

Besides the ridge road to Wells through Whatley and Little Elm, the Frome Trust maintained roads to Nunney, Mells and Coleford, which served Fussells' edge-tool works and the eastern edge of the coalfield. Most of Frome's coal, however, was hauled over the Radstock Trust's road through Buckland Dinham. It is significant that this Trust was established 5 years after the discovery of coal at Radstock in 1763; it also maintained the road from White Post to Kilmersdon and Norton St Philip to give a through route from Wells to Trowbridge and Devizes and so to London.

On the southern flank of Mendip the Bruton Trust maintained two roads to Frome, originally via Batcombe and later via Wanstrow (the modern A359), and also a road that struck north and west from Nunney through Whatley and Mells, meeting the Radstock Trust near Babingtonn giving direct access to the coalfield. Finally, the West Harptree Trust turnpiked the road that runs beneath the northern escarpment of Mendip from Churchill Gate through Blagdon, Harptree and Chewton Mendip as far as Emborough on the road from Bath to Wells.

So by about 1800 the turnpike pattern was almost complete. There were good through roads from Bristol and Bath to the country south of Mendip, though there were still a few important improvements to be made in the 1820s; the market towns were linked with each other and with most of their surrounding villages; and a close network of toll-roads served the industrial districts of eastern Mendip.

The most obvious visible relics of the turnpike era are the mileposts and the toll-houses that survive. Each Trust had its own individual pattern of milepost, some with metal plates affixed to stone blocks, others made of cast iron with two faces recording the mileage to the towns in either direction, and in some cases with the name of the Trust and the parish and the mileage to London thrown in for good measure. Shepton Mallet and Radstock Trusts both set up extraordinarily elegant and well-proportioned mileposts with excellent lettering.

Most of the toll-houses were purpose-built: neat little buildings flush with the road, sometimes with bay windows through which traffic approaching the gate could be observed more easily. But their siting has made them especially vulnerable to schemes of road widening and the improvement of visibility at dangerous crossroads. Churchill Gate, for instance, on the A38, was demolished in 1961, but a surprising number have survived, though often enlarged and modernised almost out of recognition as at Soho near Leigh-on-Mendip. Five of the Wells Trust's toll-houses still stand, and seven of Shepton Mallet's, though some of them are hardly recognisable as such today: the one at Long Cross bears the date 1790, and that at Cranmore on the A361 competes with those at Shipham and Kilmersdon as being the most attractive survival of the turnpike era in the Mendip country.

The roads themselves we take for granted because we use them daily on our lawful occasions, and we are likely to forget how much we owe to the surveyors and engineers of the turnpike age. In particular, three splendid pieces of new road were built about 1830 on the very eve of the Railway Age: from Churchill to Star, a heavily engineered stretch of road, replacing the older road which climbed over Churchill Batch; Stoberry Hill by which the Bristol road curves down into Wells with easier gradients than those of the original alignment which can still be followed as a footpath between Pen Hill and Priors Hill; and between the Mendip Inn and Downside on the A37 where the old road from Bristol to Shepton Mallet stormed straight over the Masbury ridge, and survives for about half a mile as an untarred lane with wide grass verges—like the stretch of the Fosse Way near the Beacon, a mile to the east.

The coming of the railway sounded the death-knell of the turnpikes, and coaching inns like Old Down and those at Cross were to find their main function had disappeared overnight. Not quite overnight, however, because except at the east and west extremities of Mendip the railways, as will be shown later in the chapter, did not really arrive until 1860–70, and a good deal of traffic must have continued to use the roads. The Turnpike Trusts of north Somerset were wound up at various dates between 1867 and 1883, and the Act of 1888 established the county council as the statutory highway authority with responsibility for the roads within its territory.

MODERN DEVELOPMENTS

The road system which we have inherited is a compound of many samples—prehistoric trackways, Roman arteries, Saxon and medieval byways taken over and developed by the Turnpike Trustsn and tinkered with by the local highway authority in the present century. Basically our roads are those of the early decades of the nineteenth century, which were never designed for the traffic they are now asked to carry. On minor parish roads blind corners have sometimes been cut back, hedges replaced by fencing to improve visibility and passing places squeezed in for stone lorries. On the main roads a few sections have been straightened out—the bypasses at Bleadon for instance on the A370 and at Lower Langford and at Cross on the A38, the direct road from Banwell to Weston-super-Mare mentioned earlier, and between Ston Easton and Old Down on the A37; but many miles of arterial road wind amiably through the Mendip countryside, carrying no more than a single stream of frustrated motorists in each direction—there are no stretches of dual carriageway on any road in the area. One thinks of the A368 between West Harptree and Banwell and the A371 between Wells and Cheddar, or its continuation eastwards to Shepton Mallet and Frome where it carries very heavy stone traffic as well as a great deal of holiday traffic from the Midlands to the West Country which has to negotiate the notorious bottlenecks at Charlton Cross and at Cannard's Grave.

At Radstock the closure of the two working collieries, and of the railway that serves them, will eventually eliminate the hazard of two level crossings and an excruciatingly difficult junction between two major roads. Wells and Shepton Mallet and Frome wait indefinitely for their bypasses or ring-roads while traffic lumbers through their narrow streets and local shoppers compete with each other for the inadequate supply of parking places. Axbridge has been saved from strangulation by a bypass built along the abandoned Cheddar Valley railway, but at Banwell and Winscombe the traffic problems are still unsolved.

Apart from the locally generated traffic—and there is enough of this within the Bristol and Bath commuter zones and in the more heavily industrialised areas of eastern Mendip—the main types of traffic that occupy the roads are the long-distance heavy transport vehicles by day and by night; the holiday traffic to the West with its seasonal peaks at a few summer weekends; and the ordinary tourist attracted by the historical interest and the scenic beauty of the area, who simply wants to drive out, perhaps past the Chew Valley Lake 'to the North Brow of Mendip', or up one of the combes, for the sake of the fresh air and the vision splendid which he and his family will be able to indulge in.

It is too early to forecast the ultimate impact of the M5 on Mendip. Its route cuts between Locking and Banwell and then down the valley of the Lox Yeo before crossing the Axe below Loxton and striking south across the moors. If the M5 has syphoned off a good deal of the through traffic from other routes, it is equally likely to bring a large inflow of visitors to whom Mendip has now become easily accessible.

Road Services

Along the turnpike roads moved a continuous flow of vehicles at varying speeds: private vehicles such as post-chaises, calashes and barouches; stage coaches going down from Bristol and Bath to Exeter and Weymouth, or on local services as far as Farrington Gurney or Frome; and the mail coaches averaging 10mph in their last years of fame before the arrival of the railway. In 1836 the up mail from Exeter called at Wells at 4.55pm, Old Down at 5.35 and reached the General Post Office in London at 6.51am next morning.

For the conveyance of goods and poorer passengers to whom time was no object, there were the ponderous stage wagons, ancestors of the carriers' carts which held their own in the Railway Age and survived well into the present century. Perusal of almost any early edition of *Kelly's Directory* will show that the majority of Mendip villages were served several days a week by carriers to Bristol, Bath or Frome—except apparently in the Cheddar Valley where none are listed in or out of Wells. In 1889 omnibuses to Bristol served Banwelln Cheddar and Blagdon: Joseph Saint's omnibus returned from the Hope & Anchor on Redcliff Hill at 4.30pm on Mondays, Thursdays and Saturdays.

This sort of service was still maintained within living memory. There were fewer of them in 1919, but carriers ran to Frome from Coleford and Mells, Valentine Currell went to Bristol from East Harptree three days a week, while John Marsh from Ubley maintained the traditional stand at the Hope & Anchor. The shape of things to come, however, was Jacob Lyons' motor-bus which ran to Bristol from Blagdon four times a week.

The first motor-bus to reach Mendip was the service started in 1906 by the Bath Tramways Co from the tram terminus at Glasshouse on Odd Down to Midsomer Norton, taking 55 minutes over the journey, for which the fare was 9d (4p). In the postwar period both the Bath and Bristol Tramway Companies began to spread their services over Mendip: Bristol to Wells in 1920, to Cheddar in 1921, to Shepton Mallet in 1924, Bath to Wells in 1928—killing off any competition from small local operators in the process. By 1930 most of Mendip was served by buses from Bath or Bristol, Weston-super-Mare, Wells or Frome. Even Priddy enjoyed a minimal service for a few years, though no service buses have ever used the scenic route up Burrington Combe and down Cheddar Gorge.

Most of these services still operate, with a certain amount of pruning in latter years, and often sadly uneconomic. On the south side of the hill, a few independent operators keep their services going: from Shepton Mallet to Sparkford and Yeovil, for example, and by circuitous routes between Shepton Mallet and Frome and Bruton. The last-named originated in 1923 as market-day services from Batcombe to Shepton Mallet and Frome, and before the war they were operated by the Boyce family.

Rivers and Canals

Although prehistoric man kept to high ground, avoiding if possible the marshlands and densely wooded river valleys, there are two instances where very early use may have been made of Mendip rivers. The bluestones, from the Prescelly Mountains in Pembrokeshire, which were erected at Stonehenge, were probably brought by raft up the Bristol Avon, and then up the Frome to a point near the present town of Frome, which afforded the shortest possible land portage to the upper waters of the Wylye near Warminster on their way to Salisbury Plain. The stones of Stanton Drew were probably also moved by raft down the Chew from the neighbourhood of Harptree.

In historical times, however, navigation was impossible on the swift-flowing Mendip streams with their many weirs and mills, and it was only on the moorland rivers that an approach could be made by water. There is evidence that the Wring Yeo was navigable as far as Congresbury and perhaps farther, and light craft may have made their way up the Banwell river.

The Axe was navigable until comparatively recent times. By means of the fifteenth-century Pillrow Cut or Mark Yeo, which linked the Axe with the Brue, direct access to the sea was available to the monastic community of Glastonbury, who also used waterways to reach parts of their estates such as the Pilton vineyards. Boats came up the Axe as far as Clewer near Wedmore, and up the Cheddar Yeo as far as Hythe, where remains of wharves are still visible. The most important port was at Rackley near Compton Bishop (see p 85), first mentioned as Radeclive (Redcliff) in 1178 and served by a track which brought lead down from the Mendip mines. Later on, salt and slate and coal from South Wales were brought up the old course of the Axe from Uphill and stored in sheds on the wharf. But following the Act of 1802 for the enclosure and drainage of the Axe valley, a flood-gate or clyst was built near Bleadon, preventing further navigation, though even after the opening of the Bristol & Exeter Railway in 1841, small colliers used Bleadon wharf, and the little harbour at Uphill was in use into the present century and is still a useful anchorage for pleasure craft.

Late in the eighteenth century two attempts were made to construct waterways to serve the Somerset coalfield in order to provide better means of transport than those afforded by packhorses or wagons that had to be hauled through the hilly countryside. A branch of the Somersetshire Coal Canal was cut in 1799 from Radstock to near Wellow from which point a tramroad linked it with the main line of the canal at Midford: this was finished about 1804 but apparently little used until converted to a tramroad in 1815, linking up with existing tramroads from collieries at Welton and Clandown which had fed into the basin at Radstock. The tramroad itself was bought by the Somerset &Dorset Railway in 1870 and incorporated in their Bath Extension.

Even more abortive was the Dorset & Somerset Canal, originally planned to link Bristol and Poole by way of Frome and Wincanton. Under an Act of 1796 a start was made with the 9 mile branch from Frome to serve the collieries in the Nettlebridge valleyn with a terminal basin on Stratton Common. Money ran out, work was abandoned in 1803, and later efforts to revive the scheme about 1825 also failed. The course of this sad little venture can still be followed, especially in the Coleford area, and at Barrow Hill near Buckland Dinham, where a patent Balance Lock designed and built by James Fussell at his iron works at Mells was successfully tested in 1800 and 1802.

Railways

The railway reached Mendip comparatively late. In 1841 the Bristol & Exeter main line cut through the western end of the range at Uphill. In 1854 the nominally independent Wilts, Somerset & Weymouth Railway, soon to be absorbed by the GWR, opened an $8\frac{1}{4}$ mile branch from Frome to Radstock, for mineral traffic only, to tap the Somerset coalfield rather more successfully than the Dorset & Somerset Canal had managed to do, 60 years before (see Fig 19).

Both these lines were built to Brunel's broad gauge of 7ft $0\frac{1}{4}$in: so was the East Somerset, another local company that was in due course absorbed by the GWR. This was opened from Witham (on the WS&W line) to Shepton Mallet in 1858 and to Wells in 1862, climbing over the southern slopes of the Mendip ridge with a summit level of just over 650ft above sea level near Cranmore. At Wells the East Somerset terminus confronted the terminus of the Somerset Central which had been extended from Glastonbury in 1859. The promotion of the East Somerset had in fact balked the Somerset Central's original intention of

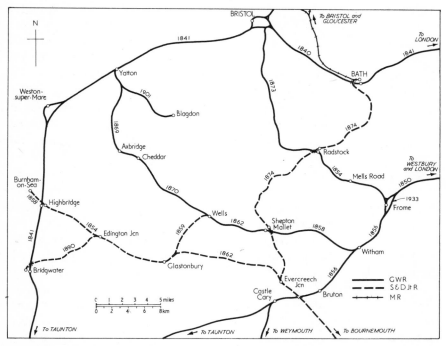

Fig 19   The railway pattern of north Somerset as it affected the Mendip area in 1914.

striking east to link up with the ws&w line at Frome. In the event, however, the scr was extended farther south along the Mendip foothills to Evercreech to meet the Dorset Central at Cole, amalgamating with that company in 1862 to form the Somerset & Dorset Railway with a through line from Burnham to Poole.

The scr had begun life as a broad-gauge protégé of the Bristol & Exeter by whom it was worked from 1854 to 1862; the Dorset Central, however, was built to the standard gauge of 4ft 8½in as befitted a protégé of the London & South Western, and on amalgamation the scr immediately introduced the mixed gauge, finally removing its broad gauge rails entirely. The Somerset & Dorset had in fact become a standard gauge cuckoo in the broad gauge nest—albeit in a state of permanent impecuniosity which compelled its directors to strive to tap more remunerative traffic to the north of Mendip.

Their first proposal, to reach Bristol along the Cheddar Valley and (with mixed gauge) over the Bristol & Exeter from Yatton, was thwarted by the b&e who opened their own broad gauge branch from Yatton to Cheddar in 1869 and to Wells in 1870, tunnelling through Mendip at Shute Shelve. In 1870, therefore, Wells boasted three termini, each owned by a different company, and all within a few hundred yards of each other. But by 1876 the GWR had absorbed both the Bristol & Exeter and the East Somerset, converted them both to standard gauge and laid a link between them *through* the S&D yard and station. In 1878 through working began from Yatton to Witham on what was henceforth known as the Cheddar Valley line.

The Somerset & Dorset's final ploy was to build a 26 mile extension from Evercreech right over the top of Mendip, reaching a summit level of 811ft at Masbury, to link up with the Midland Railway at Bath and provide a through route from the Midlands and the North to Bournemouth. This ambitious scheme brought the company (not for the first time) to the verge of bankruptcy, and in 1875 the line was leased to the Midland and the LSWR, remaining a Joint line until the nationalisation of railways in 1948.

The Bath Extension was opened in 1874. Meanwhile the S&D had bought out the Somersetshire Coal Canal tramway over which much of the produce of the Radstock coalfield had been moved to the canal at Midford since 1815. Radstock in fact had become a railway centre almost overnight, for the year before the arrival of the S&D, the Bristol & North Somerset had reached Radstock from Bristol, in 1873. The B&NS was a standard gauge line, and the earlier broad gauge mineral line from Radstock to Frome was forthwith converted to allow a through passenger service from Bristol to Frome from 1875.

The pattern of Mendip railways was now complete with the exception of the Wrington Vale Light Railway which was opened from Congresbury to Blagdon as late as 1901 and worked by the GWR. The first motor-cars were already spitting and grinding their way about the countryside, and though few could foresee what was to come, the writing was already on the wall as far as branch lines of railway were concerned; and with the exception of the Somerset & Dorset line, all the lines that served Mendip can be described as typical Great Western branches, whatever their origin. (An East Somerset overbridge was instantly distinguishable from one on the Wilts, Somerset & Weymouth, while the buildings on the Cheddar Valley line—described by Jack Simmons as 'spiky Gothic stations' with magnificently solid goods sheds—were all built of local Conglomerate.)

The branch lines, like most branch lines in England, played a modest but none the less vital role in the Mendip countryside; they can never have been real money-spinners, but although they seem to have done nothing to arrest the slow but steady decline of population in the rural areas during the second half of the nineteenth century, they were economically viable for slightly more than half a century. The Cheddar

Valley line always carried a fair number of passengers to Bristol or during the summer months to Weston or Clevedon; the grandiose station at Cheddar suggested high hopes of tourist traffic in 1869; Wells was only 3 hours from London by rail. Quarries provided the main freight traffic (at Sandford, Cheddar, Wookey, Dulcote and Cranmore), apart from the few hectic weeks of strawberry traffic and the perennial milk traffic whose loss to road collection in the late 1920s was a severe blow.

After the initial flow of traffic involved in the construction of the Yeo Reservoir, the Blagdon line was only the quietest of backwaters and the first to succumb to road competition, but the Radstock–Frome line carried a heavy mineral traffic from the collieries and from the east Mendip quarries, and was actually doubled between Radstock and Mells Road.

Over the years a wide variety of locomotive types worked the branches, with a heavy emphasis on various generations of 0-4-2T and 0-6-0T, both saddle tank and pannier tank, Dean Goods and the later Collett 0-6-0s, and 45XX and 55XX 2-6-2Ts bustling along with their two-coach sets. One of the early diesel railcars introduced by the GWR in 1934 made sporadic appearances, but the passenger services were steam-hauled to the bitter end.

The Somerset & Dorset was a very different affair. This was something more than a local line; in fact under the excellent management of the MR and the LSWR it was a very useful crosscountry link in the British railway network, and—at any rate until after the 1914–18 War—a reasonably profitable concern. There were the through expresses from the North including *The Pines* which ran throughout the year from Manchester to Bournemouth; there was a steady flow of excursion trains to the seaside during the summer months; there was through goods traffic off the Midland, routed via Templecombe on to the South Western—the historical consequence of the standard gauge breakthrough into the broad gauge empire; and there was the heavy mineral traffic from the Mendip collieries and quarries.

Most of the expresses were double-headed, while the freight trains were banked up the long haul to Masbury summit with a ruling gradient of 1 in 50 on both sides of Mendip: the journey over Mendip from Radstock to Evercreech was indeed a memorable experience. Apart from the high standard of locomotive work demanded, there was the scenic attraction of the route—the view southwards from near Masbury station was unforgettable—and a series of splendid viaducts, all built of local limestone.

Until 1930 the S&D, although it was jointly owned by the LMSR and the SR, still had its own stud of locomotives and rolling stock with magnificent blue livery; thereafter LMS types predominated, notably class 2P 4-4-0s, class 3F and 4F 0-6-0s and the black Stanier class 5 4-6-0s, until the eventual arrival of standard BR types; the exception were the class 7F 2-8-0s specially built for the SDJR in 1914 (and a second batch in 1925) for working heavy freight trains. In the postwar years the Mendip section of the line became something of a Mecca for railway fans and photographers, reaching a climax on the occasion of the final working of *The Pines* on 8 September 1962 when it was appropriately hauled by *Evening Star*, the last steam locomotive to be built by British Rail, and again at the closure of the line 5–6 March 1966.

The S&D, as all who knew it will readily admit, was a line of character, and an essential part of the Mendip scene. Its sights and its sounds linger yet in the memory, for it had become something of a legend in its own lifetime, and its nickname, 'Slow and Dirty', was a typical example of the affectionate understatement with which the Englishman refers to what is often dearest to his heart.

The dismemberment of the railway system of north Somerset covered several decades. The Blagdon branch went first (passenger service withdrawn 1931; freight beyond Wrington 1950). The Wells branch of the S&D was closed in 1911. The passenger service between Bristol and Frome was withdrawn in 1959, but freight traffic continued over the Bristol–Radstock section until 1968. The Cheddar Valley line was a victim of the Beeching axe; the passenger service was withdrawn in 1963, though freight traffic eastwards from the Cheddar quarries continued until 1968. The East Somerset section from Dulcote siding to Witham has remained open to serve several industrial sites, a new branch 1½ miles long being opened near Cranmore in 1970 to Foster Yeoman's Merehead quarry (see p 158). The Somerset & Dorset, as we have seen, was closed completely in 1966 except for a short section to Writhlington colliery near Radstock, which was closed in 1973.

The railway situation as far as Mendip is concerned is now almost identical with the situation on 14 November 1854 when the mineral branch was opened from Frome to Radstock. The only passenger services use the lines that cut across the eastern and western extremities of the range. The closure of the last two Somerset collieries in 1973 has deprived Radstock of its function as a freight terminal, though the line from Frome remains open, serving the great quarry at Whatley. A few miles of the original East Somerset line also bring stone traffic on to the Western Region main line at Witham.

Elsewhere the abandoned trackbed can be followed for miles across country, increasingly smothered in vegetation as the years pass: hundreds of acres of wasted land, and thousands of tons of useless ballast.

The possibility of using the abandoned lines for walking or riding has been balked by the removal of many of the bridges, though the magnificent Charlton viaduct at Shepton Mallet has been acquired by Showerings and incorporated in the garden adjoining their factory, and there have been proposals to make a linear park along the old s&D line between Radstock and Midsomer Norton. Most of the railway buildings, except on the Cheddar Valley line, have been demolished, though some of the station houses (at Masbury for instance and Blagdon) are occupied as private dwellings; some have been accquired by industry as at Shepton Mallet (High St) and Draycott; Midsomer Norton has been taken over by the Somerset Education Committee to create a field study and project centre for practical work to be undertaken by local secondary schools, and at Lodge Hill in the Cheddar valley the station building is used as a field centre by Bristol Grammar School.

As far as the ordinary public was concerned, the closure of the Somerset & Dorset in 1966 marked the end of an era in the history of Mendip communications. The outward flow of roadstone from the eastern flanks of Mendip is likely to increase year by year, and there has even been talk of reopening the northern end of the Cheddar Valley line as far as Winscombe to take away stone from the quarries between Cheddar and Sandford. But in the last two decades railhead has become increasingly remote for large areas of Mendip: coal must be hauled long distances by road instead of being delivered by wagon-load to the coal merchant's wharf at the local station; parcels traffic is distributed from Bristol—if handled by rail at all; and except at the eastern and western extremities of Mendip, would-be passengers face a long and tedious drive to catch their trains at Bristol or Bath or even at Westbury or Castle Cary.

Industrial Railways

A number of privately owned lines, some of them standard gauge, some narrow gauge, fed the systems worked by the GWR and the SDJR. Some have been mentioned in the previous section, but to complete the picture of the Mendip railway network it is simplest to start at Radstock and move clockwise round the hill before finally considering the s&D which ran right across the rest of the pattern (see Fig 20).

RADSTOCK–FROME

At Radstock short branches from Farrington Gurney, Old Mills, Old Welton and Wellsway collieries connected with the Bristol–Frome line,

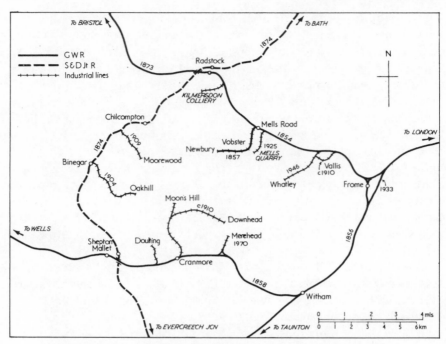

Fig 20   The railways of eastern Mendip, including the industrial lines.

as did Tynings and Ludlows; from Kilmersdon colliery at Haydon wagons were worked over a short branch by a Peckett 0-4-0T locomotive before being lowered down a rope-hauled incline to the main line. This was the last steam working in north Somerset which survived the withdrawal of steam over the WR in 1966 and continued until 1972.

At Mells Road a 2½ mile branch formerly served Mells colliery, Vobster quarry, and Newbury and Macintosh collieries (with a narrow gauge feeder from Vobster collieries). It was originally built by the Westbury Iron Company in 1857 as a broad gauge line to carry coal and limestone to their iron works at Westbury, and was worked until 1966. Another branch also served Beauchamp Brothers' Mells quarry.

At Vallis, 1 mile from Frome, a standard gauge branch served large limestone quarries, and this was extended as far as Whatley quarry in 1946; this carries considerable traffic in roadstone and in ballast for British Rail. The tortuous course of the line through the wooded gorge of the Mells river has recently been re-aligned and shortened by driving two tunnels near Great Elm, thus enabling BR diesels to work up to Whatley quarry and take away full train-loads of stone.

WITHAM–WELLS

Near Cranmore a 1½ mile branch to the Merehead Stone Terminal serves Foster Yeoman's Torr Works. Three quarters of the output of the vast quarry—between 3 and 4 million tons a year at the time of writing—is now conveyed by rail.

At Cranmore (where there is now a bitumen re-handling depot) there was formerly much stone traffic: a standard gauge branch from Waterlip quarry replaced an earlier narrow gauge line which climbed over the Mendip ridge to serve quarries at Moons Hill and Downhead. West of Cranmore station, Doulting stone was handled at the works to which it was conveyed over a horse-drawn tramroad from the qurries at Chelynch.

Dulcote siding serves another of Foster Yeoman's quarries.

Wookey an aerial ropeway at one time brought stone from Underwood quarry to a siding on the Cheddar Valley line; another siding served St Cuthbert's paper works. At Sandford quarry a standard gauge branch brought stone down to the station.

SOMERSET & DORSET LINE

At Radstock the s&d took over the tramroads from the collieries at Welton and Clandown which had been built in the eighteenth century to feed the Somersetshire Coal Canal and the tramroad which replaced the branch canal in 1815, but in course of time Welton Hill, Old Welton and Wellsway were all linked up with the Bristol & North Somerset line.

At Midsomer Norton, Norton Hill colliery was served from 1899 to 1966, the yard being worked by main line locomotives as well as by standard gauge locomotives belonging to the colliery, sturdy little tank engines with names like *Leonidas* and *Lord Salisbury*.

At Emborough a narrow gauge branch served Moorewood colliery (1½ miles away), and at different periods two aerial ropeways and two different sets of sidings served Emborough and Cockhill quarries.*

At Binegar a narrow gauge branch served Oakhill Brewery from 1904 to 1921, bringing Oakhill Stout across the fields to a large shed at Binegar station which has survived the demolition of the station itself.

---

* In the 1860s and 1870s a branch was planned down the Nettlebridge valley to serve a number of collieries and to join the GWR line at Mells Road, but this was never built.

At Winsor Hill, three quarries fed the line, one of them with a short branch off the main line controlled by a signal box which was closed in 1940.

Notes to this chapter are on pages 273-4.

28 Old Frome industries: malthouse *(left)* in the Frome United Brewery yard, and Rawlings cloth mill off Broadway – both demolished in the 1960s to make way for council housing

29 Recently excavated furnace on the site of Fussells iron works in the Wadbury valley below Mells

30 The line of the Dorset & Somerset Canal, abandoned in 1803, winding through the hills near Coleford

31 The New Frome Quarry at Whatley creeping towards the Conservation Area at Mells

32 Banwell Brewery *c* 1916: until 1850 the pond supplied a paper mill, and the site is now a bowling green

7

Industry

Robin Atthill

INDUSTRIAL MENDIP: A CONTRADICTION in terms to those who think of Mendip as a limestone ridge of hills straddling most of the holiday routes to the south-west of England, and to those who see it simply as farming country (with a strawberry belt) or as tourist country defaced here and there by quarrying. Motorists on the Fosse Way thread their way through the Norton–Radstock urban complex, full of visible evidence of the now defunct mining industry, and at Westfield, and a few miles farther south at Shepton Mallet, they pass factories belonging to the two largest firms operating in the Mendip area—Clarks and Showerings. On the other through routes there is hardly a sign of industrial activity except for the quarries on the Frome–Shepton Mallet road: at worst one is liable to meet the occasional lorry carrying roadstone or ready-mix concrete emerging suddenly from a byroad which was obviously not intended to carry such traffic.

But Mendip has a long and varied industrial history. Until the boundary changes of 1974, Somerset was the seventh largest county in England and in 1831 ranked eighth in population with 404,200 inhabitants. Except for Bath, Frome was the largest town in the county with 12,240 inhabitants against Taunton's 11,139, while 30 years earlier in 1801 Taunton had only 5,794 inhabitants against Shepton Mallet's 5,104. A glance at the 1817 Ordnance map shows how thickly populated much of north Somerset was, with villages and small towns clustered around the foothills of Mendip, and a maze of lanes serving industrial hamlets and villages on the northern and eastern flanks of the range. Many of these villages (Mells, for instance, or Nunney, or Batcombe, or Croscombe) had a much smaller population in 1931 than in 1831, though modern housing development has in some cases brought the population figures up again towards their former level.

The older Mendip industries were indigenous: their location depended upon the physical geography of the area, and its geology in particular. Either they needed water-power (or the peculiar quality of

Mendip water)—hence the industrialisation of the eastern valleys with their fast-flowing streams; or they were concerned with the mineral resources of the hills. From end to end of Mendip in fact there is hardly a parish which has not been the scene of mining activity over the centuries.

This chapter deals first with the extractive industries as being the oldest and the longest lived; then with the older manufacturing industries, most of which are now extinct and replaced by ubiquitous and non-native industries in the sense that they depend neither upon local materials nor upon local power nor upon local markets.

The Extractive Industries

(1) LEAD

Lead mining was the earliest known and the longest lasting industrial activity on Mendip. Lead objects from the Glastonbury and Meare Lake villages prove that lead was being worked 200–300 years before the Roman invasion of AD 43; St Cuthbert's Works at Priddy closed in 1908.

The area of mining lay almost entirely to the west of the Bristol–Wells road (A39), stretching from Green Ore to Charterhouse. Some account of developments in the earlier centuries has been given in Chapters 3 and 4. Apart from objects in museums, there is practically no definite evidence in the Mendip landscape of this early mining in the Roman or medieval periods, simply because the same sites have been re-worked again and again almost to within living memory.

By the middle of the sixteenth century the mining area was organised into Liberties administered by the four Lords Royal of Mendip—the Bishop, and the Lords of Harptree, Chewton and Charterhouse. They issued licences to mine; they claimed 'lot-lead' which was 10 per cent of any ore produced on their land; they administered in their own courts a code of ancient bylaws relating to the mines, and each Liberty had its own minery where there was an adequate supply of running water for washing the ore. This last factor determined the location of the mineries at Charterhouse, at Smitham Hill above Harptree, and to the east of Priddy, where Chewton minery and the Bishop's minery were practically contiguous. Several of the old maps of Mendip—the Ashwick Court map, for instance, at the Wells Museum, which is Elizabethan, and the Waldegrave map, now at Taunton, which dates from the seventeenth century—depict the mineries by means of the large bellows which provided the draught for the hearths where the lead was smelted.

Most of these old maps also contain the code of ten mining laws or customs applicable to the whole area, giving the Mendip miners a peculiar standing like the lead miners of the Peak and of Alston Moor, or workers in the stannaries of Devon and Cornwall. These laws governed the main working conditions of the lead industry in the sixteenth and seventeenth centuries: getting a licence from the lord of the soil; 'throwing the hack', by which the miner stood in his 'groove' up to his waist and threw the hack or pick in either direction along his 'rake' or seam to measure out his claim; and the ruthless burning from the hill which awaited the lead thief. He was brought to his house or work where he kept his tools, the house was set on fire about him, and he himself—if he escaped—was banished from the hill for ever.

Some of the miners were 'free-miners' working one-man mines; most of them were in small partnerships; but there were also occasional small-scale capitalists as well as notorious adventurers such as the Elizabethan Bevis Bulmer, and Thomas Bushell (1594–1674), who had grandiose ambitions and limited success. The mines seem to have achieved their greatest peak of production between 1600 and 1670 when the chance survival of a set of lead reeve's accounts among the Waldegrave papers enables us to examine in detail at least one part of the working of the industry at its height, though it is unwise to attempt to estimate the output of lead from all four Liberties on the basis of these figures. (See Gough pp 114-15). Where rich veins of lead were suspected or discovered, every yard of ground must have been explored: the grooves and shafts were often embarrassingly close to one another, and there were frequent instances, involving proceedings in the minery courts, where miners broke into one another's workings underground.

After about 1670 a long period of decline set in: the more accessible seams were worked out and deeper mining was beyond the technological skill of the age when only the occasional horse-whim or horse-driven windlass supplemented the hand-worked windlass and bucket. The crucial problem was the continual flooding of the deeper and more lucrative workings. In 1657 the miners had actually petitioned Cromwell about the recovery of 'the vast Mineral Treasure known to lie in the drowned and deserted works of that ancient Forrest called Mendipp-hill'—with special reference to the 'Millions of wealth' at the fabulously rich Rowpits in Chewton Minery. Over 100 years later, John Billingsley proposed the driving of an adit or horizontal shaft 450 feet below the hill, from Compton Martin to Wookey Hole, to carry off the watern but the truth is that Mendip lead was inferior to Derbyshire, the methods of working were oldfashioned and wasteful, and there was nothing to justify heavy capital expenditure or the introduction of modern equipment. The mines died a lingering death. Day & Masters' map of 1782 marks Edgar Pitts and Wheel Pitts on the plateau above East Harptree to the north of Chewton Minery, but there is nothing marked on the 1817 os map and in July 1815 Skinner described Priddy which had once been 'a far more considerable place . . . during the time the lead mines were worked' as a 'miserable straggling village'.

But when all seemed finished a new era began. There was to be no more mining, however, only re-smelting of the gigantic heaps of refuse left by the crude techniques of earlier centuries. Smelting on a small scale was going on at Charterhouse in 1824, but from 1850 onwards there was considerable activity in all four mineries. Cornish mining engineers such as Nicholas Ennor appeared on the scene; unscrupulous company promoters enjoyed a brief heyday; capital was raised; and new buildings and expensive machinery such as reverbatory furnaces and round Cornish buddles were installed—the latter being circular pits lined with masonry for preparing the refuse for smelting. Long horizontal flues were built along hillsides in which the smoke from the furnaces, heavily charged with lead vapour, was induced to deposit some of its content before escaping from tall chimney stacks. A small amount of silver was also produced by the Pattinson process at Charterhouse.*
Practically all the lead produced was used for making shot, much of it at the shot tower in Redcliffe Street, Bristol, by Messrs Sheldon Bush. But the industry never really flourished, and after 1880 only St Cuthbert's works at Priddy Minery remained in production until finally closed down in 1908. A few photographs record the final stages of this age-old Mendip industry.

Sixty years ago there was still a good deal to be seen in all four mineries: six chimneys still stood, and both at Priddy and Charterhouse a number of gaunt ruined buildings survived above ground, including the appropriately named Bleak House where the manager had lived, looking down on the Blackmoor valley. Since then much has crumbled away or disappeared. Above ground Smitham chimney which was built in 1867 survives on the skyline above East Harptree—though a Forestry Commission plantation has grown up around it—and at Charterhouse the group of flue tunnels, fairly well protected from Mendip weather, are surprisingly well preserved. Elsewhere the buddle pits have been completely overgrown, and the reservoirs, which were so important for the supply of water for the lead working process, have filled up with silt and reeds. The most spectacular remains, both at Priddy and Charterhouse, are the endless mounds of glossy black slag.

* On 2 October 1720 Dr Claver Morris had difficulty crossing the bog 'near Charterhouse Cupiloe'; this probably refers to a cupola or domed furnace used for melting metal rather than to the process of cupellation used by the Romans for extracting silver. (See p 69.)

The industrial archaeologist has now arrived upon the scene—but almost too late. With the help of surving photographs and of the large-scale os maps, it is possible to reconstruct to some extent the sites of the nineteenth-century lead works. Groups of schoolchildren working from the Charterhouse Field Centre have excavated and recorded the site of the Pattinson plant in the Blackmoor valley; excavation has been carried out on the site of a horse-whim at Ubley's Rake near Ubley Warren Farm; an attempt has been made to preserve a buddle house which has survived in Biddle Combe near West Horrington; the Smitham chimney, scheduled as a monument of historical importance, has now been preserved, thanks to the initiative of the Mendip Society. This is a typical 'Cornish' chimney, tapering from the bottom two-thirds in native limestone to the upper third and cap which are of brick—an interesting link with the Cornish engineers and industrialists who worked on Mendip at this time. The most permanent feature of the mining landscape, however, is likely to be the acre upon acre of 'gruffy ground', scarred and pitted by centuries of working. (The shafts were locally called 'gruffs' or 'grooves' and the miners themselves were known as 'groovers'.) Even here the bulldozer has been at work—near Green Ore, for instance, or at Lamb Leer—bringing spoiled land back into agricultural use. On the hillside above the Blackmoor valley, however, the deep rock-hewn rakes will surely outlast human endeavour.

(2) OTHER MINERALS

The western end of the main range saw a period of feverous activity late in the eighteenth century in the search for calamine ore: this yielded zinc which was alloyed with copper at the brass foundries in the Bristol region. Calamine had been discovered near Worle in 1566 and was being worked on Mendip by about 1600. By the middle of seventeenth century the industry was fully established along the western hills. Mining was mainly concentrated round Shipham and Rowberrow: there was an intensive area of mining on the hillside above the village at Shipham, pockmarked with little workings, while in the 1790s Rowberrow Bottom contained a dreary industrial village. As with lead mining, the primitive techniques, the exhaustion of easily accessible veins, and finally the competition of cheap imported ores, brought the calamine industry to an end by about 1850. Apart from areas of gruffy ground, the only visible relic is the alleged remains of a calamine oven at Shipham.

In these two parishes, Hannah and Martha More strove to introduce some measure of Christian piety and civilisation into the squalor and poverty they saw around them. At Cheddar and elsewhere they had established schools and Friendly Societies, but it was the conditions in the mining villages that horrified them most, 'the people savage and depraved . . . brutal in their natures, and ferocious in their manners'. A stained-glass window in Shipham church commemorates the work of the two sisters, whose philanthropic zeal was inspired by their friend, William Wilberforce.

Sporadic attempts have been made over the centuries to work other minerals all along the Mendip range, but only with very limited success. Iron mining for yellow ochre was attempted in the nineteenth century at various sites from Dolebury in the west to Nunney in the east. Managanese was also worked in the nineteenth century, in particular at Higher Pitts Farm near the top of Ebbor Rocks. In fact the unprofitable exertions of the Somersetshire Manganese and Iron Ore Company on this site in 1890-1 seem to have been the last genuine mining venture on Mendip—apart from coal mining which is dealt with in the next section.

Nowhere on Mendip today is one likely to be very far from the scene of former mining activity of which there are constant reminders: it may be the ubiquitous legends on the os map—Old Pit, Shaft, Mine (disused); or a place-name such as The Miners' Arms or Smitham Hill (Smitham being the smallest of the ore that goes through the wire bottom of the sieve) or Green Ore; it may be an obvious area of gruffy ground or a pathetic little spoil heap in a field; or merely the sudden glint of metal in the grass,

> a glossy scurf, undoubted sign
> That in his womb was hid metallic ore.

(3) COAL

Morden's map of Somerset, published in 1695, pockmarks the Nettlebridge valley with 'Cole Pitts', and Celia Fiennes, visiting Warminster in 1697, commented on 'the Mindiffe Coale which is allmost as good as the sea-coale from New-Castle that is dugg out of the hills all about'. By that date, however, coal mining was already a long-established industry on Mendip. Quite apart from the possible use of coal by the Romans—the Fosse Way plunges across the Nettlebridge valley at a point where outcrops were particularly obvious and accessible—there is reference to coal working in Kilmersdon parish in 1305, and both here and in the neighbouring parish of Stratton-on-the-Fosse the raising of coal was well established by the fifteenth century. The miners at Writhlington and Kilmersdon, the last two collieries to remain open, were thus the inheritors of a tradition of mining that goes back over 650 years.

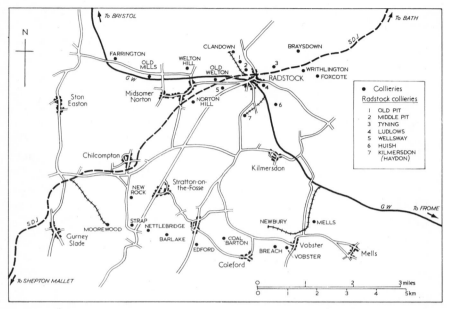

Fig 21   Collieries in the Radstock sector and the Mendip collieries with their rail connections.

The Somerset coalfield covers an area of about 100 sq miles. Apart from the northern outposts such as Pensford, Clutton and Bishop Sutton—the last-named supplied coal for the lead smelting furnaces on Mendip in the nineteenth century—most of the collieries were clustered along three valleys, the Cam Brook, the so-called River Somer and the Wellow Brook on which stand Radstock and Midsomer Norton, and the Nettlebridge valley.

The collieries in the Nettlebridge valley were often specifically called the Mendip collieries, but they cannot be treated separately from the central sector of the coalfield. Farrington Gurney, Midsomer Norton and Radstock all fall within the area covered by this study. It would be nonsensical to include Old Welton and Wellsway, but to exclude Welton Hill and Ludlows because they stood a few hundred yards outside an arbitrary boundary line. Norton–Radstock must be considered as a whole. Coal mining drastically affected the landscape and was the decisive factor in the social and economic development of two or three small villages into a sprawling urban complex of about 15,000 people.

Except for Norton–Radstock, this was essentially a rural coalfield: sometimes the group of colliery buildings and the spoil tip (or dirt batch in local parlance) stood incongruously by themselves in the middle of green fields as at Mells or New Rock, or at Moorewood and Vobster in the heavily wooded Nettlebridge valley; it was a coalfield where miners naturally lent a hand in the hayfield during the summer months when they were liable to be on short time.

Practically no heavy industry developed within the coalfield apart from Evans' foundry at Paulton which later moved to Radstock. In the 1850s there was the intention of building blast furnaces at Coleford, but in the end both coal and limestone from the Vobster quarries were carried over the Newbury railway to the iron works at Westbury in Wiltshire. The edge-tool industry depended almost entirely on water-power, as did such cloth mills as survived in the eastern Mendip valleys.

Until nationalisation in 1947, the pits were owned and worked by small local groups or private companies with only limited capital. They therefore remained small: Norton Hill, the largest and most important of the Somerset collieries, employed at one time 750 men, but New Rock employed only 200, and others were smaller still. Nor was the coal easy to win: it has been said that the miners 'scratched a living in conditions that would have been the despair of miners from other areas'. The average thickness of the seams was 20–30in, involving the removal of much waste, and the seams were often violently distorted and faulted, especially in the Nettlebridge valley, where the seams not only dip towards the vertical but actually turn over so that what was the roof becomes the floor. The faulting involved wasteful expense in searching for the coal and also in haulage over unevenly graded roads.

Nor was transport from the pithead particularly easy. After 1874 a network of extended sidings or narrow gauge tramways connected most of the pits round Radstock with the GWR or the SDJR, but until 1909 when the Moorewood branch was built, only the east end of the Nettlebridge valley was served by rail, and some collieries such as Edford and New Rock were never connected to a railway. The railways actually carried less than half the total output of the Somerset coalfield; the larger part was still moved by road in 1900 and disposed of in local markets, for domestic or industrial use, just as it had been in the turnpike period before the arrival of the canal and the railway. 'To go to Mendipp for Coles' had been a common expression in the seventeenth century and the practice died hard.

Many of the techniques used in the coalfield were oldfashioned, and little or no mechanisation was introduced before nationalisation. Some of the techniques were however particularly suited to the type of seam worked and the conditions of haulage from the coal face. The guss and crook for example, the rope and chain by which the barefoot carting boys, working on all fours, hauled the putt—a wooden box fitted with runners like a sledge—survived until the 1930s because it was an effective device, and also saved the expense of cutting roadways big enough to take tubs to the coal face where narrow seams were being worked.

The individuality of the Somerset coalfield emerges in its private terminology which speaks of putts and guggs, dipples and twinways; the collieries, too, often boasted names to delight the local historian and puzzle the etymologist—Old Breach, Duck's Nest, Ringing Bell, Bilboa and Strap—while many of the seams in the different series—Dungy Drift and Butterrakes, Slyving and Peacock, Fern Rag and Blue Pot—were familiar names in 1700 and part of the long history of the coalfield.

The earliest area of working was in the Nettlebridge valley—surface workings where the lower series of seams outcropped in the Stratton–Holcombe–Coleford area; but by the fifteenth century coalpits were being operated with shafts and underground workings, and these had been driven considerably deeper by the end of the seventeenth century with the attendant problems of drainage and winding when only water-power was available. The proprietors of these coal works were either groups of working colliers, or local business men investing small amounts of capital, or landowners who anyhow drew their royalty from the coal mined on their estates. One of this class was James Twyford, lord of the manor of Kilmersdon: his 'Observations on Coleworks' provides a detailed and fascinating picture of working conditions about 1700.

The picture changed rapidly after 1763 when the Old Pit was sunk at Radstock, which was to become the capital of the coalfield, growing from a small village of 509 in 1801 to a town of 3,355 in 1901. Although mining continued in the Nettlebridge valley throughout the nineteenth century in the Coleford–Vobster–Mells area, it was the Radstock district which witnessed the intensive development of this period with at least twenty pits being sunk along the floor of the valley from Farrington Gurney to Writhlington and on the hillsides above the various valleys that meet at Radstock. Impetus was given by the introduction of steam-power in the 1780s, enabling coal to be wound from much greater depths, and by greater geological knowledge. William Smith, the Father of English Geology, was working at High Littleton in the 1790s, and commented on the technical backwardness of the area hitherto in comparison with the northern coalfields. Transport too helped to open up the area: a branch of the Somersetshire Coal Canal reached

Radstock by 1804 to be replaced by a tramway in 1815, fed by about a dozen collieries; and in 1854 the railway arrived. The last new pits to be sunk were Kilmersdon colliery in 1874 and Norton Hill in 1900.*

The second half of the nineteenth century saw the closure of many of the older and smaller pits, and the development of larger units into which much more capital was sunk, though most of it still came from local sources. This period also saw the emergence of the big owner; the Countess Waldegrave, for instance, whose agent James McMurtrie was perhaps the outstanding figure in the history of the coalfield, and the Beauchamp family, who rose very rapidly from humble origins in the mid-nineteenth century to become the owners of most of the Radstock pits: at the time of World War II their company, Somerset Collieries Ltd, was producing 43 per cent of the output of the coalfield. In 1868 there were sixty-four active collieries at work, but by 1914 only twenty-six, which produced 1,250,000 tons of coal a year, employing about 10,000 men.

The postwar years saw a rapid decline, accentuated by the strikes of 1921 and 1926, and by the mid-thirties only thirteen pits remained in production, raising about 700,000 tons of coal a year with a labour force of about 3,500 men. The coalfield was slow to modernise by the introduction of coal-cutting machines and conveyors and loading machines—the inevitable result, perhaps, of the isolation of the small coalfield from the rest of the country. Until 1963, for example, all the coal at New Rock was being wound up a shaft 1,182ft deep but only 4ft 6in in diameter.

This was the situation when nationalisation of the coal industry came in 1947. The National Coal Board proceeded to close the older and less profitable pits and to concentrate on those where heavy capital expenditure was thought justifiable by the introduction of modern equipment and methods which were essential to combat the shortage of manpower. By 1959 only five collieries were still at work, though until 1962 production was kept up to about 600,000 tons a year. Thereafter there was a further rapid decline: Old Mills and Norton Hill were closed in 1966 and New Rock in 1968, after a working life of almost 150 years.

Thereafter only Writhlington and Kilmersdon remained open, working at a loss and producing in 1972 about 150,000 tons of coal. At the end only about 400 men were employed. The real end came on 28 September 1973 when the last load of coal was brought to the surface, though dismantling and salvage work continued for another year.

* The later pits at Dunkerton 1903, Pensford 1910, and Priston 1914, are outside the Mendip area. Moorewood 1909 and Strap 1954 resuscitated old workings.

As the NCB moved out, the historian and the industrial archaeologist have moved in, and indeed there is still much to observe and record. The steam winding engine from Old Mills, made by William Evans at Paulton in 1861, has been preserved by Bristol City Museum. The history of almost every known site has been scrupulously recorded by Down and Warrington with some indication of what is still visible today. Sometimes only a grass-grown or tree-covered dirt batch, a few ruined walls or a concrete cap over a long-disused shaft, spell out the site of a colliery to those who have eyes to see. Elsewhere industry has taken over the buildings, at Wellsway, for instance, at Edford and at Newbury; at Moorewood, 40 years after its closure, the derelict buildings, chimney and all, were still standing in a green field until 1974 when the chimney was felled and the winding-house refurbished to become the central feature in a scrap-merchant's yard, but at Norton Hill the site has been almost entirely flattened and cleared.

Most of the buildings that survive, including some fine nineteenth-century engine houses, are built of local stone, as were many of the ranks of miners' houses, especially in the Radstock area where Countess Waldegrave made a real effort to provide good housing for her workmen.

To the passing traveller it is such sights as these, and the variously shaped spoil tips, sometimes planted with softwoods and slowly beginning to take their place as permanent landscape features, which distinguish the area of the coalfield on the northern fringe of Mendip. So do the miners' welfare halls in a number of villages; so too do the old miners, squatting on their hams beside the road, their minds perhaps brooding over the past, recalling who knows what details of long-forgotten pits with abandoned shafts and worked out seams where even older men had got coal for at least six centuries.

(4) Stone

The geology of Mendip has been described in Chapter 2. Like lead and coal and other minerals, the stone of which the hills consist has been worked by man over many centuries—primarily the various types of limestone, but also the sandstone and the basalt which outcrops to the east of Beacon Hill.

Until the middle of the nineteenth century most buildings in rural areas were built of local stone quarried on the spot. For the manor house and the parish church, stone might be transported a few miles, but at West Harptree the church and the two principal houses, both dating from the seventeenth century, are built of the local Dolomitic Conglomerate. Other church towers were built of the creamy oolitic limestone from Dundry or from Doulting, whose medieval quarries supplied the stone for Wells Cathedral and Glastonbury Abbey at least from 1180 onwards. The demand persisted. In 1817 the Rev John Skinner wrote in his Journal: 'At Doulting they dig freestone, and supply the neighbourhood for miles round with the article.' Later in the nineteenth century, the stone was moved along a horse tramway to works beside the railway where it was prepared and finished by machinery before being dispatched over the East Somerset line. The same beautiful stone is still worked today at St Andrew's and Chelynch quarries.

Doulting village is built almost entirely of this stone. Moving about Mendip, indeed, one is constantly aware of the subtle variations of the texture and type of stone, at any rate in the older parts of each village: one moves from stone to stone within a mile or so. Kilmersdon and Mells are of oolitic limestone; Holcombe is pinkish Pennant Sandstone, but Stratton-on-the-Fosse is White Lias; Litton is grey limestone, but the Harptrees are Dolomitic Conglomerate, perhaps the most typical material of the villages that lie under the northern and southern escarpments. The old quarries from which these building requirements were supplied can often be identified in fields near the villages, but when Coleford Church was being built in 1829 it was stipulated that the field from which the stone was to be dug should be made level when all needs had been met.

Local quarries also met the requirements of the turnpike trustees, the stone being broken to the right size by hand on the spot (as indeed was done in certain areas until well into the present century). Stone for the walls of the new enclosures on top of Mendip was usually dug on the spot; the farmhouses and barns grew, as it were, out of their own allotments. And to improve these allotments lime was needed, and limekilns were built on many individual farms.

The railways, when they came, required stone for ballast, and also built their bridges and stations of local materials, Mountain Limestone on the Somerset & Dorset, and Dolomitic Conglomerate on the Cheddar Valley line. But the real importance of the railways was the facilities they offered for transporting stone in bulk: from 1857 limestone was being moved over the Newbury railway to the Westbury iron works—early plans of Vobster quarry show stone-crushers already installed there—and by 1875 William Beauchamp, who had started his quarry business in 1867, was sending away stone from Winsor Hill on the Somerset & Dorset, as well as from Cranmore on the East Somerset line, advertising 'Mendip Granite' for macadamising as well as building stone, gravel, asphalt and lime.

In the early part of the present century most of the large quarries were linked with either the GWR or the s&D, directly or by narrow gauge branches. Typical of this period were the group of quarries near Emborough. Quarrying at Emborough began in 1901; sidings were built off the s&D; stone-crushers were erected; an aerial ropeway conveyed stone across Emborough Pool, and the same ropeway was later re-erected to bring stone from Cockhill quarry at Gurney Slade to a tarmac plant at Moorewood sidings, while another quarry in Gurney Slade village was connected by aerial ropeway with stone-crushing plant beside the line at Binegar.

The interwar years saw the rapid growth of demand for roadstone and the development of modern quarrying techniques. These quarries, including a number of new sites opened up in the 1920s and 1930s (such as Dulcote, which was started in 1922), were owned by small local groups which coalesced in 1934 to form Roads Reconstruction with its headquarters at Cranmore and later at Frome. Most of the quarries of this earlier period have been closed and their rail links removed: Winsor Hill and Waterlip, Downhead and Vobster and Vallis. The abandoned railway formations can still sometimes be traced across country; the quarries themselves are sometimes full of water, sometimes overgrown with scrub, sometimes littered with rusting plant and spoil heaps, sometimes strangely moving and beautiful.

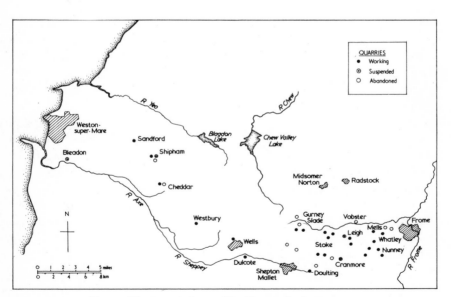

Fig 22 The stone industry: Mendip quarries in 1975.

Already fears were being voiced about the effect on the landscape of uncontrolled quarrying. This was especially the case near Wells where Milton Hill and Dulcote Hill were both being devoured, although both were features of very great natural beauty in the environment of the city and its cathedral. (Following a public inquiry in 1947 an order was issued to preserve the overall appearance of the skyline at Dulcote.)

But it is in the years since World War II that the quarrying industry has developed with such rapidity and voraciousness as to cause alarm and despondency in many areas and on many counts. The reason is the unprecedented and unforeseen demand for roadstone and other aggregatess as well as ready-mix concrete and other concrete products. Mendip quarries are the only really adequate source of supply for road development in the South of England, and also for replacing the falling reserves of gravel in the South and South East. Output has escalated from 1.2 million tons in 1947 to 3 million tons in 1965, 8 million tons in 1970 and 10 million tons in 1973. Present trends suggest that 20 million tons a year might be extracted by 1988 if the annual increase of 6-8 per cent were maintained (see Fig 22).

Most of this stone is won from new quarries or from large-scale development on earlier sites. These concessions were granted uncon- ditional planning permission under the Town and Country (General Interim Development) Order 1946, in some cases without adequate safeguards as to the working requirements or the possible effects on the environment and amenities of the area. The postwar years have seen the rapid installation of larger and more complex machinery for the treat- ment of the raw material and its preparation in numerous marketable forms. The Nordberg gyratory crusher at Merehead, for instance, is the largest of its kind in Europe. All this demanded large-scale capital investment, with the result that many of the quarries have now been acquired by large public companies such as Amey Roadstone Corpora- tion or English China Clays, though some of the major quarries are still owned by local family groups: John Wainwright, for instance, who acquired Moon's Hill in 1904, and Foster Yeoman who started work at Dulcote in 1922 and at Merehead in 1958, and two or three others.

Only two of the working quarries—New Frome Quarry at Whatley and Merehead Quarry at Cranmore—are served by rail. The rest of the stone produced is moved by road, nearly 2,000 lorry-loads a day on an average moving along roads, many of which are no more than country lanes, utterly unsuitable for ever-larger vehicles including the latest ten-wheel hopper or tipper type of lorry of 32 tons gross weight. The traffic

---

* Aggregates may be roughly defined as quarried stone, sand and gravel used in nearly all forms of modern construction and civil engineering.

generated by the quarries is one of the main causes for local concern, not only in narrow lanes, but in the village streets and towns through which it has to pass; in the Cheddar–Wells area it conflicts with heavy holiday traffic, while much of it feeds on to the A361, which is an important through route from the Midlands to the South West, though often capable of carrying only a single line of traffic in each direction for miles on end.

The other nuisances associated with quarrying affect the immediate neighbourhood: noise, both from blasting and from machinery, the latter continuing all night in some areas; atmospheric pollution from dust; and above all the visual impact of the workings on the eye of the beholder and the general loss of amenity—glaring examples are at Sandford and at Batts Combe, Cheddar, in thickly populated and much visited areas, and the blight of Asham Wood.

Further consequences are water pollution, the long-term effect on the water table, the destruction of cave-systems and of archaeological sites, and the loss of agricultural land. The over-riding consideration, however, is the fact that many of the major quarries are situated, if not in an Area of Outstanding Natural Beauty, at any rate in an Area of Great Landscape Value. This conflict of interests will be discussed further in the final chapter of this book. The inescapable facts are that limestone is essential to the modern economy and that the demand for limestone in many forms and byproducts is still rapidly increasing. The basic problem is how to meet this demand by controlling quarrying operations in such a way as to minimise the damage to the environment.

The situation today is that there are now twenty-four operating units on Mendip, some of which will grow to many times their present size before their concessions are exhausted, quite apart from concessions where quarrying has not yet started (see Fig 22). The units fall into three groups: five on western Mendip from Bleadon to Cheddar, all visually offensive as they eat into the bold sculpture of the hillsides in a favourite tourist area; five on central Mendip from the skyline quarry at Westbury on the southern escarpment through Milton Hill and Dulcote as far east as Gurney Slade; and fourteen on eastern Mendip beyond the Fosse Way, including the two basalt quarries at Stoke St Michael and the large group in the area contained by Cranmore–Nunney–Mells–Leigh-on-Mendip. Because of the terrain, these are less obtrusive to the eye, but they appear destined to destroy a great deal of the landscape during the next few decades, including some of the beautiful deep wooded valleys that are such a feature of eastern Mendip.

Little has been written about this subject until recent years except in professional or technical journals. The present situation however has been fearlessly and concisely assessed by Dr W. I. Stanton in a paper published in *Man and the Mendips* (1971). His main findings were that eastern Mendip should be designated a sacrifice area, but even here it was essential that the limestone should be worked to its absolute maximum by constructive quarrying which would involve deep sub-water-table working. Somerset County Council has also published its full-length survey *Quarrying in Somerset* by C. L. Keeler of the County Planning Department: an impartial appraisal of every aspect of the quarrying and transporting of stone from Somerset. In the words of the preface, 'it is to attempt to provide the information upon the basis of which a future policy aiming to reconcile the demands for this stone with the necessity to protect the living conditions, recreational possibilities and scenery of the beautiful County of Somerset that this appraisal has been attempted'. The future development of Mendip will largely depend on the policy adopted as a guide to the control of quarry development as a result of this survey.

The ancillary industries linked with the extraction of stone can be dealt with more briefly.

Lime burning seems to have begun at the time of the enclosures on Mendip towards the end of the eighteenth century, lime 'the grand manure of the district' being required in considerable quantities to improve the newly won fields. Billingsley, writing in 1794, describes the kilns of this period: 'their form is that of a French bottle, the height seventeen feet, the length of the neck, in which the calcination is wholly effected, seven feet; its diameter four feet, and the diameter of the belly in the largest part twelve feet. They are built on the side of a hill, by which means the top is on a level with the adjacent rock.' These old kilns are still to be seen dotted about all over Mendip, where names like Limekiln Lane and Limekiln Wood recur, as does the legend LK on early editions of the six-inch OS.

In the 1880s *Kelly's Directory* lists fifteen lime burners, but only five in 1919: latterly production was carried on at Callow Rock and Gurney Slade, but only at Gurney Slade are the old methods still in use with hillside kilns fed from the higher level, heated by solid fuel and emptied at lower ground level. Here the firm of Francis Flower has burnt lime since 1873. Modern kilns, often nearly 100 feet high with unit output of up to 100 tons, fired by liquid or gaseous fuels, form a striking contrast to the traditional Mendip methods. The purity of the limestone in certain areas makes it particularly suitable for metallurgical use, but the recent planning permission to install two large kilns as part of a £3 million

33 The nineteenth-century façade of the paper mill at Wookey Hole bought by Madame Tussaud's in 1973 together with the Caves

34 Shepton Mallet: the abandoned Somerset & Dorset Railway loops round the Showering industrial complex while the old town lies farther down the valley

35 Cricket on the Cathedral Green at Wells *c* 1790 from a water-colour drawing by Turner

scheme for the development of Batts Combe quarry has caused some alarm among certain sections of the community in the Cheddar area from anxiety about the chemical efflux from the kilns and the danger that might arise from an accident to a tanker carrying butane gas to the quarry through narrow streets, though the gas has now been routed to reach the quarry without touching any built-up area.

As distinct from ready-mix concrete in its various forms, some quarries specialise in concrete products, as do several firms who also produce various forms of reconstructed stone: at least three of these—at Edford, at Newbury and at Vobster—occupy the sites and buildings of abandoned collieries.

The Dolomitic Conglomerate all round the foothills of the plateau was put to many building uses. Round Draycott in particular it was cut for features such as gateposts or the pillars of verandahs or even for drinking troughs or corn staddles. At Bryscomb quarry the stone from certain beds was found to take a polish, and machinery for cutting and polishing it was eventually installed in a block of buildings now converted into dwelling houses. This use of the stone was known before 1600, to judge from tombstones at Wedmore and in Wells Cathedral, where there are also four pillars at the west end of the nave. 'Draycott Marble' was a nineteenth-century product: at Ashwick the church was rebuilt in 1876–81 and the pillars of the nave which came from Draycott are similar to some almost contemporary work at Ammerdown House near Kilmersdon. At the other end of Mendip, Loxton church was re-paved with Draycott stone as late as 1913.

Although one associates brickfields with the Taunton–Bridgwater–Highbridge area, there were formerly many small brick-works around Mendip which supplied local needs before the era of mass production and rapid and cheap transport. A painting of Old Down Inn in 1769 shows a kiln at a brickyard which is also marked on the 1817 os map; this map also marks a brick kiln near Banwell, where brick making continued throughout the nineteenth century. There must have been various beds of clay at Emborough, for in 1873 T. J. Hicks leased land here to work beds of clay and brick-earth, and this developed into the Somerset Brick and Tile Works, with another yard at Ever-creech Junction on the s&D line; by 1900 garden pottery was also being made here, and fuller's earth and ochre and umber were also worked. In fact there was 25 years of industrial activity on the Emborough site before stone quarrying began. There was always a demand for bricks in connection with mining activities; thus there were brickyards on the site of Moorewood colliery in the 1860s (and later also at Clandown) and also on Smitham Hill, East Harptree, close to the lead works. There were brickyards too at Midsomer Norton and at Welton, the latter with ten kilns and a 140ft chimney, served by an aerial ropeway which brought clay down from the top of the ridge near Paulton. This brickyard worked until 1940.

The only bricks made on Mendip today are manufactured from limestone aggregate by the Somerset Brick Company at Cranmore, yet another example of the many uses to which Mendip stone has been put. ‑

An altogether earlier venture was the Wanstrow pottery. This belonged to the Yeoman family, and part of the diary of John Yeoman (1748–1824) survives, describing his trips to London in 1774 and 1777 on which he visited several potteries, carefully comparing other 'pott-houses' with his own methods. This concern was still flourishing about 1825. There is no sign of it today except for the name 'The Pottery' applied to the lower part of the village. A little distance to the north, however, was a field called Claypitts, and here was a brickyard throughout the nineteenth century. The site is still marked on the 2½in map but recently the field has been used as a refuse tip by the local council and all evidence is now obliterated. The name Brickyard Lane, however, is an important piece of evidence for the local historian, recording the existence of yet another of the old industries that have vanished from Mendip.

The Manufacturing Industries (see Fig 23)

(1) CLOTH

The closure of the Wallbridge Mills at Frome in 1965 marked the end of a long chapter of Mendip industrial history. Appropriately enough, the mills belonged to Alfred H. Tucker Ltd, for a tucker was a fuller—there is a Tucker Street in Wells and several Tucking Mills survive in north Somerset valleys—a direct reminder of the medieval origins of an industry that flourished round and about Mendip for more than six centuries.

By 1300 the export of broadcloth was beginning to replace the export of wool as the basis of England's commercial prosperity. The second half of the fourteenth century was a period of rapid industrial expansion and the first period of prosperity in the West Country woollen industry. This had originally been an urban industry, but the restrictive practices of the urban craft guilds in Bristol hampered the expansion of production, and this factor as well as the requirements of fulling led to the migration of the industry to rural areas.

North Somerset became one of the leading areas of production in England. The aulnager was the State official who collected the payments made by the sellers of cloths which he sealed as conforming to certain statutory requirements, and although the accuracy of the figures in the aulnage accounts has been questioned, the accounts at least indicate the districts where the trade was flourishing. In 1394-8, for example, Frome and Wells were producing between 1,000 and 2,000 broadcloths a year (as were Pensford and Bath); Batcombe, Croscombe, Mells and Shepton Mallet between 200 and 800; Axbridge, Chewton Mendip, Harptree, Kilmersdon and Nunney between 25 and 200.

Leland, riding around Somerset in the 1530s, noted village after village that was 'much occupied with making of cloth', and the outward and visible sign of the prosperity stemming from the wool and cloth trades was the splendid series of Perpendicular churches round Mendip, mostly fifteenth-century rebuildings of earlier structures: Chewton Mendip, whose 'goodly new high tourrid steple' Leland observed c 1540, and Mells, whose fair church had been built 'yn tyme of mynde'. At the other end of the hill the magnificent fifteenth-century church at Axbridge epitomises the medieval prosperity of the little borough.

Wool was supplied by the local breed of Mendip sheep or from the sheep-bearing uplands of neighbouring counties; fuller's earth for cleansing the wool was obtained from the Inferior Oolite in the ridges to the south-east of Bath; but the basic requirement was water, both for the actual process of fulling—the thickening of the cloth by felting the fibres—and for power to drive the earliest piece of machinery used in the industry, the fulling stocks or heavy wooden hammers. Hence the location of the industry on the upper reaches of the swift-flowing streams that cut back into the eastern end of the Mendip range: the Chew, the Mells river, the Frome, the Brue, the Alham, the Doulting water and their many tributary streams.

The clothiers, who owned the mills, bought the wool and sold the cloth; carding and spinning and weaving were cottage industries, after which the cloth was brought to the mill for fulling. *The Young Man's Looking Glass*, a poem about Shepton Mallet written by Richard Watts in 1641, lists the different craftsmen involved in the manufacture of cloth before the introduction of machinery: the parter, the dyer, the mixer, the stock carder, the knee carder, the spinster, the weaver, the brayer, the burler, the fuller, the rower, the shearman and the drawer. Many of the small clothiers were no more than the social equals of other workers in the industry, such as weavers, but some prospered exceedingly, rising into the ranks of landowning gentry: such were the Strodes of Shepton Mallet and Cranmore, the Bisses of Batcombe and Croscombe, and

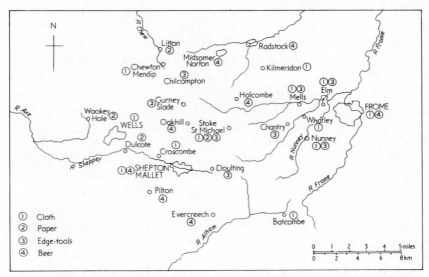

Fig 23   Manufacturing industries before 1914: 1 Cloth, 2 Paper, 3 Edge-tool, 4 Beer.

James Ashe of Batcombe who was thought by his neighbours to be worth £15,000 in 1637.

By the beginning of the eighteenth century, Frome had taken the lead as the largest town in the area: Defoe, who visited it in the 1720s, observed that the trade was 'so prodigiously increased within these last thirty or forty years that they have built a new church and many new streets of houses'. This prosperity continued until the 1820s, although Shepton Mallet had gone into permanent decline by 1800.

If to some extent the industry was beginning to draw in upon urban centres with larger units of production, many of the rural mills were working well into the nineteenth century, mainly for fulling but later with a certain amount of machinery driven by water-power. Under an Act of 1727 broadcloths were again measured and sealed by a government inspector in each district: Frome, Shepton Mallet (covering the mills from Doulting to Wells), Mells (with the tributary valleys down to the outskirts of Frome), and, at any rate until the 1770s, the smaller districts of Batcombe and Harptree, the latter extending northwards down the Chew.

It is only partially true that the ultimate failure of the Somerset woollen industry was due to its backwardness as compared with the advanced technology of the West Riding. The initial impetus had not been lacking. Shepton clothiers, led by John Billingsley, had set up an experimental carding engine and spinning jenny in 1776, but this was wrecked by a mob from Frome and Warminster; the same thing happened at Frome in 1781. Although so close to a coalfield which would have enabled them to drive the new machines by steam and to become independent of the limitations of water-power, the clothiers were apparently reluctant to persevere with their experiments, and the workers were unwilling to accept the new machinery; 'until the Yorkshire manufacturers have stolen the article away from us, we are almost afraid to introduce it', as a witness reported to the Parliamentary Committee of 1803.

As late as 1822 the military were called in at Frome to quell disturbances sparked off by attempts to introduce the spring loom. In 1826 Cobbett visited Frome, and his embittered description of the ragged weavers turned road menders and receiving 2s 6d a week from the parish, with their best clothes, their bedding, their looms and their furniture in pawn, is a classic picture of the first fruits of the Industrial Revolution—the disastrous inability of a long-established industry to adapt to new conditions.

After 1821 the population of Frome and of many neighbouring villages decreased, often very markedly. At Shepton (where some of the mills had turned over to making silk and crape and velvet) there was only one small woollen mill still at work in 1838, two each at Croscombe and Elm, and one each at Nunney and Whatley—employing in all about 100 workers. Sheppards, the largest firm in Frome, whose connection with the trade went back at least to the early eighteenth century, had introduced steam-power in 1811 and kept going until 1878 when their factories at Pilly Vale and Spring Gardens were advertised for sale.

The ruined walls still stand beside the River Frome at Spring Gardens, and many east Mendip valleys are dotted with derelict mills or at least with the traces of the leats which once served them. The history of many Mendip industries is writ in water. Some mills were adapted to other uses as the woollen trade declined—gunpowder, paper, edge-tools or even grist, which will be referred to later in this chapter. Along the river at Shepton Mallet, as far down as Bowlish and Darshill, the occasional mill survives, well-proportioned buildings of the late eighteenth or early nineteenth century, built of local grey stone with well-spaced windows and a dignity of their own. Likewise the solid Georgian houses of the prosperous clothiers, both at Shepton Mallet and Frome, and in villages like Batcombe. For earlier generations there are only the memorials in the churches and the churches themselves. On the dark oak roof of the fifteenth-century church at Croscombe are two bosses portraying a clothier and his wife, to judge by the rolls of cloth spread open before them and the large pair of shears at the man's side.

A word about some ancillary industries. Woad was widely cultivated as a crop from which dye was made. In the sixteenth century, clothiers at Mells and Westcombe made bequests in their wills of their woad vats. In Elizabethan times the woad industry was protected by bans on the import of indigo from the East and of logwood from America. Woad was still being cultivated in the Keynsham area at the end of the eighteenth century, and Billingsley mentions the existence of a woad mill and drying sheds at Mells about 1750, the mill serving to crush the leaves to pulp from which the dye was made.

From the mid-seventeenth century, logwood was imported through Bristol. The logs were chipped and ground in a mill and used for a black dye—processes carried on at Keynsham Mill until 1064. In 1784 a logwood mill was advertised for sale near Stoke St Michael by Messrs Billingsley & Bowles, drysalters who had 'declined that business', and significantly enough there was a field called Dye House Ground near Ham Mill, a mile from Stoke Bottom. Frome later became the centre of the dyeing industry where at least half a dozen firms flourished during the nineteenth century, notably the Olives, whose main business was in Willow Vale, where they employed fifty men with twelve vats and seven furnaces, with another establishment in Justice Lane.

The card makers of Frome also played an important part in the cloth industry, making the wire-toothed instruments, and later the machines, which carded the wool. Several hundred people were employed in this specialised industry during the eighteenth century, the firm of Rawlings continuing from before 1700 until 1972—a fine record.

Teasels, a crop now grown only in south Somerset, were formerly grown extensively along the north side of Mendip between Wrington and Harptree, and also near Shepton Mallet where a teasel-drying shed survives along the road to Croscombe. Their hooked bristles were well suited for raising the nap while certain sorts of cloth were being dressed. The 'rower' mentioned in Richard Watts's poem in 1641 used teasels to draw loose fibres from the body of the cloth, just as Langland three centuries earlier had described cloth as 'cratched with teasels'. It was entirely appropriate, therefore, that Frome Urban District Council should have adopted the teasel in its crest.

A rather different sort of industry was the knitting of stockings, carried on from Axbridge in the west to Shepton Mallet in the east. In 1831 Shepton was referred to as still maintaining 'its ancient manufacture of fine knit hose'. 'Knitter' appears frequently as an occupation in early census returns. 'Stocking-makers', like clothiers, were likely to be men of considerable substance and of some social position. The 'stocking-factory' at Nettlebridge may have been no more than a warehouse where the finished products were collected, but 'an extensive stocking manufactory' was advertised for sale at Ashwick in 1796, and other references to 'stocking utensils' suggest that a number of stocking frames were brought together in a single workshop, though hand knitting was also carried on in the area at the same time. As late as 1872 William Urch of Nettlebridge is described as 'hosiery manufacturer'.

(2) IRON

'Iren owr found a late in Mendipe,' Leland wrote in the 1530s, 'and yren made ther.' In the following century Camden refers to the pits of coal in the Nettlebridge valley 'made use of by smiths as most proper to soften iron'. It was in this valley that the Fussells established themselves at Mells in 1744, though it is not clear where they got their iron. There is evidence of sporadic attempts to dig iron ore at various points on Mendip—Iron Pit Bottom is mentioned near Ebbor in 1752, and fields called Great Iron Pits and Little Iron Pits appear on the Stoke St Michael tithe map—but none of the nineteenth-century projects appears to have prospered. The output from an ironstone mine at Nunney, opened in 1873, was sent away by rail from Frome to the Black Country.

Apart from the supply of iron, the essential ingredient in the development of the iron industry that grew up in the eastern valleys was water: as a source of power, and also for hardening the edge-tools, for which the water emerging from the Mountain Limestone was particularly suitable. Besides Fussells, there were other forges established by the beginning of the nineteenth century: Samuel Dunkerton's edge-tool mill at Pilton was advertised for sale in 1833, Stoke Lane Iron Works appears on the 1817 os, and the Steeds family were established at Gurney Slade by 1831. This was a typical family concern, employing perhaps a dozen men at most, turning out edge-tools of all sorts, and axles for the tubs used in local collieries; the forge, with two water-wheels driving the hammer and the grindstones, continued to work until the death of Arthur Steeds in 1934. Other firms that continued well into this century were Coombs of Doulting and Padfield of Chilcompton–three generations of them spanning a century. In every case the sites of the ruined mills and forges can still be seen, while tools stamped with the maker's name are jealously preserved in private hands.

Such firms, however, were very small beer compared with Fussells of Mells. Their business expanded rapidly from the single mill erected at Mells in 1744 'for grinding edge-tools and forging iron-plates' until there were six separate branches at work—at Great Elm, Chantry, Railford, Nunney, and the Upper and Lower Works at Mells. From these factories flowed a continuous stream of edge-tools of all sorts—scythes, hay-knives, reaphooks, billhooks, axe-heads, spades, shovels and garden tools—different patterns for different districts, both for the home trade and for export.

The Fussells themselves became rich, rising from village craftsmen into the ranks of local squirearchy: they built themselves mansions, they founded the parish of Chantry, and built the church and school there. They had financial interests in collieries and woollen mills and in the abortive Dorset & Somerset Canal. But in the latter half of the nineteenth century the business seems to have declined: there was the disastrous collapse of English agriculture in the 1870s; the Fussells themselves seem to have lost interest—at any rate none of the younger generation went into the business, and in 1884 it was taken over by Isaac Nash of Stourbridge, and closed down in 1894.

Like the clothiers, the Fussells were probably too slow to adapt to new techniques which would have enabled them to compete with rival firms in the Midlands and the North. Although coal was available on their doorstep, it was late in the day when they introduced steam-power at Mells and substituted rolling mills for the older methods of hand forging. Once again water-power, on which they had depended for so long, had proved inadequate, and today the Mendip streams wash past the ruined walls of their factories, almost buried in the undergrowth of deep wooded valleys that were for long the scene of intense industrial activity.

The recent discovery of a large-scale plan of the Mells Iron Works dating from the late 1840s has helped the groups of industrial archaeologists who are at present engaged in the excavation of the site. Their efforts have so far revealed a furnace of unusual design, dating from the first half of the nineteenth century, a large number of forges, and such spectacular items as the framework of an 11ft wrought-iron water wheel—all giving a vivid impression of a large and complex industrial set-up built on a very difficult site.

(3) PAPER

The earliest reference to paper making in Somerset is a Deed of Sale dated 1610 referring to 'all those two turking [sic] mills under one roove whereof one is now converted to a paper mill'. This was the Wookey Hole Mill, where hand-made paper was produced for more than 350 years until its closure in 1972.

Quick streams and clear water were essential to the paper makers; hence the location of the mills right up against the flanks of Mendip, as close as possible to where the water broke out of the hill, as at Rickford

and Sherborne and Stoke Bottom, and above all at Wookey Hole, where
a leat brought water direct to the mill from the very point where the Axe
emerges into the light of day. There were also mills at Banwell, Compton
Martin, West Harptree (on the Chew) and Dulcote, and several mills on
the Axe below Wookey Hole and on the Cheddar Yeo.

The majority of these mills were in production by 1800. They were
small family concerns, containing only one or two vats and employing
perhaps a dozen people. The paper was made from rags that were
pounded into pulp in troughs (or later in a shredding machine known as
a Hollander); each sheet was made separately by the vatman in a mould
and then pressed and dried and finished. Paper making as carried on at
Wookey Hole until 1972 was a traditional craft process.

But the increasing demand for paper in the nineteenth century led to
the application of steam-power to driving the Hollanders and the new
machines invented about 1800 which pressed the pulp on to an endless
belt to form a continuous roll of paper. This was the beginning of the end
for many of the small Mendip mills with their limited output, unless they
were able to keep going by concentrating on specialised trade demands
such as paper for bank notes, legal documents or high-class writing
paper. Compton Martin and Stoke Lane were finished before 1840,
Banwell by 1850; the last of the Cheddar mills closed in 1900.

Wookey Hole, however, took on a new lease of life when it was acquired by William Sampson Hodgkinson in 1852: the mill was rebuilt
and enlarged, eventually containing fourteen vats and employing about
120 workers, including many women. Much of the village was also built
by the Hodgkinson family—the church, the school, the club and
workers' houses, all built of local stone. The village in fact was a thriving
industrial community in a completely rural setting. Gradually the trade
declined between the two World Wars, and when the mill was taken
over by the Inveresk Paper Co in 1950 only two vats of hand-made paper
were maintained, the rest of the mill being converted to machinery.

Inveresk had also acquired St Cuthbert's Mill, originally known as
Lower Wookey, half a mile down the Axe. This was at work by 1816, but
the fine façade presented to the road was added much later when the
mill was mechanised and enlarged. (Workers at Hodgkinsons would
always refer, not without a sense of scornful superiority, to 'the machine
mill'.) Today St Cuthbert's is the last survivor of the Mendip paper
industry, producing many different sorts of paper to meet specialised
requirements, including a limited amount of hand- and mould-made
paper, this section having been transferred from the upper mill when it
was closed.

Wookey Hole Mill was acquired by Madame Tussaud's in 1973 and the premises are being adapted for the entertainment of visitors to Wookey Hole caves by adding exhibitions and explanations: among the exhibits it is planned to re-install some of the old paper making equipment and to display to visitors something of the industry and the techniques of this old Mendip industry.

(4) Corn Mills

For the industries so far considered, water-power was essential, at any rate until about 1800, and, as we have seen, many industrial units never adapted themselves to newer forms of power. Even so one is surprised at the number of mill sites that can still be identified all round Mendip and the variety of uses which they served. Moreton, for instance, now drowned by the Chew Valley Lake, had a mill at the time of the Domesday survey, and this was grinding corn within living memory, but in 1799 it was a gunpowder mill.

Many of these vanished mills appear on the 1817 os map (including a windmill at Hutton) and on the 1886 six-inch edition, and their abandoned leats and pools are often shown on modern maps, but of many more no trace remains. According to Collinson, towards the end of the eighteenth century the Cheddar Yeo drove thirteen mills within half a mile of its source: by 1791 there were still seven, three paper mills and four corn mills. On the upper reaches of the Alham around Batcombe the mills were thick upon the ground (Higher Alham, Westcombe, Pughs Bottom, Middle Mill, Lovely), presumably all involved in the woollen industry, quite apart from Batcombe Mill and Spargrove which were corn mills. The late J. A. Garton said that at the beginning of the present century it was possible in the course of a 6 mile walk from Doulting to Dulcote to count forty mill-races.

The archetypal mill, however, was the corn mill. There was at least one on nearly every manor, and they were duly recorded in the Domesday survey of 1086: Max Mill at Winscombe, Stratford Mill at West Harptree and Mells, to give three examples. Many of these mills were still at work well into the present century. By the 1880s some millers like the Orledges of Croscombe had installed boilers to implement water-power when the streams were low. This was the case at Coley near East Harptree, which worked until 1930, after which it was bought and demolished by Bristol Waterworks and only the leat remains today. About 1906 the owner, E. W. Masters, acquired a Foden steam wagon proudly named *The Western Triumph* for haulage, and later a motor-lorry was used to fetch corn from Avonmouth Docks, though local farmers also brought their grist to the mill. In the Nettlebridge valley within 3 miles of one another, mills were working at Gurney Slade, Benter, Ham and Coleford, the last named being acquired by the local RDC who installed a pump to raise water to a reservoir in the upper part of the village.

No water-powered mill is working today in the Mendip area, though a few miles to the north, at Priston near Bath, the corn mill is still powered by a water-wheel. Stratford Mill, one of the many mills on the upper reaches of the Chew, was dismantled at the time of the construction of the Chew Valley Lake and re-erected in 1954 in the grounds of the Blaise Castle Folk Museum on the outskirts of Bristol—a late-eighteenth-century corn mill in full working order with an undershot water-wheel to drive the applewood machinery. Where mills are still at work, they are powered by electricity; at Spring Gardens near Frome for instance, at Wells and at Bleadon at the western end of Mendip. Water-power would in any case be inadequate and insufficiently reliable for modern needs, but sometimes one wonders how ever there was sufficient water to drive the mills that once clustered the banks of the little streams. It must be remembered that over the centuries the water-table has fallen considerably, that where springs have been tapped by Water Supply authorities the flow of water in the streams has inevitably diminished, but above all that in past centuries the stream courses and the leats and mill-ponds must have been scoured and cleared and maintained with anxious care, for on their maintenance depended the livelihood of each individual miller.

(5) BREWING

On 25 November 1823 the Rev John Skinner of Camerton sent his servant, John Goold, to Oakhill 'to settle the brewer's account there'. This is an interesting reference, showing that Oakhill, founded in 1767, already had something more than a purely local reputation. Earlier breweries were small concerns, generally attached to public houses, where beer was 'home brewed'. There was a public brewhouse in Banwell in 1530, and in 1608 Edward Hort of Wells, brewer and tippler (a tippler was a retailer of liquor), was prosecuted for unlawfully maintaining in his house 'a common shuffleboard whereupon divers persons resorted to play'. Even in the mid-nineteenth century the Fire Engine and the Duke of Wellington in the mining area of the Nettlebridge valley both had their own breweries.

It was in the nineteenth century, however, that brewing developed as an organised industry, following the lead set by Oakhill, though Frome in 1721 had been noted for its 'rare stale beer which they keep to a great age, and it is not only esteemed by the common people but many of the Gentry prefer it to the best French or Port-Wines'. All round Mendip breweries sprang up: at Holcombe in 1800, at Cross by about 1840, at Banwell (on the site of the old paper mill) in 1850, at Pilton and at Stoney Stratton, near Evercreech. About 1840 a derelict woollen factory was converted into a brewery at Charlton on the outskirts of Shepton Mallet, while the enormous and unsightly Anglo-Bavarian Brewery was established in the town itself in 1864.

In Wells there were several small breweries in the 1860s but none survived into the present century. On the north side of Mendip the needs of the mining communities were met by Coombs of Radstock (and Clandown) from about 1860, and at least four breweries at Midsomer Norton and Welton, of which Thatchers was the largest and best known. In 1881 there were nine breweries in Frome, though these were in process of being amalgamated into two: Lamb Brewery and Frome United.

This was, in fact, the shape of things to come. *Kelly's Directory* for 1889 lists seventeen breweries in the Mendip area, but only eight in 1919. Today there are none, though the buildings often survive, put sometimes to strange uses—at Holcombe a garage, at Shepton Mallet a trading estate, at Welton a paper bag factory.

The location of the breweries was obviously decided by the needs of the local population. They were much thicker on the ground in the industrial areas of eastern Mendip, where the heavy industries of quarrying, mining and iron making, as well as textiles, were clustered. But like so many other industries, brewing depended upon water: Oakhill is situated on the spring line, Holcombe beer derived its quality from the purity of the water flowing off a bed of clay, and at Welton and Evercreech and Banwell the quality of the water was renowned.

Some of the brewery buildings were of considerable size (Wickham says that Holcombe brewery was facetiously known as 'Beer Abbey'), what with the grain store, maltings, cooperage, bottling store, wagon sheds and stables.

It is difficult to assess the output in the absence of documentation. Oakhill at its peak was said to produce 2,000–2,500 barrels a week, but this was hardly typical, as the firm owned a large chain of public houses, and their stout at any rate was distributed all over England. The fortuitous survival of the brewer s daybook from Evercreech gives a better indication of the production of the smaller breweries. Over the last few years before closure in 1893, Hill Bros averaged 133 brews a year, brewing about 1,000 gallons a time—KK, XXX, porter and stout. In 1891 the excise duty payable amounted to £1,140 6s 3d (£1,140.31p) which was charged on 139,744 gallons, equal to 3,881 barrels.

In a period of increasing commercial pressure and the need for cen-tralisation, the smaller units could not hope to survive, and take-over, which probably spelt closure, was inevitable. More modern equipment demanded more capital and also larger markets than the villages or small towns that lay within the range of horse-drawn drays. Oakhill used traction engines to put their famous Invalid Stout on the Somerset & Dorset Railway, and eventually built a light railway to Binegar station which operated from 1904 to 1921. But the future was dictated by motor-transport, delivering beer from larger breweries over much wider areas.

A disastrous fire at Oakhill in 1925 marked the end of brewing there and a take-over by Bristol United. Collings' brewery at Cross, Coombs at Radstock and Thatchers at Welton also survived into the 1920s before closing. Brewing ceased at Charlton in 1961: by then Bristol United, with whom Charlton had amalgamated in 1937, had in turn been amalgamated with Georges and in due course became part of the Courage group.

Most of the breweries had their own maltings, usually on the same site, though sometimes separate, as at Frome where Bailys, who owned the Lamb Brewery, had a large malting establishment near the railway station. In the last century maltings were sometimes to be found on outlying farms—at Stratton-on-the-Fosse, for instance and at Yelling Mill near Shepton Mallet—which must have supplied malt to local breweries. Close inspection of what appear to be ordinary farm buildings sometimes reveals a line of windows whose constant opening and closing by the maltster controlled the germination of the barley on the open floor, while one end of the building is generally identifiable as the kiln-house.

At Banwell, where brewing stopped about 1909, the malt-house still stands, and also at Charlton, a delightful little building erected in 1844 with pyramidal roof and capped vents. At Holcombe brewing had stopped by 1904, but malting continued until 1930, as it does at Oakhill today where the maltings were mechanised in 1960 and have since been extended to establish Oakhill as an important unit in the Courage group.

In the last two decades Shepton Mallet has been the scene of the most spectacular development in the drink industry. The Showerings were an old-established Shepton family owning a small brewery in Kilver Street which produced cider as well as beer. Soon after World War II they evolved a clear sparkling drink made from pear-juice and marketed since 1953 as Babycham. In 1956 Showerings amalgamated with R. N. Coate, the cider-making firm of Nailsea, where cider-making was concentrated, while the Shepton factory was devoted to the production of enough Babycham to meet the ever-increasing and world-wide demand. Recently, however, cider has been developed to such an extent that a new cider-making complex has been built at the eastern end of the town where Showerings have now concentrated the cider production of their constituent companies. Showerings' offices occupy what was once a Georgian woollen mill, whose mill-ponds have been used as features in a delightful piece of landscape gardening, set against the back-drop of the disused Charlton railway viaduct.

The newest and yet in a sense the oldest manifestation of the drink industry is at Pilton. Here, where the Glastonbury monks cultivated their vineyard as early as 1189, on the steep southward-facing slope behind the manor, 4 acres of vines have now been planted from which a full-bodied white wine known as Pilton Riesling is produced and marketed. Another vineyard is also established in the neighbouring village of North Wootton.

(6) MISCELLANEOUS

It seems appropriate here to include a brief account of a number of interesting local industries that grew up apparently in isolation at various points along Mendip in the last 200 or 300 years.

Such was the spade and rake handle business at Leigh-on-Mendip, carried on for well over a century by two small family firms, Thomas Ashman & Co and Rossiter & Co. These must have been linked with the local edge-tool industry; at Mells, William A. Fussell ran a separate firm who made wooden handles for the tools made by other members of the family at their various mills. Thomas Ashman—a staunch nonconformist who built the Methodist churches at Leigh and Stoke St Michael and elsewhere on eastern Mendip—was also a timber merchant with a steam sawmill whose chimney still stands across the street from the church. His firm too carries on, producing general turnery from home-grown timber. Much of the raw material must always have been locally grown, and auctioneers' posters dated 1817 show that regular sales were held in local inns (at Tadhill and at Leighton, for example) to dispose of timber felled in Asham Wood.

Another business which supplied the needs of agriculture and other local industries was rope making. In 1808 Thomas Hobbs established his factory at Downside on the outskirts of Shepton Mallet, where the remains of the now derelict ropewalk can still be seen, dating from the first half of the nineteenth centurym

Cheese must more properly be considered as an agricultural rather than an industrial product. *Kelly's Directory* for 1889 lists only two cheese makers for the whole of Somerset but 'in addition most of the farmers in this county make cheese'. Cheese factors, however, who collected and stored cheeses from the farms and then supplied the provision merchants, needed large storage premises: such were the old brewery buildings at Stoney Stratton and the Old Passenger—ie the East Somerset—station at Wells, and William Small's warehouse at Cheddar. In the present century large dairy firms have grown up at Evercreech and at Wells, and are now incorporated in the mammoth Unigate.

Turning to metal industries, there was a notable line of clock makers at Ashwick and Oakhill: Hardwick, Roper, Green, to say nothing of William Steeds. Charles Roper Green who died in 1904 proclaimed on his bill-heads that his business was established in 1733, tracing the line back through Nicholas Roper to Richard Hardwick (1697–1770). Examples of their work can be found in local homes, and Hardwick clocks in particular are collectors' pieces: there is a fine specimen in the National Trust house at Tintinhull near Yeovil. Clocks were also made by the Bilbies of Chew Stoke, one of whom, John Bilbie, moved to Axbridge where he set up business on his own, and another, Edward Bilbie, to Rodney Stoke.

The Bilbies, however, were primarily bell founders: their business at Chew Stoke flourished from about 1660 until about 1800 and many Mendip churches—Batcombe, Winscombe and Mells, to select three almost at random—contain examples of their work. They were said to be an eccentric family, devoted to the mystery of their craft. One of their trade secrets was alleged to be the use of calamine from Mendip, and their bells were apt to be inscribed with crude verses extolling the virtues of their own products and denigrating those of their rivals.

The most famous of these were the Cockeys of Frome who arrived from Warminster about 1690 and established a foundry in Bell Lane. They continued bell casting until about 1850, though after 1750 the casting was mostly done elsewhere. By the beginning of the nineteenth century they had established an iron foundry off Bath Street, making gas-holders and other equipment for gas as well as a variety of other products, which kept the firm going until a few years ago. A number of Somerset towers contain Cockey bells, including the Mendip villages of Nunney, Wanstrow and Whatley. The nicest juxtaposition occurs at Kilmersdon and at Pilton, where bellls by the great rivals, Bilbie and

Cockey, hang side by side, ringing in perfect harmony.

Another Frome foundry was that of the firm founded by J. W. Singer (1819-1904). Originally a watch maker, Singer began making ornamental metalwork for churches—screens at St John's, Frome, and at Kilmersdon are fine examples of his work—and then branched out into making castings for statues for which the firm became world-famous.

One last industry that deserves mention sprang up at the beginning of this century for a few years in a complex of buildings that still survive at Cutlers Green near Chewton Mendip. Here a small self-contained engineering works with antiquated machinery produced a variety of 3 and 5 ton steam wagons, petrol-driven vans and lorries, and 'Mendip' motor-cars, the only surviving specimen of which is being restored at Cheddar.

Modern Industry

Most of the industries so far described are no longer active. Of the mineral resources of Mendip, only stone is being exploited today; of the manufacturing industries, a few have roots in the more or less distant past—paper at Wookey Hole, malting at Oakhill, the drink industry in general, and the processing of cheese and other dairy products.

It only remains to take note of some of the newer industries which have replaced, or are replacing, the older basic industries such as mining, cloth making or even brewing. They have already been described as ubiquitous, not indigenous, industries, dependent neither upon local materials (except in the case of dairy products), nor upon local power, nor upon local markets. At sight they would appear to be a haphazard collection, and any complete survey would rapidly deteriorate into a mere catalogue. What is much more important to consider is their location and their effect on the environment as a whole.

Sometimes old sites have been put to new uses: the last of the Frome cloth mills is now a carpet factory; the old paper mill at Wookey Hole is in process of conversion into a museum and leisure centre for the tourist industry; old collieries, as at Coleford, or old quarries, such as Chelm's Combe at Cheddar, have new occupants. Otherwise, industries are generally sited on the outskirts of larger villages or market towns, and in the specific areas scheduled under the County Development Plan of 1053 and its First Review. The other important consideration is the availability of labour, though mobility is no longer so much of a problem in the age of the private motor-car: some of the larger firms such as Showerings and Clarks operate their own coach services to collect workers from outlying villages.

36 The Axe emerging from Wookey Hole Cave – from a water colour painting by
Michael 'Angelo' Rooker *c* 1795

37 Priddy Fair 1974 – the 627th great annual sale of sheep in progress on the Green

38 Emborough Pool beside the road from Wells to Bath, 700ft above sea level

At the western end of Mendip the Bristol Aerojet factory at Elborough near Locking can almost be regarded as an outlier of Weston-super-Mare; Banwell produces agricultural machinery; at Langford, market gardening and canning go hand in hand. Cheddar appropriately makes cheese straws, and incongruously and unobtrusively houses the National Tower Testing Station in an old quarry.

Between Wells and Wookey Hole there is a large factory belonging to emi which concentrates on the production of small electronic equipment as well as on research activities. Until 1951 the site was occupied by another firm who had been evacuated to Wells during the war and later moved out along the Wookey Hole road beside what had been a prisoner-of-war encampment.

At Wells and at Evercreech there are large milk factories where cheese and other dairy products are processed and stored, both now part of the Unigate empire, but once operated under the more homely banners of Wilts United Dairies and C. & G. Prideaux. Clares now make protective clothing behind the town hall in Wells, and further industrial development is now planned along the disused railway south of the town, but because of the proximity of Shepton Mallet, Glastonbury and Street, it seems unlikely that any large-scale factory development will be necessary at Wells.

Shepton Mallet—which until 1951 was roughly the same size as Wells with a population of about 5,000—has for centuries been an industrial as well as a market town, though few of the old mill buildings survive and fewer still are used. A trading estate now occupies the vast premises of the former Anglo-Bavarian Brewery and at the east end of the town, close to the Showering complex, a new industrial estate is being developed on the site of the former Somerset & Dorset Railway station at Charlton Road.

One of the most interesting developments has been the arrival on Mendip of C. & J. Clark of Street. Instead of continuing to expand in their home town, the firm planned to move up into areas where labour was likely to be more readily available: this was specially true of Norton–Radstock, the centre of a coalfield already on the decline before the war. In 1946 Clarks arrived in Shepton Mallet where they now employ 500 people; a few years later, after a temporary sojourn in Midsomer Norton where they took over an old shoe factory—here, and at Paulton, boot and shoe making was an old industry tied up to some extent with coal mining—they built a large new factory beside the Fosse Way at Westfield, which was opened in 1956, and where 750 people are now employed, and 60,000 pairs of children's shoes are produced weekly.

Norton–Radstock itself is a messy area: a group of mining settlements which have coalesced into a sprawling conurbation where a heterogeneous collection of industries have replaced—and are still replacing—the collieries. The factories are haphazardly spread about, sometimes occupying colliery sites, but now becoming grouped in more clearly defined areas—along the valley from Welton into the Radstock basin, and up the first Mendip slopes through Westfield.

Here, indeed, one may find strange bedfellows in the industrial scene. Heavy industry traditionally associated with a coalfield is represented by Evans' foundry, an old family business which moved from a site at Paulton on the Somersetshire Coal Canal to Radstock in the nineteenth century. There are engineering works, and railway wagon works. There is a joinery works, and a paper bag factory occupying an old brewery, while at Westfield two long established local firms—Edgells and Prattens—specialise in producing prefabricated wooden buildings.

The largest employers of labour on the north-east fringe of Mendip are Purnells of Paulton. Founded in 1849 as small jobbing printers, the firm expanded spectacularly in the 1930s and the postwar years, and their factory now covers 50 acres and employs 2,000 workers. In 1964 a merger resulted in the Purnell group of companies becoming part of the gigantic British Printing Corporation. In the same year one of the companies then associated with the corporation, and concerned with the manufacture of flexible packaging, established itself at Norton Hill, where a large new factory now adjoins the site of the largest of the Somerset collieries which closed in 1966. Here as elsewhere on Mendip 'the old order changeth, yielding place to new'.

Apart from J. W. Singer & Sons, mentioned in the last section, and now making hot brass pressings, Frome's most widely-known industry today is probably printing. Butler and Tanner, founded in 1845, moved in 19p8 from the middle of the town to a site near the railway where they now employ nearly 600 people. Cockeys, Singers and Butler & Tanner are in fact all examples of new industries which developed in the second half of the nineteenth century to replace the collapsed cloth industry and so salvage Frome's economy.

Frome, indeed, with a remarkably stable population from about 1850 to 1950, is notable for a continual reorganisation of its industrial economy throughout that period, constantly attracting and developing new industries. Today the breweries have all gone and the last of the cloth mills closed in 1965, but after 1918, and again after 1945, new industries bolstered Frome's prosperity and provided remarkable variety: apart from those already mentioned there are plastics, furniture, metal products and various other forms of light engineering.

This is largely due to the fact that Frome has always been able to supply sites and labour. Old sites have become available from time to time: the silk and crepe factory in Merchants Barton was taken over by Nott's for engineering, the Houston cloth mill by Wallington & Weston for plastics. The Marston Trading Estate was set up by the council in 1965, and a further 63 acres are earmarked under the County Development Plan for expansion if needed. Housing has been reasonably adequate and Frome has always been well placed as a focal point in the network of communications necessary for the handling of raw materials and of the finished products, even if road has now replaced rail as the chief distributor.

The factors which have governed the expansion and prosperity of Frome as an industrial town are also pointers to the conditions which will control the development of industry elsewhere around Mendip in the years to come. Industry will go where labour is available, and to some extent this is dependent upon housing, though a certain amount of commuting by car and coach will be inevitable—while oil is available. Adequate roads are necessary for both intake and output, for only the quarries are now served by rail. Further industrial development within the Area of Outstanding Natural Beauty is now unthinkable, despite the proximity of the M5, and the closure of the last collieries means that—apart from quarrying—the future is concerned with light industries. This would appear to limit any problems of pollution: there will be no more spoil heaps—and a spoil heap at a paper mill can be as much of an eyesore as one at a derelict colliery, and perhaps less amenable to landscaping.

The siting of industry under the County Development Plan is made with reference to both the pattern of town life and the rural environment. Here Mendip has so much to offer: the towns and surrounding villages are small and pleasant to live in; the richly varied landscape is full of amenities for recreation; and less than an hour's drive distant are the varied fleshpots of Bath and Bristol, Taunton and Weston-super-Mare.

Notes to this chapter are on pages 274-5.

8

Recreation

Robin Atthill and D. I. Smith

Social Gatherings
ROBIN ATTHILL

FROM ABOUT 1739 until 1834 the Wells summer race-meeting was held up on Mendip in mid-July. It concluded with a ball, an assembly, and back-sword and cudgel playing: obviously a major social event for all classes. At Callow races too in 1823 there was single-stick playing both morning and afternoon, 'and liberal encouragement given'. Just such an entertainment on Shipham Green is vividly described by Walter Raymond in *Two Men O' Mendip,* where the young 'groover' Giles Standerwick triumphantly defeats the champion from the other side of Taunton. Even at the beginning of the present century there were boxing booths at Binegar fair: one is reminded of the May morning in 1769 when Parson Woodforde's brother John came up to Cannard's Grave 'to see a famous boxing match between Parfitt Maggs and one Darck a Londoner', where the local champion was beaten.

Binegar fair survived as a horse-fair until 1955, an assembly point for gipsies and copers and cheap jacks. In the eighteenth century it had been a much bigger event lasting the whole of Whitsun week, during which time the churchwardens hired two men to guard the church which stood close to the fair-field. As well as horses, cattle, sheep, woollen cloth and toys were sold at the fair which was said to have moved up on to the hill from Wells during a visitation of the plague, just as Priddy fair is by tradition the Wells summer fair which moved there at the time of the Black Death.

Before 1914 there were fairs in a dozen or so Mendip villages from Banwell to Nunney and from Ubley to Pilton, sometimes more than once in a year.[1] Of these Priddy is the sole survivor—apart from the swings and roundabouts at Wells and Frome. Priddy fair takes place on a Wednesday in the second half of August: formerly it was always 21 August, and the first rain after Priddy fair is the traditional beginning of winter as far as Mendip folk are concerned.

No longer do the gipsies come, no longer is an ox roasted whole on a spit and gargantuan helpings of beef and vegetables doled out for 1s 2d (6p). Instead there are cattle trucks and motor cars everywhere, ice-cream vendors and cheap jacks and their wares. But the real object of the exercise takes place on the green itself—the sale by auction of thousands of sheep, and the meeting and greeting of farmers from all over Mendip, meeting and greeting perhaps for the only time in the year, just as their forebears had done over the centuries.

The race-meetings, the boxing matches, the cock-fighting, the bull-baiting and the single-stick playing—all these brought people together, and dotted about the calendar they provided opportunities for relaxation and recreation and the chance to get away from the harsher realities of life in isolated rural communities.[2]

This was also a by-product of the Friendly Societies. The primary function of these clubs was to alleviate poverty and to provide sick pay and a decent burial in the days before the National Insurance Act: a man drawing sickness benefit today is still referred to as being 'on the club'. Club Day was one of the highlights of the year in the village: the procession to church, the feast, the dance, the sports and all the fun of the fair, the ribbons, the club banners and staves—all then made for a really festive occasion. Clubs flourished in many Mendip villages: the brass pole-heads at Radstock and at Shipham for instance depicted a set of miner's tools. The great day was usually Whit Monday or Trinity Monday. At Priddy, founded 1814, and at Westbury-sub-Mendip, founded c 1760, Club Day is now held on the Spring Holiday in May with a roll call at the village inn, a procession to church, luncheon and sports; while at Witham Friary the club founded c 1786 survives as a Benefit Society with a share-out once in five years, known locally as the 'Quinquennial Parting'.[3]

Compared with such junketings, the fête on the rectory lawn or the village flower show are only pale shadows, but they are at least a visible symbol of the local sense of community. So are the spectacular November carnivals which take place in a number of Mendip towns and villages, and the larger Mid-Somerset Show at Shepton Mallet and Frome Cheese Show—all of which are social as well as commercial events. The largest gathering of all is the Bath and West Show which in 1965 established itself on a permanent site of 212 acres between Shepton Mallet and Evercreech on the southern foothills of Mendip.

LOCAL NEWSPAPERS

Much of the flavour of social life, the day-to-day events of a bygone age, can be recaptured from the files of local newspapers, published weekly, and read avidly and lovingly throughout the area in which they circulate and posted on to exiles all over the world. Many such journals have been established for well over 100 years, fulfilling their function of accurately and faithfully reporting purely local news. While Bristol and Bath papers have always circulated in the Mendip area, as has the *Western Gazette* (published at Yeovil since 1736), we are here concerned with more specifically local papers published on or under Mendip.

The oldest paper in the area is the *Weston Mercury* which circulates at the west end of the range, covering an area as far east as Cheddar and Blagdon; this was established in 1843 as the *Westonian,* 'a Monthly Arrival List and Directory for Weston-super-Mare and Journal of local Intelligence', became a weekly journal in 1855, and maintained its identity through a number of changes of title and amalgamations.

The *Wells Journal,* however, has maintained its title as well as its identity since 1851. It is now published by Clares in the mid-Somerset series of newspapers which includes the *Shepton Mallet Journal* (1857), the *Central Somerset Gazette* (1861) which circulates from Glastonbury, and the *Cheddar Valley Gazette* (1954) which revived the title of an independent journal published from 1926 to 1935, itself the successor of the *Cheddar Valley Times* (1908–26).

High up on eastern Mendip, J. C. Tucker, formerly a colliery blacksmith, established a printing press at Coleford from which he published the *East Somerset Telegraph* from 1859 to 1886. This venture certainly survived longer than many ephemeral productions such as the *Wells Guardian* (1859–60), the *Frome Advertiser* (1876–8) and the *North Somerset Independent* (1931–3).

Another example of longevity is the *Frome Times,* which was established in 1859 and succeeded in 1886 by the *Somerset Standard* which later incorporated the *Somerset & Wilts Journal* before itself being taken over in 1962 by Wessex Newspapers as one of the Bath Chronicle Series and combined with the *Somerset Guardian and Radstock Advertiser* (founded in 1893): one says 'combined' advisedly, because the *Somerset Standard* and *Somerset Guardian* are now identical in format, and with a certain amount of overlap they cover between them the whole of the north-eastern end of Mendip.

The files of all these journals (often fascinatingly excerpted under such titles as 'Fifty Years Ago'), the work over many decades of hundreds of reporters and local correspondents, give us a vivid and accurate picture of daily life in Mendip villages and market towns. Almost every issue can provide valuable material for the local or social historian—not least the advertisement columns. As L. E. J. Brooke has written, the files of local weekly newspapers 'hold fascination for all who delight in drawing aside the curtain of time to read not only matters of importance, but of those trivialities which throw interesting sidelights on the habits and customs of a bygone age . . . which go to make up the pattern of our English way of life'.[4]

Field Sports

HUNTING

Hunting is the archetypal sport on Mendip: a beautiful decorated glass bowl from the late Roman villa at Winthill near Banwell depicts a Roman, mounted on a pony, hunting a hare into a net with a couple of hounds. King Edmund's adventure in 941, when a hunted stag and hounds went over the cliffs at Cheddar in a thick fog, was to be repeated in 1895 when part of the pack of the Wells Harriers went over the cliff. The history of the 18forest of Mendip and of the hunting lodges from which the royal hunting rights were exercised has already been dealt with in Chapter 4 (see p 90).

The hunting of fox and hare, as we know the sport today, originated with the private packs of the eighteenth-century squires. Most of Mendip seems to have been hunted by the Tudways of Wells from c 1760 to 1859: their packs were at first harriers, but after 1837 foxhounds, kennelled presumably at The Cedars. At the east end of the hill the Blackmore Vale were making regular points to Asham Wood, described in 1826 as 'a Cover of 600 acres and full of rocky precipices and main earths'. In the 1850s an occasional deer was uncarted on Mendip to be hunted by the Bath Staghounds.

The main tradition of Mendip hunting was maintained by the Wells Subscription Harriers from 1860 to 1920. This pack, hunting fox and hare, was kennelled at various places at various times, but finally at Coxley, and some account of its activities is to be found in the *Reminiscences* of H. W. Selby Lowndes who was Master from 1895 to 1897. Perhaps the most famous local Master was Louis Beauchamp of Norton Hall (1902–13) where up to 200 would sit down to breakfast before the opening meet.[5]

The revival of foxhounds on Mendip was due to the initiative of H. A. Tiarks of Webbington and his brother F. C. Tiarks of Loxton. In 1914, despite considerable opposition, they got together a pack of foxhounds and founded the Mendip Hunt, only to be stopped by the outbreak of war. In 1920 however the Wells Harriers and the Stanton Drew Harriers, who were founded in 1855, amalgamated and started hunting again with a pack of foxhounds kennelled at Ston Easton, the harriers being retained to hunt hare on certain days. The hounds were moved from Ston Easton to Priddy during the mastership of the most famous of all Mendip Masters, C. Hilton Green (1921–4), and in 1922 the pack again became known as the Mendip. Herman Tiarks returned as Master from 1924 to 1928 with Will Morris as Huntsman.

The Mendip Farmers Hunt now covers most of the Mendip upland, and also the country to the north and south of the main ridge, with twenty-four couple of hounds kennelled at Priddy, hunting two and sometimes three days a week.

'A sea of grass and jumpable stone walls' was how Selby Lowndes described the country in the 1890s, and it is still 70 per cent pasture, though arable has increased since the war, and fields of kale are now the most likely covers to harbour a fox. In some areas walls and hedges are being demolished to make larger fields, and quarrying has eaten voraciously into woodland areas towards the east end of the hill, but the railways have disappeared, there are comparatively few major roads, and it is still wonderfully unspoiled sporting country that provides many splendid runs and extends the strongest horse.

South of the Shepton Mallet to Frome road (A361) is country hunted by the Blackmore Vale (now the Blackmore & Sparkford Vale since 1971), as indeed it has been hunted since their foundation in 1826. Their *Hunting Journal* for 5 March 1831 records in detail a 'curious and extraordinary chase' which lasted 4hr 45m and covered 25 miles extending through thirteen parishes. They had found in Batcombe Wood and hunted through Asham 'direct for the alpine heights of Mendip . . . over the heaths and furzes of that wild and romantic region to a place called Lye, where the fox was apparently lost in a heavy fog and rain, having been headed by some furze-cutters on the moor'. The fox however was recovered and hunted through Mells Park to Vallis and Little Elm where 'in the rocky gorge of the valley, at the base of a tree overhanging the mountain torrent, the hounds were at bay, and on the top of the tree, twenty feet above the ground in a mass of ivy the fox was seen at perch; from whence he made his leap into the stream below, a favourite hound and the fox sinking to the bottom together'.

The Weston Harriers hunted over the western end of Mendip from about 1850, hunting hare on the Levels and fox on the hills. In 1970 they amalgamated with a private pack of foxhounds at Banwell to become the Weston and Banwell Harriers, now kennelled again at Webbington where the Tiarks brothers had once maintained their own pack of harriers.

This pack now hunts fox at the western end of Mendip from the sea as far inland as the A38 at Shute Shelve, and also on the moors on either side of the hills; a very sporting piece of country with great variety—'the worst and roughest and hilliest of any country in England', as Herman Tiarks described it, though he also delighted in what he called the 'enormous water country where you meet rhine after rhine', and gives his opinion that any horse that would jump those rhines would jump any country.

Beagles are comparative newcomers on the Mendip scene, though they hunted around Wells in the late nineteenth century. A photograph taken at Fenny Castle c 1895 shows a meet of beagles attended by no less a celebrity than Dr W. G. Grace. This may well have been one of a number of short-lived private packs or a visit from the Clifton Foot Harriers.

Since World War II two packs have hunted the hare on Mendip. The Downside Beagles, formed in 1946, largely on the initiative of Dom Ceolfrid O'Hara, met twice weekly during school term until the pack was dispersed in 1958. Today the Chilmark Beagles, maintained by the Harland family at Glastonbury, hunt over Mendip one day a week.

RACING

The only race-course that survives on Mendip today is at Nedge near Chewton Mendip, where the open down affords a splendid view of the 3-mile circuit. Three point-to-point meetings are now held here: the Mendip Farmers, the West Somerset Vale and the Weston & Banwell Harriers. (The Weston Harriers previously used a course at Wolvers Hill near Banwell.)

Until 1932 the Mendip had held their point-to-point meetings on Chewton Down just to the north of the village. This meeting had been inaugurated by the Wells Harriers in 1903, but racing originally took place on the north of the down and not, as later, on the south side towards Emborough. When the Wells Harriers held their first race-meeting, attended by more than a thousand spectators, it was described as 'a revival of olden times', as it was over forty years since anything of the kind had taken place in the parish. This tradition is confirmed by the report of a hunt in 1852 which ran 'across the Chewton race-course'.

This was by no means the only Mendip race-course. On 2 July 1718, for instance, Dr Claver Morris of Wells rode out to Masbury Castle to see a horse-race from Masbury to Priddy at which he won ten shillings—a real point-to-point race across unenclosed countryside.

The enclosures towards the end of the eighteenth century obviously affected racing on Mendip. A race-course at Banwell for instance—on common land on the hill to the south-west of the village—was enclosed under an Act of 1795. The last race-meeting was held on 12 October 1796: 'an immense concourse of people from the surrounding country assembled, and gentlemen's carriages, post-chaises, gigs etc were seen round the stand in great number'.

The old Wells race-course at Whitnell Corner near Slab House was also affected by enclosure about 1800, and the races were transferred to Prior's Hill, the outlying ridge of Pen Hill between the old and new Bristol roads. This was a real race-meeting, figuring in the *Sporting Kalendar* and other hand-books of the turf, and usually held in mid-July.

Among the Axbridge records preserved at the local museum is a poster headed Axbridge Diversions, advertising three races to be held over the Callow Course on 17 September 1823: the best of three heats twice round the course for purses of ten sovereigns, five sovereigns and a handsome bridle and saddle. These diversions continued as late as 1872 when the Log Book of the British School at Cheddar mentions Callow races as being a contributory cause of the low attendance at school on 16 August.

Farther east there were pony races at Cranmore on a course parallel with the Shepton Mallet road from the Doulting parish boundary to Cranmore Piers, and a short-lived series of meetings at Nunney Catch in the years immediately following World War I.

The race-meetings have in a sense been replaced by the numerous gymkhanas which have come into fashion since World War II, when motor transport became available to get both horse and rider to gatherings many miles away across the hills. Pony Clubs flourish too, and the Mendip Farmers Hunt organise many horse activities, culminating in a week-long meeting, held each year in open country near Priddy, which is really an extended working rally. Riding schools flourish round the western end of Mendip where there is more open country readily available, but almost anywhere along the hill one is likely to come upon riders, both young and old. Riding is certainly a recreation that adds a dimension to one's knowledge and love of Mendip, and an activity to be encouraged, so long as care is taken not to trespass inside the Forestry plantations or to damage bridlepaths which are also footpaths used by walkers.

SHOOTING

Shooting, unlike hunting, is essentially a private sport. Until 1914, and even in some cases until 1939, the larger Mendip estates included well-stocked coverts tended by gamekeepers whose cottages sometimes survive, buried deep in the woods. Such shooting as is enjoyed today, mainly of pheasants, is likely to be leased out to syndicates, and with the decrease of the rabbit population because of myxomatosis there is less rough shooting over farms. There were formerly a number of rabbit warrens, dating from the Middle Ages. The names alone survive on the map (see p 92). Billingsley, writing in the 1790s, says that the warrens were formerly much more extensive, and comments wryly on the depredation of two-legged and four-legged vermin.

A more specialised activity was rifle-shooting, and a number of ranges are marked on old Ordnance maps. While never as ubiquitous as the butts which each village was bound to maintain in medieval times to ensure that every man should be able to shoot with bow and arrow—the name survives in Butts Hill at Frome and elsewhere—rifle ranges were established at various points along Mendip during the nineteenth century, usually at times of national emergency or invasion scares: there were ranges at Uphill and at Dinder, on Wavering Down and in Lower Twin Brook Combe on the northern slopes of Black Down. In 1907 Holcombe Miniature Rifle Club was started with a 100yd range. Here and elsewhere the remains of the large mounds of earth which served as butts may well perplex the archaeologist in centuries to come. The most spectacular relics can be seen on the south side of Beacon Hill above Shepton Mallet where there was a 650yd range on which Volunteer prize shoots were taking place as long ago as 1886.[6]

The modern range at Yoxter Farm, near the top of Cheddar Gorge, was opened about 1935 by the Territorial Army and the Auxiliary Forces Association, with a small range camp. This was enlarged during World War II, and in 1968 the camp became the County Training Centre for the Army Cadet Force, while the 600yd range belongs to the Territorial Army and Volunteer Reserve Association for Western Wessex and is in constant use all the year round. The military in fact own about 900 acres of Mendip upland, although by no means all of it is used as a training area, and a good deal of it is still farmed. The Danger Area now marked on the Ordnance Survey extends past Stowbarrow, one of the historic boundary marks mentioned in medieval perambulations of the Forest of Mendip, almost as far as Bowery Corner near the Hunt Kennels.

Local memory and tradition recall two olden time fowling activities. Before World War I there were shooting matches, at East Harptree for instance. These were organised competitions with referees, in which rabbits, pigeons, starlings and sparrows were released from traps, the winner scooping the pool of entry fees for each round. These were clearly the forerunners of the clay pigeon shoots held in various areas today.

The duck decoys really belong to the Levels, but close up under the southern scarp of Mendip—at Cheddar, Nyland, Rodney Stoke and Westbury, there were decoy pools on which duck alighted, to be lured into the curving 'pipes' which led only to the nets where they met their doom at the hands of the decoyman. Decoy Pool Farm at Nyland marks the site of one, and the remains of another can be found near the confluence of the Cheddar Yeo and the Axe (ST 435523). The Westbury pool was certainly in use by 1652, the others are all marked on the 1817 OS, but with the draining of the Levels they all went out of use during the nineteenth century.

FISHING

During the last hundred years or so, following the Bristol Waterworks Company's Act of 1846, a number of reservoirs have been constructed around Mendip in connection with the supply of water to meet the ever-increasing needs of the city of Bristol. On the north side of the range these form a delightful landscape feature ('Bristol's Lake District') and provide varied opportunities for recreation, quite apart from the casual pleasure afforded to motorists and holiday-makers and in particular to anybody wise enough to walk on the northern escarpment of the hill.

The two small reservoirs at Sherborne near Litton were the earliest. They were completed in 1853 to provide compensation water in the Chew valley when springs at Chewton Mendip were piped to the reservoirs at Barrow Gurney which supplied Bristol. The Sherborne reservoirs lie in a secret valley between Litton and Coley, cradled by the hills; they are pleasant little stretches of water, best appreciated from hillside footpaths towards Hinton Blewett.

Blagdon Lake is much better known (though most people are probably content to enjoy glimpses of it from their cars) and much larger, nearly 2 miles long, $\frac{3}{4}$ mile wide at one point and 7 miles in circumference. It was completed in 1901 when the dam impounded the River Yeo, drowning about 450 acres of farmland and forming what appears to be a natural lake, lapping the contours of the Mendip foothills and holding 1,700 million gallons of water which is in due course pumped to Barrow Gurney.

From its earliest days Blagdon became famous for its trout fishing, producing fish of almost legendary size which throve in the shallow waters extending over newly drowned land. Boat fishing is traditional at Blagdon, and the setting and the sport provided by both brown and rainbow trout have drawn fishermen from all over the world. The trout are bred at the Ubley hatchery at the upper end of the lake, from which embryo trout have been exported to many parts of the world.

The Chew Valley Lake is even more beautiful, folded into the surrounding hills, broken by the subtle contours of Denny Island, and carefully landscaped by the planting of 40,000 trees of many different varieties which will add to its charm as the years pass. This is a larger lake than Blagdon, 10 miles in circumference, the dam near Chew Stoke impounding 4,too million gallons covering nearly 1,200 acres.

Authorised in 1939 but delayed by the war years, the lake was begun in 1951 and inaugurated by the Queen on 17 April 1056. Skirted by two main roads and with a new road built across the great dam, it has become such a popular resort for Bristolians and others that a landscaped carpark and picnic area has now been brought into use at the north end near the dam. It has become a bird sanctuary too where literally thousands of birds may be studied and enjoyed: more than 200 different species resident or migrant have been observed. Near Herriotts Bridge at the southern end of the lake is a Nature Reserve. A Nature Trail has also been planned in the Moreton–Stratford area.

Like Blagdon, the lake has become a fisherman's paradise stocked with fabulous trout of a special strain evolved at the Ubley hatchery, and well over 10,000 fish are now being caught each year. For some years fishing was only allowed from the bank or from the inshore shallows, but fishing from motor-boats is now allowed with certain restrictions against entering the specified sailing area. Since 1967 dinghy sailing has been allowed, so that now the intricate and ever-changing pattern of coloured sails adds yet another feature of beauty against the background of the hill country.

Beyond the barrier of Mendip the Cheddar reservoir, completed in 1937, presents a strange contrast, perhaps more in keeping with the rectilinear landscape of rhines and droves. It is a great circular bowl, $\frac{3}{4}$ mile in diameter, lying to the south of the road from Axbridge to Cheddar and holding within its artificial embankment 1,300 million gallons of water stored from the springs at the foot of Cheddar Gorge. Yet here too there is good sport to be enjoyed: dinghy sailing and racing under the supervision of the Bristol Corinthian Yacht Club, and spinning for pike and other coarse fish.

It must be emphasised that all these pieces of water are private property and not public recreation centres: there is no right of access except by road or by definitive public footpaths. Fishing permits must be obtained, sailing is only possible for authorised groups, and entry permits must be requested by ornithologists and recognised societies or individuals engaged in scientific studies for whom amenities such as hides have been constructed at Chew. First and foremost the lakes exist to provide a reliable supply of pure water for Bristol: we are indeed fortunate that they also do so much to preserve the wild life and the natural beauty of the Mendip countryside and that they can provide recreation and pleasure for many of the inhabitants of a great city.[7]

Apart from what is offered by the lakes, there is only a limited amount of fishing around Mendip. There is coarse fishing in the lower reaches of the Axe and other moorland streams at the west end of the hill, and on some of the little rivers at the east end. Most of this fishing belongs to the riparian owners—as does the coarse fishing at Emborough Pool and at one or two other small lakes in private demesnes. Perhaps the most interesting development is at Marston Bigot, where the lake in the park has been restored and stocked by the Frome Angling Association, who also control 7 miles of fishing along the River Frome and the Mells river as far as Murtry.

Tourism

Fishing, bird-watching and nature study in general are contemplative recreations, usually enjoyed in peace and quiet and comparative isolation; they require some degree either of manual dexterity or of scientific or intellectual ability. Likewise painting, which is essentially an individual pastime, even if based upon such a place as the Mendip Painting Centre at Rickford or deriving from courses at one of the technical colleges farther east along the hill. It is obvious from work observed at local exhibitions that the Mendip scene appeals to an increasingly large number of artists, both amateur and professional. Among the professional artists Peter Coate and Anthony Rossiter have produced outstanding work that has gained them wide recognition.

Less effort is required of the tourist, and indeed pleasure motoring is now easily the most popular of all outdoor recreations. Mendip is easy of access and covered by a network of roads—there are no large areas of wild to be approached only with difficulty and on foot, as is the case with Exmoor, Dartmoor or the Brecon Beacons, to name the three nearest National Parks—and many people spend their weekends and holidays driving, sight-seeing, sitting about and picnicking.

For many hundreds of years Mendip has attracted the curious traveller: in 1150 Henry of Huntingdon came to Cheddar and described the gorge as one of the four wonders of England; in 1470 William of Worcester was at Wookey Hole; and about 1540 Leland on his peregrinations made a number of shrewd and observant comments on the Mendip scene. Most travellers seem to have visited Wookey

Hole—Celia Fiennes for example and Daniel Defoe; and Michael 'Angelo' Rooker painted the entrance to the cave late in the eighteenth century when Turner was painting the west front of Wells Cathedral. The Picturesque Travellers—Gilpin, Maton, Warner—took these sights in their stride on their western tours.[8]

Local inhabitants too went sight-seeing. Dr Claver Morris of Wells took a party to Wookey Hole on 23 July 1709: there was no guide, but it cost them half-a-crown for beer and candles. The Rev John Skinner was there in 1797, and from Camerton he would sometimes drive his visitors over Mendip to show them the splendours of Cheddar Cliffs. By now the new turnpike roads had made travelling very much easier and safer than it had been for earlier travellers like Leland and Celia Fiennes, who had made their way on horseback as best they could.[9]

The arrival of the railway from 1850 onwards brought a new type of traveller—the day-tripper. Excursions were run to Wells over the Somerset Central which reached the city in 1859, three years before the East Somerset which arrived from Shepton Mallet in 1862. The Cheddar Valley branch did not get there until 1870, but Cheddar station with its imposing overall roof and refreshment room was a clear indication of the tourist traffic that was expected over the line. The opening-up of the newly discovered Gough's Cave in 1890 was an added attraction.

The Somerset & Dorset line from Bath was opened over Mendip in 1874, and circular trips were eventually run to Wells, returning via the Cheddar Valley and Bristol. In 1902 Saturday afternoon excursions were advertised: 1s 3d return to Chilcompton (for Downside Abbey); 1s 6d to Masbury, where trippers were met by a horse-brake and taken down to tea in Wells and back up to Masbury. By 1923 a charabanc had been substituted for the horse-brake, and the combined rail and road trip took 75 minutes from Bath to Wells.

The charabanc however was to win the day, and coaches were to bring far more tourists to Mendip than ever travelled by train. By the early 1920s day-trips from Weston-super-Mare or Bristol were labouring up Burrington Combe, down Cheddar Gorge and on to Wells.

In 1927 Wookey Hole cave was opened up and made more easily accessible to the public, with electric light, and other amenities such as a swimming pool added during the 1930s. In 1973 the empty paper mill nearby was acquired by Madame Tussaud's to be developed as an entertainment centre. Even so, Wookey Hole mercifully manages to retain the atmosphere of a village and has so far avoided the intense commercialisation that has done so much to spoil Cheddar.

This indeed pinpoints an unresolved conflict. Local authorities must make provision for the influx of tourists, but they must also attempt to preserve the quality of life in any given area: after alln it is the local inhabitant who pays the rates. While the owners of commercial amenities are concerned to attract the largest possible number of visitors, only a limited number is desirable where natural amenities are the attraction. Ebbor Gorge is now a less pleasant place to visit than it was before it was made over to the National Trust; and a cable-car would not add attraction to the top of Cheddar Cliffs and could only result in irreparable harm to the environment.

Ball Games

It is when we come to consider the more active forms of recreation that we realise how many opportunities Mendip has to offer—both above and below ground. 'Above ground' should by rights include gliding, but this is not an activity available to the general public: the Gliding School at Halesland above Draycott is available only for the training of cadets. On the ground the new sport of stock-car racing in the stadium west of Charterhouse beyond Tyning's Farm, and the motorcycle scrambles at Leighton near Nunney, give much pleasure to participants and spectators alike, though they shatter the silence of the hills—for a few hours on a limited number of days in the year. But at the same time there are probably a far greater number of people actively involved, whether as players or spectators, in the traditional ball games.

Fives or handball is the earliest ball game on Mendip to which reference is found. It was first played against church towers which provided gratis a high wall, and buttresses, and a flat court stretching into the churchyard. In 1635 the Locking churchwarden was summoned to Wells to discuss the prevention of 'those that played fives in the churchyard'. Windows had to be re-glazed or boarded up, and digging up or trenching the fives place is a recurrent item in parish accounts. At Ashwick in 1763 the churchwardens got the consent of the Archdeacon to the removal of the churchyard cross and its re-erection 'in the vifes [sic] place in order to prevent the young people from spending so much idle time in that sort of exercise'.

Five-players were finally extruded from churchyards, and resorted—especially in south Somerset—to courts provided by innkeepers, much as skittle-alleys are provided in our own time to attract custom and stimulate thirst. One such court was briefly exposed and then demolished in Shepton Mallet during the recent rebuilding of the town centre—a lofty redbrick wall with two rougher stone walls splaying out at an angle and a paved forecourt. This may however have been a school game rather than an inn game, as the old Grammar School

39 The Netherworld of Mendip: cave decorations at St Cuthbert's Swallet

40 The village school at Charterhouse was closed in 1947 and has now been reopened by the Somerset Education Committee as an Outdoor Activities Centre

41 Cheddar Cliffs as seen by the Picturesque Traveller (from an early nineteenth-century print)

stands close by, and at Downside School, a few miles to the north, handball was played against walls from 1814 until a magnificent new ball-place was built in 1854.

The regular team games—cricket, football Zunder both codes) and hockey—have long been played by local clubs in villages and towns all round Mendip. Turner's well-known water-colour of Wells Cathedral, dating from the early 1790s, shows a game of cricket in progress outside the west front. At Evercreech the club records go back to 1853, when the village played Chewton Mendip for a barrel of beer. There are many pleasant village grounds all along Mendip and some more sophisticated set-ups in the urban areas.

Somerset 2nd XI have played matches on the excellent ground at Midsomer Norton; a County Championship match was staged at Downside School in 1934 between Somerset and Glamorgan, then captained by M. J. Turnbull, an Old Gregorian; and the Australian touring team of 1930 appeared on the same ground. Championship matches have also been played at Frome and at Wells, both before and after World War II. At Wellsn Arthur Wellard made history by hitting five sixes in one over in 1936, following this up with five sixes and a single, two years later, off no less a bowler than the immortal Frank Woolley.

Association football is much more widely played than cricket at present, and there are many leagues where village or local works teams play each other. The larger town clubs play in the Somerset Senior League, but Frome Town and Welton Rovers, both professional or semi-professional clubs, play in the Western League. Welton Rovers, representing Midsomer Norton, are perhaps the outstanding club in the Mendip area, with a history dating back to 1887 and a long sequence of successes in League and Cup competitions.

Rugby football is only played in a few towns or large villages, generally where there is a strong nucleus of Old Boys from local rugby-playing schools. Hockey is perhaps played even less, mainly from the lack of all-weather pitches in an area of considerable rainfall. The hockey festivals on the sands at Weston and at Brean can hardly claim to be Mendip activities.

While giving evidence in a trial at Wells Assizes about 1685, Tobias Salmon, then aged 97, declared that he had played bowls on Lipyeat Green near Kilmersdon in the days of James I, but since then bowls seems to have become an urban game, with two notable exceptions: at Wookey Hole, where the rink is laid out in front of the nineteenth-century paper-mill and the village club still plays as Hodgkinson's, thus commemorating their link with the family who created the environment in which they play; and at Banwell, on the site of the village pond whose springs once supplied a paper-mill and later a brewery.

Although not actually a ball game, the ancient game of quoits has for long been associated with the inn, and until World War II was played regularly in the Radstock and Frome districts, which produced several All-England champions. The game has lately been revived at the Tyning Inn at Radstock where quoits weighing 7–11lb each are pitched 18yd to a pin set in the centre of a specially laid clay bed. Traditionally the season began on Good Friday, and early in the present century there was a North Somerset League in which a number of teams from local inns competed, including outlying villages such as Nettlebridge and Gurney Slade.

Unlike all these team (or spectator) sports, golf as played on Mendip is essentially an individual recreation: it has only developed in the present century and to some extent depends upon the motor-car, though only one Mendip course lies any distance from a centre of population.

The Weston-super-Mare golf course—the club was founded in 1893—lies just north of Black Rock, but is so close to the boundary of Mendip as to merit mention, lying as it does on the outskirts of Uphill with fine views of Brean Down and the mouth of the Axe.

The Wells club dates from 1913 though golf had been played on the nine-hole course some years earlier. It lies pleasantly along a sheltered valley among the foothills of Mendip, under the flank of a wooded hill crowned by the Iron Age encampment known as King's Castle, though now threatened by one of various proposals for a ring-road.

A few miles away and in a very different setting is the Mendip club, founded from Shepton Mallet. By 1895 golf was being played on Doulting Sheep Sleight to the south of the town, but in 1909 a new nine-hole course was opened on top of Mendip. This was laid out by A. Vardon, brother of the famous Harry Vardon, at an estimated cost of £30, and extended to eighteen holes in 1965. The course lies along the summit of the eastern Mendip ridge, between the old Bristol–Weymouth coach road and the Iron Age fortress at Masbury, rising at one point to 974 feet above sea-level. The beautiful downland turf and the panoramic views, from the Welsh mountains to the Dorset Heights and from Cotswold to Exmoor, ensure that despite the hazards of wind and fog a game of golf at Masbury will be a memorable and satisfying experience.

The newest course, the Fosseway, was opened in 1970 on the outskirts of Midsomer Norton along the lane to Charlton. This is a nine-hole course (designed by Messrs Cotton, Pennink, Lawrie and partners) and if scenically less exciting then the other Mendip courses, it provides recreation for the growing population of the Norton–Radstock area.

Walking

Most people arrive on Mendip by car today, and driving about to arrive somewhere, or just driving hopefully, they can get a good general impression; but only on foot can they acquire any intimate knowledge of Mendip. There is little pleasure to be got walking along many of the long straight roads, despite the attraction of the wide grass verges; many minor roads may be traffic-free, but they are surfaced with tarmac and hard on the feet; a small number of bridlepaths and drove roads attract the eye on the Ordnance maps, though, like the Fosse Way from Oakhill to Charlton, they can be pretty tough going in winter and summer alike.

The real key that unlocks the heart of Mendip to those who wish to find it is the footpath. The rights of way are now marked in red on Sheets 172, 182 and 183 of the 1:50,000 os map, but on the last edition of the One-inch (Sheets 165 and 166) they were not marked in the area covered by the former Wells RDC. It is still possible to explore enormous areas of Mendip by footpath: in all they must traverse hundreds of miles of the countryside, but there is, alas, no guarantee that they are kept open for the casual walker who is likely to be the only person wishing to use them. A few are signposted, some parish councils have formed footpath committees and the Mendip Society has undertaken to help with the construction and erection of footpath signs. At present an inviting stone stile or a green lane may sometimes lead to a stretch of impenetrable jungle or a difficult confrontation with barbed wire or a tatterdemalion gate buried in thirty years' growth of hedgerow. Elsewhere there are paths scrupulously kept open, though never used by the local community. Towards the eastern end of the hill, a glance at the map reveals a tightly woven network of paths concentrated in what was once a flourishing industrial area, converging on collieries or mills, on church or pub, linking the numerous hamlets and villages.

The types of walk offered vary all along the range. At the western end, Brean Down, Crook Peak and Wavering Down offer short turf with the limestone rock close underfoot, and superb views across water or moor to distant hills, with a sense of elevation quite disproportionate to the actual height attained. Black Down is the only considerable area of open heather-covered top, but here, and farther east along the plateau, a number of splendid walks strike right across Mendip—from Dolebury or Burrington to Cheddar, for instance; from Cheddar past Charterhouse and down to Ubley or Compton Martin; or from Wookey Hole to Chewton Mendip or Litton. The official *Guide to Wells* carefully describes a number of possible routes in that area. Farther east there are pleasant paths to discover in places like Ashwick Grove or down the Nettlebridge valley past Coleford, along the towpath of the ill-fated Dorset & Somerset Canal; across Doulting Sheep Sleight and over the splendid hills behind Evercreech and Batcombe; or from Downhead through Asham Wood (preferably at the weekend when the quarries are silent). Farther east still there is the great wooded fastness of Postlebury Hill—difficult indeed of access—which few realise to be higher than the much more famous Crook Peak at the other end of Mendip.

These are paths for the general walker. More specialised are the Nature Trails, carefully waymarked, with details generally available in leaflets at sites in the Wells area (Biddle Combe), at the National Nature Reserve in Ebbor Gorge and in the Reserves at Black Rock and Long Wood above Cheddar. In the Priddy area an Archaeological Trail is to be established, guiding the walker across country to a number of the most interesting geological, archaeological and industrial sites. Another project prepared, but as yet unrealised, is the proposed long-distance path from Avebury to the sea which it is hoped will reach Mendip near Batcombe, and give a high-level footpath along the southern scarp, continuing over Black Down and along the western hills to the mouth of the Axe at Uphill. This will indeed be a magnificent walk.

Walks are organised by groups like the Ramblers' Association, the Mendip Society and the Shepton Mallet Society, and by specialist groups such as geologists, natural historians and ornithologists. Orienteering is mainly concentrated on the area of woodland at Stock Hill near Priddy.

Only one Youth Hostel is now open, at Cheddar, though for many years there were also hostels at Wookey Hole, Hutton, Burrington and Croscombe. On top of the hill there are practically no recognised camping sites west of A39, though eastward from here, along both flanks of the hill, and all round the western end, there are facilities for holiday caravans to park as well as some permanent caravan sites.

The most interesting project which brings a large number of children to Mendip every year is the Charterhouse Field & Outdoor Activity Centre. Charterhouse school was built in 1861 and closed in 1947. In 1964 it was re-opened as a residential centre which now operates with a full-time warden throughout the year. Wooden chalets, a study room and an observatory have been added, to accommodate about forty people at a time. School parties ranging from 9-year-olds right up to sixth-formers, youth groups and teachers on training courses are here able to benefit from a tremendous variety of field studies available—ecological, geological, and historical, with special potential for industrial archaeology; while many sorts of exciting outdoor activities, including rock-climbing and caving, are available in the area.

Caves and Caving

D. I. Smith

The recreational opportunites afforded by the Mendip caves can best be discussed under two headings: the commercial show caves at Cheddar and Wookey Hole, and the sporting caves.

There are two major show caves at Cheddar, both now under the management of Cheddar Caves Ltd. The largest is Gough's Cave, with its associated tourist attractions of restaurant and museum, and the smaller, less frequented, Cox's Cave. Neither of these caves exhibited natural entrances in historic time. Cox's Cave was discovered during road widening operations in 1837 and was opened, by Edward Cox, on a commercial basis shortly afterwards. Gough's Cave was dug into by Richard Gough and his sons during the 1890s, after many years of diligent searching in the Gorge, and opened as a show cave in 1899. Before this exciting discovery, Gough had acted as the guide to the cave now known as Gough's Old Cave, which is located behind the modern Cave Man Restaurant. This was probably the first of the Cheddar show caves, but suffered severely from the competition of Cox's Cave, and was abandoned for commercial purposes after Gough's Cave was opened.

Wookey Hole Cave, with its imposing entrance forming a rock arch from beneath which rises the River Axe, has a very much longer history. Indeed, until the last century it was the most famous cave in the British Isles and was known as a natural curiosity throughout Europe. Commercialisation in the modern sense did not commence until electric light was installed in 1927. Visitors were conducted around the three chambers that form the initial section of the cave. Until about 1852, two further chambers were accessible, but the construction of a small dam, built in conjunction with the nearby paper-mill, raised the water level so that entry to these was submerged. Cave diving had, by 1971, extended the number of cave chambers as far as 'Wookey 22' (the twenty-second chamber). The problem is that between each of these chambers there is a flooded length of cave passage. The cave tour for visitors has been extended, since early 1975, by the construction of a tunnel, so that parties can now pass from the third chamber to view chambers seven, eight and nine, returning to the surface to observe the ravine with the River Axe and complete their tour along the canal that originally fed the paper-mill.

The importance of these caves as a tourist attraction is very considerable. Cheddar Caves are visited by half a million tourists each year and Wookey Hole Cave by some 200,000, a figure likely to increase in the light of the new developments at that cave.

The show caves, however, form only a fraction of the known cave passages in the Mendip Hills. An excellent guide entitled (very appropriately) *The Complete Caves of Mendip* was compiled by Barrington and Stanton (1972). This lists all the known caves and associated features on Mendip, together with precise details of their location and dimensions, and a bibliography to the literature of each individual cave. Additional details are given as to how to obtain access to those caves that are 'gated'. There are well over 400 features listed, and the total length of cave passage on the Mendip Hills is in excess of 15 miles. The largest and most famous of the individual caves is Swildon's Hole, near Priddy, with nearly 5 miles of passage and a vertical range of well over 500 feet. Over twenty of the known caves have total passage lengths in excess of 1,000 feet.

Caving as a sport is purely a twentieth-century pastime. While the caves of Mendip do not have the impressive vertical pitches of the Yorkshire 'potholes', or the length of passage of some of the Welsh caves, as far as the history of cave exploration and scientific study are concerned they are outstanding. They are also one of the most popular caving regions in the country. The Mendip Nature Research Committee, founded in 1906, was the earliest caving club on Mendip and one of the earliest in Britain. The University of Bristol Spelaeological Society, which dates from 1919, was the first university caving society, and the Wessex Cave Club, founded in 1934, is probably the largest caving club in Britain with over 300 members. The growth of the sport is spectacular. In 1950 there were some sixty caving clubs in the country (excluding school clubs) and thirteen of these were based on Mendip or carried out most of their activity on (or under) Mendip. Hanwell (1971) writes that the number of local caving club members was some 350 in 1950; by 1955 this had risen to 635, to over a thousand (from twenty-five clubs) in 1960, and in 1970 to almost 2,000 from sixty clubs. The projected figures are that, by 1980, there will be at least 5,000 cavers belonging to the clubs and societies in the Mendip region. Those familiar with caving clubs will realise that such societies vary from the very small informal group, whose existence is ephemeral, to the long established and well organised. What is important is that of the cavers to be found on Mendip on any given day, many will not belong to Mendip-based caving clubs. Additional cavers can come from clubs whose base is far from Mendip, they can be among the many cavers who do not belong to a club at all, or they may be young folk enjoying caving under the auspices of a variety of recreational bodies. These include local youth clubs, Boy Scout groups, adventure training from schools under the control of local educational authorities, often associated with the Duke of Edinburgh Award Scheme, or from the armed forces. Many of these bodies, and many of the caving clubs, maintain 'huts' on Mendip, and such huts can vary from dilapidated wooden structures to luxurious premises complete with showers and running hot water. Much of the weekend popularity of Mendip caving is because it is the nearest major caving region to London and the populous south-east.

The distribution of the caves is controlled by the geology and hydrology of the Carboniferous Limestone of the Mendip Hills (see pp 18–31). Few of the caves had obvious natural entrances, and the majority have been discovered as the result of arduous digging combined with a varying degree of scientific expertise and the judicious use of explosives. Of the major caves, only Goatchurch Cavern and Wookey Hole Cave have natural entrances that lead unhindered into any form of extensive cave system. It is possible to classify the caves according to differing sites within the landscape (see Fig 5, p 28). Possible entrances occur at the swallets where stream waters disappear underground, or at the sites of former swallets associated with earlier periods of landscape evolution. The largest cave systems (for example, Swildon's Hole, St Cuthbert's Swallet and Stoke Lane Slocker, location shown on Fig 3, p 20) are of this form. It is also possible to enter the subterranean drainage from the rising (or spring) end of the system. Wookey Hole and Gough's Cave are of this type, although it is the abandoned cave risings that are normally more easy of access. To break into the drainage system that connects the swallet to rising at other points is more difficult. Lamb Leer Cavern with its Great Chamber is the best example of a major cave virtually isolated from the swallet to rising hydrological system. It was entered during mining operations in 1674 and the descent of the 65ft drop into the Great Chamber by the owner, John Beaumont, must rank highly in the early annals of cave exploration. The cave was abandoned about 1700 and rediscovered in 1880. The descent into the Great Chamber is still one of the most exciting experiences in Mendip caving. Many other minor caves have been entered by excavation into the closed depression features that mark the surface of Mendip; Cow Hole and Pine Tree Pot are examples.

A history of Mendip caving by Johnson (1967) is available, and this presents a chronological approach to the sporting and scientific aspects of the subject. The era of modern caving began at the end of the last century and in large part this grew from the interest in the archaeology of the cave entrances and rock shelters. These early interests are so intimately associated with the endeavours of one man, Henry Ernest Balch, that caving and cave science before World War I are synonymous with his name. Balch was born in Wells in 1869, was awarded a scholarship to the Blue School in that City, commenced employment as a post office messenger at the age of 14, and rose to the position of Head Postmaster of Wells in 1928. In his early years, he pioneered the exploration of the cave systems at Swildon's Hole and Eastwater Cavern. In both cases, access was gained by excavation of the debris where the stream waters seeped underground. Balch, in joint authorship with E. A. Baker in 1907, produced *The Netherworld of Mendip,* the first book in the English language that dealt specifically with caves and caving. This was followed by six further books concerned with Mendip caves and archaeology. His work was recognised by the award of an Honorary MA degree from the University of Bristol in 1927 and the Honorary Freedom of the City of Wells in 1944. A biography and bibliography of this famous caver by W. I. Stanton, *Pioneer under the Mendips,* was published in 1969 to mark the centenary of his birth.

What of modern cavers? Generalisation is difficult, for there is no type caver. From its earliest beginnings the pastime has spanned age and education, upbringing and interest. Always a proportion of the youthful become addicted and as more and more of the young have some experience of caving, so the number of dedicated cavers grows. This band of enthusiasts tend to develop a range of specialist interests. Of the interests that can be classified as essentially sporting, the search for new caves, the surveying and extension of known caves and cave-diving spring readily to mind. It is possible on most weekends, summer and winter, to find small groups of 'mature' cavers engaged in dirty, hard manual labour, excavating surface depressions in their search for new caves. Such groups can include well-known local representatives of the medical and teaching professions, company directors, solicitors, office workers and schoolboys. Cave-diving is undoubtedly the most specialised and adventurous of the caving specialities. The first organised cave-diving on Mendip was at Swildon's Hole in 1934, and the primitive apparatus used was described many years later by one of the participants: 'the respirator was a crazy thing, made from a piece of an old bicycle frame and fitted with an inlet and outlet valve enabling the diver to inhale through a 40-foot length of garden hose'. From these humble beginnings cave-diving has become a highly sophisticated sport in which Wookey Hole Cave has played a special role in the history of British cave-diving. Lest this should give the impression that caving is dangerous and foolhardy, for many years a highly organised Mendip Cave Rescue Organisation has existed. This works in co-operation with the local police, and can muster teams of trained cave rescue personnel, including doctors, within a short time of an emergency call.

The caves form an integral part of the character of the Mendip Hills, linked with history and science, literature and legend. Mendip without its caves could be likened to Egypt without its pyramids, or Cheddar without its cheese! Both the twentieth-century show cave visitor and the sporting scientific caver have their earlier counterparts, but modern developments in transport and in recreational leisure time have greatly increased their numbers. It is important that we should not abuse the cave heritage of Mendip; it must be conserved so that its fascination can be shared by the ever-growing number of participants. It can only be hoped that conservation and growth can, in this case, be successfully combined.

Notes to this chapter are on pages 275–6.

9

The Changing Face of Mendip

Robin Atthill

CENTURY BY CENTURY the face of Mendip has changed. Different peoples have come and gone, leaving their mark upon the hills: Palaeolithic and Neolithic, Iron Age and Bronze Age man, Celt, Roman, Saxon and Norman. The forests were felled and the marshes drained; the early enclosures were made and settlements grew into hamlets and villages which flourished, or decayed, or revived, century by century. In *East Coker,* T. S. Eliot has succinctly and perceptively outlined the long process by which so much of the scene with which we are familiar has been created:

> In succession
> Houses rise and fall, crumble, are extended,
> Are removed, destroyed, restored, or in their place
> Is an open field, or a factory, or a by-pass.

Two comparatively short periods in Mendip's long history have probably seen greater change along the hill than any others. The first was the period between about 1770 and 1820 when the enclosures were completed and the landscape of the high plateau as we know it today, was created; the second is the period since 1918—the age of the internal combustion engine—'the lifetime of one man only', to use Eliot's words again. The first saw agriculture replace mining as the chief occupation on top of the hill, and the impact of the Industrial Revolution on the north-east fringe, where Radstock was to become the capital of the Somerset coalfield, while the completion of the pattern of turnpike roads provided Mendip with its first adequate transport system. The second period saw the end of Mendip's isolation, for despite the turnpike roads and the marginal impact of the railway, large areas of Mendip country experienced very little change between the completion of the enclosures and the end of World War I.

In 1918 the high plateau was still a world of its own, remote from the valleys to north and south, and incredibly remote from Bristol or Bath. It was only 10 years since the closure of the lead works at Priddy, and less than 20 since the railway reached Blagdon, where the lake had already become an accepted feature of the view from the northern escarpment; away to the east the Somerset & Dorset line struggled over the crest of the hill with stations at Binegar and Masbury.

It was a world as yet hardly impinged upon by the telephone or the motor-car or the motor-bus: most of the surrounding villages were still linked with the nearest markets, or with Bristol or Bath, by carriers' vans; there was no electricity, no mains water or sewage system—and no BBC.

Today all modern conveniences are taken for granted even in the most isolated farmhouse. Yet in a sense this is still a world of its own, for there has been only a very limited increase in population on the top of the hill in the last 60 years, despite its increased accessibility and the growing wish of many to escape from city life. The climate, and now the planners, are the chief reasons for this, and Mendip has retained something of its old sense of isolation and loneliness, especially during the winter months; for man is by nature a gregarious animal.

This is clear when one compares the population figures in the census returns for 1921—immediately after the 1914-18 War and at the beginning of the motor age—with those for 1971. Some of the figures are misleading because of boundary changes, but putting aside the purely urban areas (Frome, Norton–Radstock, Shepton Mallet and Wells) and suburban areas such as Hutton and Locking which are peripheral to Weston-super-Mare, and Selwood which surrounds Frome, an interesting pattern seems to emerge across the Mendip parishes, always bearing in mind that certain civil parishes include more than one village.

Ten parishes—Burrington, Farrington Gurney, Leigh-on-Mendip, Litton, Pilton, St Cuthbert Out, Stoke St Michael, Ubley, Witham Friary and North Wootton—show no significant change in population between 1921 and 1971; six of them in fact contain slightly fewer people than they did in 1911. Eleven more parishes, all lying east of the Bristol–Wells road (A39), show significant *decreases* of up to 25 per cent between 1921 and 1971, and even more significant decreases in some cases if compared with the figures for 1911. These parishes with declining populations are Ashwick, Batcombe, Binegar, Chewton Mendip, Dinder, Doulting, Downhead, Elm, Mells, Upton Noble and Whatley. The paradox is that while a lot of new houses have been built in some of these parishes, the size of the average family has declined, and a number of older houses, often in outlying parts of the parish, have disappeared: some have simply disintegrated; elsewhere two or three cottages have been knocked together during conversion into superior middle-class residences.

The remaining twenty-three parishes, where a reasonably accurate comparison can be made, show significant *increases* of population between 1921 and 1971, ranging from about 10 per cent at Compton Bishop and Croscombe through 25 per cent at Bleadon, West Harptree and Wanstrow to 50 per cent at Rodney Stoke (which includes Draycott) and Holcombe. At Banwell, Churchill, Shipham and Winscombe the population has more than doubled in the last 50 years.* Most of the largest increases occur at the west end of the hill in the Bristol and Weston-super-Mare commuter zone, though a number of parishes east of A39 also show significant increases. Here too certain parishes where boundary changes have occurred, such as Chilcompton, Stratton-on-the-Fosse, Coleford and Nunney, have obviously increased in population considerably.

Quite apart from the overall increase in population, there are of course far more people about on Mendip than there were 60 years ago, for one reason and one reason only: the invention of the internal combustion engine. There is also more noise both on the roads and in the fields, where a single tractor may have replaced anything up to half a dozen agricultural labourers. It is still possible to walk for hours on Mendip without meeting a human being, except perhaps where one has to cross a road; it is harder however to get beyond the sound of motorcars, especially at weekends or during the holiday months.

Since 1918, within the space of a single lifetime, tremendous visual changes have taken place all over Mendip with considerable impact both on the environment and on the lives of the people. A number of features have disappeared from the scene, probably for ever, some of them of great historic interest as contributing to the unique quality of the area. The last traces of the lead industry have now almost vanished, at any rate above ground: in 1918 there were three chimneys standing, and a number of buildings, but today, apart from the restored chimney on Smitham Hill, only the crumbling stone flues at Charterhouse and at Chewton minery, and the reedy reservoirs, survive. The collieries too have closed: most of the sites have been adapted to other uses, but some have reverted to wild, with their batches grass-grown or tree-covered. Only in the Norton–Radstock area is one really aware that the getting of coal once dominated men's lives on this side of the hill.

---

* At Priddy, oddly enough, the population has also doubled from 142 in 1921 to 271 in 1971, though this is still well below the peak of 313 which was reached in 1841.

Sometimes the curious searcher will stumble across the remains of the little railways that served a number of the collieries or quarries. The standard gauge railways too have disappeared into limbo except for the two sections serving east Mendip quarries: many of the stations have been ruthlessly demolished, though a number have been converted, sometimes to ignoble uses. So have the breweries, which were formerly a characteristic feature of the local scene and an important factor in its economic life.

The landscape too has suffered change. Familiar woods have been felled, the tree-stumps grubbed out and the land brought under cultivation. Chilcompton Wood has gone, changing the whole appearance of the valley to which it was such a noble ornament; Burnt Wood on the Bath–Wells road near Slab House has gone, and here the stone walls which are such a basic ingredient in the visual pattern of Mendip have been replaced by concrete posts and barbed wire. Elsewhere, afforestation of open hillsides has completely changed the scene, especially in two areas which attract visitors—Rowberrow Warren at the west end of Black Down, and Stock Hill to the east of Priddy Pool. Elsewhere unenclosed land—not common land, for there is very little common land on Mendip—has been enclosed by fences: on the southern slopes of Black Down, for instance, near Tyning's Farm, and beside the road from Priddy to Wookey Hole over Deerleap. Good farming perhaps, but a pity, because it limits access to open spaces for many who come to Mendip for recreation and pleasure.

On the other side of the picture are the changes that have taken place and are still taking place to affect the overall image of Mendip: new factories and new industries have replaced the old, new housing areas have spread out from the towns and from many of the villages, at first haphazard and uncontrolled, with some appalling examples of ribbon development and inappropriate building material, but later controlled by the provisions of the County Plan, whether council housing or private residential development in what one may loosely call the commuter areas.

There have been few major improvements on the roads: none of the towns has yet been bypassed, except for Axbridge, and this only became possible with the closure of the Cheddar Valley railway in 1963; the villages of Cross and (rather surprisingly) Litton were given their bypasses in the early 1920s. Elsewhere it has been a matter of sporadic widening or the elimination of blind corners, but the work involved has been negligible compared with the work carried out by the turnpike trustees 150–200 years before.

Along the Mendip roads subtle changes are continually affecting the landscape pattern: the draughtsmen responsible for the First Edition os map of 1817 were so delighted with the pattern of the new Mendip enclosures that they sometimes drew in the field boundaries (along Dursdon Drove for instance between Rookham and Deerleap). The 1886 Six-inch map shows the ultimate perfection of this field-pattern, with minute spots of blue depicting the ponds that were to be found in the corner of almost every field before the arrival of mains water. Our own age has seen hedges grubbed out and walls demolished to make the larger fields that are easier and more economic to work with modern machines. Wire fencing and concrete posts have often replaced the older hedges and walls, for few farmers can afford the time or the money to rebuild dilapidated walls, even if they could find the skilled labour. Many acres which were previously rough grazing land, or even gruffy ground on the high plateau, have been reclaimed and brought under cultivation during or since the 1939–45 War—a sight which would have delighted the heart of John Billingsley.

Afforestation, too, would have delighted him. 'Systematic plantation is but little studied,' he lamented in 1794, though no 'speculation can be more profitable or more pleasing than planting'. The Forestry Commission admits to the same priorities, first the growing of trees for timber, and secondly the provision of recreational amenity.

Since 1939 the Commission has leased and planted six areas on Mendip, totalling nearly 1,500 acres, from Rowberrow Warren (545 acres) on the western slopes of Black Down to Harridge Wood (97 acres) half a mile from the site of John Billingsley's house in Ashwick Grove. On Smitham Hill above East Harptree there is Frances Plantation (197 acres), the name commemorating the famous Frances, Countess Waldegrave; there are smaller plantations on Beacon Hill and at Cranmore Tower, and nearly 500 acres at Stock Hill north of Priddy Pool, where the historic name of Mendip Forest has been revived. Most of these are mixed plantations, containing hardwoods as well as conifers in varying proportions, and care has been taken to study the landscape and to keep in touch with various conservation bodies.

The general policy of the Commission is to encourage the public to go into the forests, wherever there are no legal constraints against their so doing, and to follow the footpaths and rides, many of which are anyhow public rights of way, thus adding another amenity to the Mendip terrain.

Afforestation has added a dimension to the hill; quarrying has removed a dimension—to the tune of about 10 million tons a year at the time of writing. The development of the stone industry has been outlined in Chapter 7; it remains to re-assess in general terms the impact of quarrying today—and tomorrow.

Modern quarrying creates more problems than it solves—and this goes for other areas beside Mendip: one thinks immediately of the Yorkshire Dales and of Wenlock Edge. The discussion of these problems generates much heat: action groups have been formed; the issues involved have reached the middle pages of *The Times*; the Minister for the Environment has appointed two committees—the Verney Committee on Aggregates and the Stevens Committee on Minerals Planning Control. There is a fierce and clear-cut conflict, so far unresolved, between the conservation of the environment and industrial development: or, to put it in its simplest terms, the paramount need for roadstone and the allied products derived from limestone.

There are a number of groups affected and involved, to a greater or lesser degree, with a certain amount of overlapping: the planners, the owners, the voluntary societies, the inhabitants and, by no means least, the tourists. As far as the older approvals are concerned, the planners have very limited powers: co-operation with the owners, rather than compulsion, is the best than can be hoped for. Under present legislation there is no question of revocation of existing concessions, as adequate compensation is far beyond the means of any local authority. Concessions could only be revoked by Act of Parliament. Later concessions have been granted under certain conditions affecting the environment. At the present time about 2,600 acres have been approved for the winning and working of limestone, and a further 200 acres for basalt.

Here, then, is the crux as far as the quarry owners are concerned: they hold enormously valuable concessions; their industry is one of fantastically rapid growth to meet essential needs of modern society; they have invested heavily in very expensive modern plant, and in the areas where they operate, the quarries provide a livelihood for a significant proportion of the population—over Mendip as a whole the quarries employ directly or indirectly about 3,000 people. If in earlier decades the quarry owners were unaware of or indifferent to amenity values, and insensitive to their quarries' impact on the environment, this is no longer so today. The quarry industry has become increasingly aware of its obligations and is now making great efforts to put its house in order: considerable sums have been spent on encasing plant to suppress or restrict the nuisance from dust, on anti-pollution measures, on screening and sculpturing the working areas and spoil heaps, and improving the surfaces of approach roads.

This change of heart is at least in part due to the concern with environment at a national level, as well as to criticisms brought to bear upon the industry locally—not only on Mendip. The voice of voluntary societies and local action groups may be a still small voice confronting the big battalions of industry or the faceless anonymity of a government department, but it is a voice that must be heard in any self-respecting democracy, a voice that asks questions, that comments embarrassingly on the emperor's new clothes and the official hand-outs, and seeks to stimulate public opinion. It is an emotive, at times even hysterical, voice but it is at least articulate.

For the silent majority of the population of Mendip are passive and inarticulate in their reaction to the quarry problem: many of them, of course, have lived with quarries all their lives and are inclined to take them for granted. But except for the central Mendip area, the lives of most inhabitants are affected to a greater or lesser degree by the quarries, and will inevitably be under greater pressures in the years to come: noise and dust, the traffic generated on byroads and main roads, and the gradual loss of visual amenity; and one emphasises that the erosion of the landscape and the gouging out of vast craters are *gradual* processes, which local inhabitants are the less likely to be aware of—until it is too late.

But for the visitor and the tourist the impact is much more immediate: horrifyingly so at Sandford or Shipham Gorge or Cheddar, and unescapably so to anybody driving along the A361 between Frome and Shepton Mallet on their way to the West. Finding one's way to the Nature Reserve in Asham Wood can be an appalling experience; so can standing in Chantry churchyard and looking south-west. At other moments, in the middle of Mells, or Leigh, or Nunney, in the heart of what has emotively been labelled the 'sacrifice area' of east Mendip, it is hard to realise that one is ringed by vast workings; and it is possible to live between two quarries, a mile away on either side—as indeed the present writer does—and hardly be aware of their existence except under certain combinations of wind and weather.

And tomorrow? If the worst prognostications are fulfilled, large areas of Mendip will be irretrievably devastated—at any rate for our own generation. Against this prospect must be set the education of public opinion and the pressure which it can bring to bear, the framing and the implementation of nation-wide policies on aggregates, and the essential need for an ever-increasing sense of responsibility among the quarry owners towards the community as a whole. In the getting of stone, where it is got and how it is got, the economic factor is not the absolute: man does not live by stone alone. What is essential for all to grasp is that the industry and the planning authorities and the conservation groups can, and indeed must, work *together*, and not *against* each other.

In the long term, time will heal some of the scars, but they will be deep

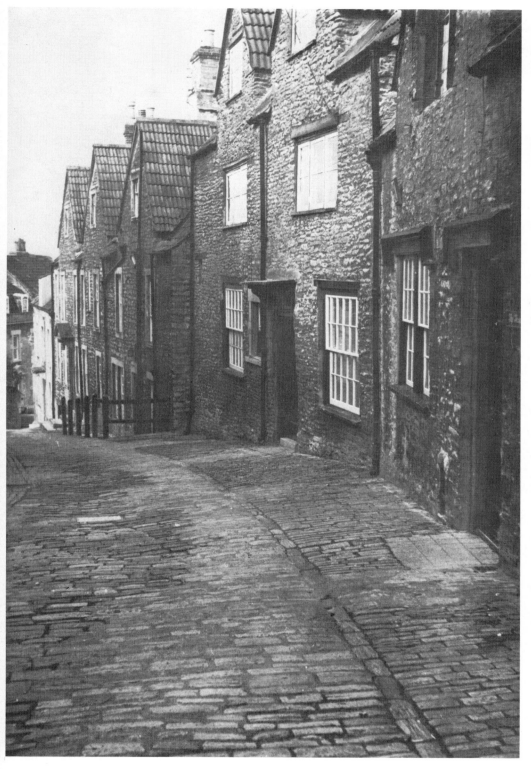

42 Frome: Gentle Street, cobbled and runnelled and lined with splendid old houses, was
once the main road to the south

43 Batcombe: nineteenth-century village school (now closed) and sixteenth-century church tower

44 Babington church (1750) on the lawn of Babington House: the site of a deserted medieval village

45 Nunney: the Georgian manor farm

scars. One thinks of the old quarry workings along Brean Down, which are now grey cliffs falling into the sea; the rock faces in some of the larger abandoned quarries already present scenes of great beauty. But these are private property, inaccessible to the public and potentially dangerous. In the years to come, if Mendip is to continue to attract large numbers of tourists, these sites must surely be put to use for recreation and amenity: for car-parks; for reservoirs; for fishing; for rock climbing; for geological and natural history studies—in fact for a host of activities in what could well become outdoor educational and leisure centres. There will be much reclamation to be done in the reshaping and landscaping of the terrain, and this cannot be done overnight—the example of the planting of trees and the slow growth of natural vegetation on the colliery tips is there before our eyes on the north-east fringe of Mendip. But if gravel pits can be transformed into beautiful landscape features providing for all sorts of recreation, and if open-cast mining sites can be reclaimed into good agricultural land, surely there is hope for the future of Mendip?

The most articulate attack on quarrying activities, and the sharpest criticism of official policies and attitudes, have come from the Mendip Society, which is by far the largest amenity society in the area. It was founded in 1965 as the Mendip Preservation Society, whose declared aim was 'to keep itself informed of anything affecting the rural amenities of the Mendip area and act in any way possible to conserve these amenities'. The society was the first to suggest that Mendip should be declared an Area of Outstanding Natural Beauty and with the Somerset Trust for Nature Conservation it produced a draft proposal for the county council.

As the Mendip Society since 1970, and representing a membership of over 2,000 people, it now proclaims that its broad objective is to preserve the beauty and character of Mendip and its surroundings. This objective it seeks to achieve in various ways: by inspecting the planning registers of the district councils and making representations on proposed developments that appear to conflict with the aims of the society; by investigation into quarrying activities and by discussions on quarrying policy; and by setting out to educate public opinion by a varied programme of lectures and meetings. At local level—there are six local committees representing the whole Mendip area—further meetings and such outdoor activities as walks, rubbish clearance and tree planting have been organised.

The most spectacular effort of the society was the Mendip 71 Exhibition, held at the Bishop's Palace in Wells, which attracted nation-wide publicity and 23,000 visitors in 3 weeks. The aim of the specially designed exhibition (whose material has since been acquired by the Somerset County Council for educational purposes) was to portray the total character of Mendip, to illustrate the pressures affecting that character and to put forward suggestions for the future use of the area. The simultaneous publication of *Man and the Mendips* presented these issues in more permanent form. The title is indeed significant: the society is intensely aware of the impact of man upon Mendip and of the conflicting pressures developing in the area; its intense and disinterested concern for the future is reflected in its activities in moulding and monitoring developments around Mendip. Its most important function may be seen to be its role as watch-dog.

The Mendip Society is concerned with all aspects of conservation. Nature conservation on Mendip is the specific concern of a number of different bodies who are involved in the management of certain areas set aside for their natural beauty and natural history importance. The primary purpose of Nature Reserves is to preserve certain habitats and thus encourage the breeding of wild plants and animals. They are often selected as outstanding examples of particular habitats and particular assemblages of species. Thus, quite apart from the enjoyment of natural beauty and the pleasures of recreation afforded, the reserves provide opportunity for scientific research and educational work. Some of the properties are owned outright; others are held on lease for longer or shorter periods.

The National Trust owns four properties totalling 638 acres: Brean Down, Cheddar Gorge, Ebbor Gorge and Tor Hill, Wells. The Tor Hill property (19½ acres), mainly woodland, preserves the incomparable view of the cathedral and its complex of surrounding buildings from the east, with a distant view of Glastonbury Tor away across the moors. Brean Down (159 acres) is leased to Sedgemoor District Council, which allows it to be used as an open space for the enjoyment of the public; much of the management is carried out by the Somerset Trust for Nature Conservation assisted by various voluntary organisations. Now designated as a Site of Special Scientific Interest, Brean Down was one of the first bird sanctuaries, established by the RSPB in 1912 and guarded for 40 years by the late Harry Cox.

Ebbor Gorge was presented to the National Trust in 1967 by Mrs G. W. Hodgkinson in memory of Sir Winston Churchill; 116 acres of woodland, rock and scree are managed as a National Nature Reserve by the Nature Conservancy Council, which has established a car-park and picnic area beside the Priddy road, and way-marked certain paths which are quite distinct from the public footpaths that make their way up and over the hill. At Cheddar the Trust owns a stretch of land

(318 acres) extending about 2½ miles up the Gorge on the north side of the road as far as Wellington Farm.

At Black Rock, near the top of the Gorge, 121 acres of the National Trust's Cheddar property are managed and controlled by the Somerset Trust for Nature Conservation, and within this reserve they have set out a Nature Trail 1½ miles long. Adjoining this reserve are the 42 acres of the Long Wood Nature Reserve, which is also managed by the Somerset Trust and is primarily an educational reserve, with a Nature Trail attracting upwards of 10,000 people a year. Another 42 acres in Velvet Bottom have now been leased by the Somerset Trust and designated as a Nature Reserve: here also there will be a Nature Trail.

The Nature Conservancy Council and the Somerset Trust also manage other reserves. Stoke Wood is managed by the Nature Conservancy Council: 86 acres on the Limestone slopes above Rodney Stoke, a fine example of dry Mendip woodland with much ash. Four more reserves managed by the Somerset Trust are set aside for more special study, and permits must be obtained for visits. There are 33 acres of Asham Wood, leased from one of the quarry companies; Chantry Lake and Woods, available to small groups for specified study; about 2 acres of woodland near Kilmersdon used as a study area by a local school; and Mascall's Wood, near Cheddar, bought by the Somerset Trust in 1974.

At Ubley Warren Farm, near Charterhouse, the University of Bristol manages an 80 acre reserve which includes some of the spectacular area known as the Rakes—winding rocky chasms pitted with old mining shafts now covered with protective grids. This reserve adjoins, and can be used in conjunction with, the Blackmoor Educational Nature Reserve, 60 acres of woodland, marsh and old minery, owned by Somerset County Council. Nearby is the field centre at Charterhouse School (see p 196), which upwards of 4,000 children from every part of Somerset are now visiting every year to enjoy part of their education in the very heart of Mendip.

The designation in 1975 of Velvet Bottom as a Nature Reserve links up the Charterhouse reserves with those around Cheddar Gorge, producing a major wild life area of almost 600 acres. The problem with this area is that visitors, increasing in number year by year, are already doing damage to the very features of the environment that are being conserved for their benefit. Trampling, litter, fire hazards and downright vandalism conflict with the enhancement of natural beauty and the conservation of wild life with which the various organisations are concerned. This was the main reason for the appointment in 1975 by the Somerset Trust of a part-time naturalist ranger, and for an attempt to bring the whole area under a unified nature conservation management.

'From every part of Somerset' does not now mean quite the same as it did a few years ago, for the western end of Mendip and the villages under the northern escarpment as far east as the Harptrees (including about one-third of the Area of Outstanding Natural Beauty) are now in Avon. The divided responsibility for the provision of educational and recreational amenities for Mendip, and the question mark hanging over the area *as a whole*, cause some uneasiness. One can at present only wait and see what degree of co-ordination develops between the county authorities of Somerset and Avon, and indeed between the new district councils along the hill: Woodspring, Sedgemoor and Wansdyke, who all march with Mendip.

This study of Mendip is concerned with the future in so far as it can be seen to derive from present-day trends, which are themselves often dependent upon the accidents or designs of past history. How far will the Mendip which we know survive the pressures which are now being brought to bear upon it—in particular, the escalation of quarrying and tourism, and the conflicting demands for recreation in the face of population growth and greater mobility? My own strong conviction is that the essential character of Mendip will survive: the upstanding western hills with their thin flowery turf and their fresh sea-borne breezes; the isolated farms of the high plateau with their windbreaks, the dry stone walls marching beside the long straight roads with their wide grass verges, the areas of gruffy ground (unlikely ever to be reclaimed), the heather-topped sandstone summits, and farther east the deep wooded and well-watered valleys with their remote and largely unspoiled villages.

From Cottle's Ash to the Black Rock is a comparatively small area—the plateau itself at its widest is no more than 4 miles across—but it is fragile and precious: it has not got the grandeur of areas like Dartmoor or the Lakes or the Yorkshire Dales, but it does offer extraordinary variety close-packed within this limited area.

To appreciate the essential character and variety of Mendip one needs to climb to some of the high places from which such panoramic views are to be enjoyed: to Wavering Down with the pattern of the broken western hills, and Brean Down thrusting out into the Bristol Channel, the low moors threaded by the Axe, which has itself emerged from the bowels of the hill, and the great bulk of Mendip curving away south-eastwards; or to Deerleap above Wookey Hole, which looks across Ebbor Gorge to a distant glimpse of Wells and along the southern face of the hill to Shepton Mallet and beyond; or to the top of Harptree Hill where the old road to Bristol drops off the ridge towards the Chew Valley Lake, and one is surrounded by new enclosures and unreclaimed gruffy ground; or farther to the east, to Beacon Hill or Cranmore Tower, where the range begins to fall away and the quarries are clustered thick upon the ground and valleys strike away north and south, and looking back along the range one sees the 900ft BBC mast on Pen Hill, pencilled bright and glittering in the smokeless air, the symbol of a new age rising above the strata of history and pre-history to face what Hardy so unerringly described as 'the gusts on Mendip ridge'.

Notes to this chapter are on page 277.

10

Gazetteer

Robin Atthill

NOTES

(1) The National Grid references are all ST, and pinpoint the parish church, or, if there is no church, the central point of the place to be described. At Frome, Shepton Mallet and Wells the reference is to the market place.

(2) Place-names: except for certain amplification in cases where there is good authority for including another explanation, the interpretation of the place-names is based on Ekwall, *The Concise Oxford Dictionary of English Place-names* (fourth edition, 1970) published by the Oxford University Press, to whom I am grateful for permission to make use of this material.

SOURCES

In about thirty of the eighty-five places described in the Gazetteer, booklets or leaflets in some form or other are available in the church, sometimes dealing with parish history as well. For the rest, see Pevsner, *The Buildings of England, North Somerset and Bristol* (Penguin, 1958), and *South and West Somerset* (1958) for Brean, North Wootton, Pilton and Evercreech. The most useful guidebooks and topographical works are mentioned in the Notes to Chapter 1. A number of short parish histories have been published, generally privately, often by Women's Institutes: most of these are available at the Local History Library, Taunton Castle. Few villages are lucky enough to have had full-length histories or studies published: Theodore Compton's *A Mendip Valley* (1892) is a collection of Winscombe sketches; J. D. C. Wickham's *Records by Spade and Terrier* (c 1912) deals with the Holcombe area; Lord Hylton's *History of Kilmersdon* (1910) and F. W. Cleverdon's *History of Mells* (Frome Society, 1974) are thorough pieces of historical research. F. A. Knight's *The Seaboard of Mendip* (1902) and *The Heart of Mendip* (1915) deal very fully with all the parishes from Cheddar and Burrington westwards, including Charterhouse-on-Mendip.

Ashwick (637484): the *wic* or settlement by the ash trees

On the NE slopes of the Masbury ridge, the large civil parish stretches as far as the Roman Fosse Way to include Oakhill and Gurney Slade as well as the hamlets of Neighbourne, Benter and Nettlebridge in their deep valley networked with lanes. This valley is well timbered, fringed with hanging woodlands, largely of ash, as if the medieval clearances had got so far and no farther. Beyond this valley is typical Mendip upland of the age of enclosure, rising to nearly 1,000ft above sea level on the golf course.

There is no village, only a widely scattered community. Near the church is Ashwick Court (c 1700); the ruins of John Billingsley's home lie near the head of Ashwick Grove, a heavily wooded gorge running away NE. The industrial archaeologist gratefully records evidence of vanished breweries, corn mills, iron works and coal workings, but the last colliery (Moorewood) closed in 1933, and a scrapyard occupies the site.

Formerly a chapel-of-ease to Kilmersdon, Ashwick only became a parish in 1826: apart from the C15 tower, the church is a dignified Victorian building (1876–81) by Browne & Gill of Bath, with columns of 'Draycott Marble' in the nave.

Axbridge (432546): the *burh* or township overlooking the Axe (see p 86)

Ever since its origin as a fortified township and as a market town serving the Saxon royal palace at Cheddar, Axbridge has been a place of importance: with a population of only 1,000 it has for centuries been a town rather than a village; until 1883 it had a mayor and corporation; until 1974 it was the seat of a rural district council.

Crammed between the steep hillside to the N and the low-lying moors to the S, Axbridge could never expand: its single winding street opens up into the little market place over which the noble church presides. From above the church—better still from its tower—one looks down upon the clustering steep-roofed houses, with long strips of garden behind: a medieval pattern dating from the time of Axbridge's prosperity in the woollen trade. Much earlier building is concealed behind the sober C17 or Georgian fronts, eg the manor house. High Street winds imperceptibly into West Street, off which is the grim block of the Axbridge Union (1837) now used for hospital management. Moorland Street—Moor Lane—drops quickly to the levels which were not drained and enclosed until the early C19: St Mary's Street becomes Cheddar Street and peters out fairly soon. The market place is the heart of Axbridge, with its old inns, its town hall of 1830 and the curving flight of steps fashioned of local Conglomerate which lead the eye upward to the church—a cruciform Perpendicular building and one of Mendip's splendours. Entered through the richly ornamented s porch, the body of the church is breathtakingly beautiful: light floods in through the great Perpendicular windows, and one notes the wooden aisle roofs, the plastered nave roof with its fantastic pendants dated 1636, the fan-vaulting under the central tower and the profusion of C17-18 monuments, and much more besides.

Through traffic now roars along the bypass, opened in 1967 on the bed of the abandoned Cheddar Valley railway, past the fine gabled station building opened with such a flourish in 1869. Without this traffic, peace has been restored to Axbridge, where we see an almost completely unspoiled C18-19 market town: no local industry except market gardening replaced the woollen trade. Framing the entrance to the square from the w is a group of C15 houses, the most spectacular of which is the magnificent timber-framed building with jutting upper storeys, dating from c 1500, but known as 'King John's Hunting Lodge': this now contains the museum full of vivid reminders of Axbridge's long and interesting past.

Babington (705570): the settlement of Babba's people

Babington stands on a little plateau on one of the NE outliers of Mendip, looking across to Ammerdown and to Cranmore Tower, and eastwards beyond Frome to Cley Hill and the Wiltshire downs. The tiny parish once included Newbury with its colliery and the eastern part of Coleford right down to the river. Throughout the C19 the population hardly ever exceeded 200, and now, shared out between Kilmersdon and Coleford, all that remains of Babington is a church and a manor house, approached along an avenue of beeches. A perfect tiny Georgian church of 1750, with clear glass windows, moulded plaster ceiling, a delicately gilded and blue-domed apse and all the original woodwork—the whole carefully restored and lovingly maintained—it stands on the lawn in front of the beautifully proportioned manor house which belonged to the Longs and the Knatchbulls, built and tiled with local oolite: a serenely satisfying pair of buildings that complement one another.

Banwell (399591): Bana's spring or stream, or the felon stream, *bana* signifying murderer

An aura of antiquity surrounds Banwell—prehistoric earthworks, caves full of bones, Roman sites and narrow winding streets that desperately need to be bypassed by the grinding main road traffic. From

Banwell Hill one looks down on the old village, dominated by the lofty church tower and centred on the springs that rose to feed the village pond: here once were mills and a brewery, where today is a bowling green. The side streets like Church Street and High Street are trim and quiet; the main street is noisy and frankly scruffy, as if despairing of the bypass. Modern housing estates line the Weston road, but Banwell still retains the air of a village. The huge parish stretches out across the moors to include hamlets like Wolvers Hill, West Wick, Way Wick and Rolstone; to the w the M5 closely follows the parish boundary down to the Lox Yeo.

The church stands proudly in its large churchyard which slopes towards the moors. The 100ft tower and the main fabric are C15 work; the interior is lofty and airy with a stone pulpit similar to Bleadon's, C15 pews and a magnificent rood-screen of seven bays dated 1520–5. Next to the church is 'The Abbey', a reconstruction of the C15 Bishop's Palace of Banwell; 'The Castle', however, is purely Victorian. Bishop Law and his son built 'The Caves' early in the C19, planting the woods and the pleasure grounds with their various follies: from the old race-course at the E end of the hill there are magnificent views in almost every direction.

Batcombe (690390): Bata's valley (name recurs twice near Cheddar)

Approached from every direction by steep hills, Batcombe is a beautiful village in a beautiful situation, lying along the deep valley of the tributary of the Alham among the unspoiled broken hill country of SE Mendip. The magnificent church speaks of past prosperity, derived from the woollen mills along the river. Batcombe was a Glastonbury manor that came to the Bisses, the great clothiers whose memorials are in the church, and one of whom added the s porch to the church in 1629. With the decay of the woollen industry in the C18, Batcombe became a purely agricultural village and has so remained, though now residential as well. The village is smaller than it looks, though the main street straggles along the hillside for nearly a mile from Eastcombe (once Ashcombe) to Westcombe, with many good stone cottages and several notable larger houses, all built of mellow golden oolite. So is the church, a lofty Perpendicular building with a tremendous w tower completed c 1540: rich fenestration, no pinnacles, a figure of Christ attended by six flying angels on the w front as at Chewton Mendip—striking from every angle, best perhaps from below Back Lane, or from Portway, the steep lane to Bruton which was once the turnpike road from Frome.

Westcombe (676392): lying to the w of Batcombe from which it is separated by the steep Alham valley

Though always linked with Batcombe, Westcombe feels like a village in its own right, a stone-built Mendip village looking across the valley to Creech Hill. A number of the cottages have been tastefully tarted up, but Westcombe House, a Georgian mansion, has been demolished except for the converted stables, below which are a grotto and some rustic walks—in a landscaped park which includes a lake formed by damming the Alham.

Binegar (615494): Benagre on the C17 Communion plate, Benhangre in 1176, the slope where beans grew

A shapeless village with no visible centre; the parish stretches this way and that as far as Old Down. Where Binegar ends and Gurney Slade begins is anyone's guess: much of Gurney Slade is in Binegar parish, much of Binegar is in Emborough parish—Binegar Green for instance, and the housing estate at Dalleston (named after a local quarry owner) facing the Portway. Lower down the hill—for Binegar is a bleak upland village on the edge of the plateau—are grouped church, rectory and school; past a grim row of redbrick houses beside the derelict railway line the road slips past the Horse and Jockey into Kingscombe and Gurney Slade. The church, which may originally have served a number of scattered settlements, is a Victorian rebuild (1858) except for the plain Perpendicular tower. Binegar today is an agricultural and quarrying community; but Binegar Fair packed up in the 1950s, Read's quarry is worked out and filled with colliery spoil, and the vanished railway station once handled most of the output of Oakhill brewery.

Blagdon (504589): the black hill, ie Black Down

The parish extends from N of the River Yeo up over Black Down to the top of Cheddar Gorge and the Yoxter ranges, including Charterhouse. Every approach to Blagdon is exciting and spectacular, whether along the wooded parklike combe from Rickford past Oatley's mock-Tudor Coombe Lodge, now the Further Education Staff College, or dropping off the Mendip plateau with the church tower seen against the background of lake and tumbling hills. From the Butcombe side one gets the clearest picture of the village sprawling against the lower slopes of Black Down: Day & Masters' map of 1782—and Day was a Blagdon man—shows three separate communities: East End, West End and Street End. In a sense this is still true, High Street, with its lack of purpose and its very nondescript and undistinguished architecture, merely linking three much more interesting areas. Street End, a huddle of old and new cottages, climbs steeply past the large new hotel with the panoramic view to reach the new enclosures on Mendip; West End has the village hall, the nonconformist churches, shops, pubs, the stuccoed Regency Court, and a network of lanes and old cottages (such as the delightful Bell Square) as well as much new housing. Across the steep little valley East End has more shops, more pubs, the village school and the parish church, rebuilt in 1909, apart from its lofty tower, in the best Somerset tradition, both in its stone and its woodwork, largely the gift and itself the memorial of members of the Wills family. It groups well with a lot of pleasing colour-washed houses in winding lanes, a prosperous and attractive area, for Bristol is only 14 miles away and much new housing has sprung up. Curiously enough the village never spread downhill to the railway which served Blagdon 1901-31; the station survives as part of a private house, close to the fine redbrick stone-faced pumping station below the dam at the bottom of the lake.

Bleadon (342569): Bleodun—*bleo*=colour—the coloured down, mottled green and grey where limestone outcrops

The village became a quiet backwater once the traffic to and from Weston had been channelled across the level, but it is almost unrecognisable to one who knew it before the last war. The agglomeration of new housing has almost smothered the pattern of the original settlement on the lower slope of the hill, and only a few farms and colour-washed cottages seem to have survived. From South Hill one gets a superb panorama of hills far and near: at one's feet the moors, the rhines, the serpentine Axe which was navigable until 1802—a quarry and concrete works too. To the N, the church with its lofty triple-windowed tower of typical West Mendip design dominates the village, with new housing all round and climbing the hill past the ancient field-system. The church itself, approached past a fine cross, is full of light and air with white walls and plastered wagon-roof; there is a stone pulpit like that at Banwell, and a simple war memorial framed in the arcade of what once must have been a N aisle above a cill of medieval tiles. From Bleadon Hill one looks w into Wales and E towards the main Mendip massif.

Brean (284590): a Celtic name, linked with Welsh *bre* or *bryn*=hill

The village of Brean, now little more than an interminable holiday camp stretching along the coast road behind the sand dunes, does not belong to Mendip. But Brean Down does, for apart from the island of Steep Holm it is the last stubborn upthrust of the limestone mass that first emerged 30 miles to the E near Frome. It is a great whaleback of a headland, rising 321ft above the sea with splendid cliffs on either side and nearly 2 miles long: National Trust property, a bird sanctuary and a Nature Reserve, covered with archaeological sites and tipped by the unexpected remains of a fort built in 1867 against threatened invasion. World War II brought more military installations. It takes a long time to get to Brean Down, except by ferry when running, by way of Bleadon or Lympsham, but it is worth every minute of the journey for the sake of walking over the short turf, savouring the wonderful views in every direction, and watching Mendip going down so bravely into the sea.

Burrington (479593): the settlement by the burg, the Iron Age camp on high ground above the village

The parish includes the summit of Black Down, the highest point on Mendip, the hamlets of Bourne and Rickford, well wooded and watered, and reaches down into the Yeo valley across the A38 to include parts of Langford. Burrington is best known for its rocky combe, honeycombed with caves, and for the splendid stretch of common land, known as Burrington Ham, looking over the Yeo valley and up to Black Down. The village itself is a cul-de-sac and remains largely unspoiled, with colour-washed houses or cottages built of local Conglomerate. The church and the Georgian vicarage are on the w fringe, looking across fields to the wooded slopes where Mendip Lodge once stood. The church, standing in a beautiful churchyard, contains too much Victorian glass, but much good modern woodwork: otherwise a simple Perpendicular building with good roof supported by angel figures; outside there are fierce gargoyles and a lofty spirelet on the rood-stair turret.

Chantry (719471): The Chantry was built c 1825 on land which belonged to a C14 chantry chapel in Whatley church

In 1846 the hamlet of Little Elm found itself metamorphosed into the new parish of Chantry. The ironmaster James Fussell had built a Georgian mansion in a small park with a lake which was both ornamental and a source of power for his edge-tool works in the valley. The Fussells also founded the parish and built the church—an early Gothic revival design by Gilbert Scott, with a neat crocketed spirelet and a profusion of carving including angels holding edge-tools and other ironmongery—and also the school, a pioneer comprehensive school (1857) which included in one building an infant school, a national school, an industrial school and a boarding school for girls. A few old cottages and an inn at Little Elm are the nucleus of what is still no more than a scattered hamlet on the old ridge road from Frome to Wells, now almost ringed by quarries with the accompanying noise and dirt.

Charterhouse (502556): the Carthusians of Witham had a cell or a grange here

The heart of Mendip: a scattered settlement surrounded by prehistoric and Roman remains where lead was worked for centuries until the 1880s, set in a wide empty landscape of rolling heather-covered or stone-walled hills, looking s over Velvet Bottom towards Cheddar Gorge and N on to Black Down, past isolated farms sheltering behind their windbreaks—a bleak, lonely world with its own fascination. The oldest houses, Manor Farm (a C17 building perhaps on the site of the Carthusian settlement) and Lower Farm, lie in sheltered hollows. The school is now an outdoor activity centre, and the Blackmoor Educational Nature Reserve extends over part of the old minery. W. D. Caroe's little church built in 1908 is a landmark: a simple, rough-cast building with a tiny spire, and a delicately carved screen in the homely interior—dedicated to St Hugh, once Prior- of Witham, to whom Charterhouse belonged.

Cheddar (459530): Ceodre, from OE *ceod,* a pouch, referring to the caves or the gorge

By 1801 Cheddar was a large sprawling village of 1,150 people; by 1901 the population had doubled, and today it is nearly 4,000, but still an enormous sprawling village rather than a town, in the middle of an enormous parish that stretches from the Axe up to Black Down and Stowbarrow on the top of Mendip. Bounded on the w by the New Road, built by the Wedmore Turnpike Trust in 1827 as a through road to Bristol, Cheddar has steadily expanded, as Axbridge could not, to fill the little plateau lying at the foot of the high hills. On the southernmost point above the moors—where Hythe was Cheddar's port until about 1800—the site of a Roman villa and a Saxon palace (marked out in front of the Kings of Wessex School), the parish church and the market cross, show where the original settlement was. Day & Masters' map of 1782 shows that the village had already spread up the slope towards the cliffs, where the Yeo worked a number of mills, including three paper mills. Tourists in search of The Picturesque were already visiting Cheddar, and the arrival of the railway in 1869 gave impetus to a wave of Victorian building. In the motor age the favourite approach is down the Gorge where cafes and gift shops have proliferated to welcome a million tourists a year.

The pleasantest approach to Cheddar is from the E, along the Wells road, or from Bradley Cross down Redcliffe Street, or along the Lippiat, with a wonderful view of the C17 hall surrounded by bungalow development. But Cheddar is worth exploring—on foot and out of season. There are many interesting buildings, from the derelict Bristol & Exeter station to the uncompromisingly modern Cave Man restaurant at the foot of the Gorge. There are old cottages dotted about everywhere, even in the shopping centre: Church Street, Lower North Street and Kent Street are full of pleasant houses—all pleasanter than Cliff Street, though farther up, the traffic can be avoided by a footpath along the stream which has been landscaped by Bristol Waterworks. There is Hannah More's school, and the Motor Museum—and the churches: the parish church, notable for its rich and lofty Perpendicular tower and the pierced parapets which bring an overall sense of unity to the several chantry chapels and porches, and inside for the gilded and painted roof and the stone pulpit—a spacious and light building with many interesting features. There is also a large Victorian Methodist church in local stone; a lofty gabled Catholic church, opened in 1966, in Tweentown; and a Baptist church of 1831 in Lower North Street, bright and light with all its original furniture.

At the top of the village, Warrens Hill is noisy with lorries from the vast Batts Combe quarry which scars the hillside; Tuttons Hill leads to the Tower Testing Station in the abandoned Chelm's Combe quarry. Sheltered by these mountainous rocky slopes, Cheddar has grown and flourished, thanks mainly to the spectacular scenery of England's grand canyon and the caves that were discovered and opened up in the last century. From Tuttons Hill one can see the whole pattern of Cheddar, from the Reservoir, dotted perhaps with sailing craft, across the market gardens with their cloches glittering in the sunlight, across areas of new housing, to the church tower, a mile and more away, and Nyland Hill rising from the misty moors.

Chesterblade (661412): the *blaed* or terrace near the fort or camp

A hamlet, and a small hamlet at that, approached by muddy lanes, in the beautiful broken hill country s of the main E Mendip ridge. A few grey cottages and farms perch on the slope looking across to the Bronze Age camp on Small Down, and through the hills to Evercreech, to which Chesterblade belongs. The tiny church, rebuilt in 1888, is whitewashed and neat within, with a good C12 s door and stone pulpit and reading desk, standing at the crossroads in the middle of this remote and unspoiled settlement.

Chewton Mendip (596531): the settlement on the River Chew

Almost always one's first glimpse of Chewton is of the magnificent church tower—perhaps the finest of all the Mendip towers—126ft high, standing alone above the village and approached by footpaths from every direction—a superb design, with a rich crown and flying angels carved on the w front. The interior, despite some interesting features, is disappointing: heavily restored and dark, with much C19 glass. The Waldegraves have owned Chewton from 1553, but did not live here till the 1860s when Frances Waldegrave, the dazzling Victorian hostess, built the mock-Tudor priory, now demolished. The village itself lies mostly in a shallow valley below the so-called Celtic fields and the long barrow on Chew Down from whose flank the Chew emerges, crystal-clear, flowing over a ford and under a twin-arched stone footbridge. Grey cottages stretch along the Bristol–Wells road and down the valley towards Litton, and there are more old cottages on The Folly. Bathway, with its Methodist church, and Cutler's Green, are separate hamlets, and the enormous parish stretching far up on Mendip includes Priddy Circles and Nine Barrows and most of the lead mining area between Priddy and Green Ore, as well as the less well known industrial site at Tor Hole.

Chilcompton (647524): the settlement in the combe, perhaps the manor of a child or youth of noble birth

The original settlement in the valley was grouped round the mill which has now disappeared, the Jacobean manor house (1611), now a farm, and the church, which apart from the tower is a fine spacious Victorian piece of rebuilding, lofty and light, with a splendid ring of bells. The stream tumbles over a series of miniature waterfalls beside the village street—described by Coleridge in 1794 in his *Lines to a Beautiful Spring in a Village* (which he called Kirkhampton). There are several good houses here, but later the village climbed up Bowden Hill towards the Somerset & Dorset Railway station, and finally ribbon-developed along the Bath–Wells road. This is all the passing motorist is likely to see, dominated by the crane in the timberyard. One or two other small industries have become established here, though New Rock colliery closed in 1968. The valley is more truly rural, though a good deal of new housing has sprung up there, separated by a narrow green belt from Midsomer Norton.

Christon (379573): the settlement by the *cruc* or hill; Crook Peak faces the village across the valley

The M5 thrusting down the Lox Yeo valley has destroyed the peace of a thousand years at Christon, which is a small, a very small village—though there is evidence on the ground that the medieval village was much larger—sheltering under the hill and looking down to the river. It consists of a scatter of houses along a winding lane, and a C17 Court with a gazebo, overlooking the road by a Victorian letter-box and a cast-iron pump with a stone trough. In the churchyard stand splendid yew trees: the church itself is Norman, overlaid with Victorian restoration in neo-Norman. The richly carved s door is hooded by a cavernous stone porch: gargoyles drip from the squat square tower, and inside, the ribs of the vaulted crossing rise from splendid dragons. The total impression is one of permanence and serenity.

Churchill (437602): the first syllable perhaps derives from *cruc*=hill, cf Christon, Crook Peak

s of Churchill Gate the A38 cuts through the N flank of Mendip between the Iron Age camps of Dolebury and Dinghurst: along this road lies the newer part of the village, noisy and bungaloid, Bristol commuter country running on into Lower Langford. The original village lies off the Weston road, with a pleasant street punctuated by the Jubilee clock tower, the Wesleyan church and Cottage Homes, all built of local Conglomerate. The parish church stands apart from the village, where Windmill Hill falls away to the moors, and overlooks the walled garden of Churchill Court. Stone effigies of the Fitzpaynes, who occupied the court in the C14, greet one in the church porch, but the church itself is a rather undistinguished Perpendicular building with a plain tower, though it contains some good woodwork and interesting memorials. Nearby, on the road to Churchill Green, is the new comprehensive school which also serves as a community centre for a wide area.

Cloford (726440): the ford where burdock grew—OE Clatford, where *clate*=burdock

A large ecclesiastical parish, but part of the civil parish of Wanstrow, lying across the upper waters of the Nunney Brook from Asham Wood to Postlebury: an open, sparsely populated area even with the hamlets of Holwell and Leighton—the latter, sombre and sad, almost depopulated within living memory. Cloford itself was once much larger, but now there are only a few farms on the common, a few cottages—and a Victorian letter-box by the little church. From here one looks across the site of the lost medieval village, across the brook to the fine C17 manor house now surrounded by enormous modern farm buildings, and beyond that to the scars and dust of the quarries and a distant glimpse of Cranmore tower. The Horners were lords of the manor, commemorated

46 Smitham Hill chimney in the Forestry Commission plantation above East Harptree: the most conspicuous relic of the lead mining industry, recently restored by the Mendip Society

47 The BBC mast on Pen Hill seen from the Iron Age hill-fort at Maesbury

48 Merehead Quarry near Cranmore with its new rail-link to the East Somerset branch from Witham

49 Sunshine and shadow in the cathedral cloister at Wells

by their arms on the w front of the tower and by two C17 monuments in the church which was rebuilt by the Victorians except for the tower: a dark interior with an over-ornate chancel, but lit by oil lamps and gaily painted candlesticks attached to the pews.

Coleford (687490): the ford over which charcoal was carried—or where coal was found

Now a large and thriving community with solid areas of postwar housing and a population of nearly 2,000, Coleford has grown from a cramped hillside hamlet looking across the Nettlebridge river towards Leigh on the main E Mendip ridge. Traces of the medieval chapel served by Glastonbury have been detected in secular buildings in the Barton, but later, Coleford was regarded as part of Kilmersdon until it became a parish in 1843. Originally it was a mining settlement—coal was got here from the C14 onwards with considerable escalation in the C18–19. (A stone and concrete works occupies the site of Newbury, the last colliery to close, in 1927.) By then the village had spread up and along the Highbury ridge where several terraces date from the 1870s. Highbury is rather depressing—a long straggle in every sort of style and material, some grim council housing at either end, and private development at Goodeaves and at Farley Dell, where there is a maze of jazzy suburban dwellings among which the British Legion Club and the Bishop Henderson School stand out. Halfway down the hill the 1831 Gothic, or rather Gothick, church with its neat little tower stands on a green knoll looking up the valley. The interior is surprising, a single wide cell, spacious and unusual rather than conventionally beautiful. Keith New's King Saul window commemorates Coleford's most famous son, William Marchant Jones, better known as Jarge Balsh. The rest of the village huddles picturesquely along the steep hillside with a towering Wesleyan chapel, pubs and shops along the narrow winding street built mostly of local brown ironstone. Two mills survive, and at the w end, below the aqueduct, the most spectacular relic of the canal which was built to serve the collieries and left unfinished c 1800, is a sudden flowering of bijou properties: against all the odds Coleford has become residentially desirable.

Compton Bishop (396554): the settlement in the combe that runs up into the hills; the manor belonged to the Bishop of Bath and Wells

A large parish extending from the Axe to the summit of Crook Peak and Wavering Down to include the hamlets of Webbington (with its Country Club and the kennels of the Weston & Banwell Harriers),

Rackley, once a port on the old course of the Axe, and Cross. There are new houses and market gardens along the road from Cross, but the old village lies in its secluded valley surrounded by the bare hills, with a fine C17 manor farm and cottages dotted about the lanes. The church stands at the head of the valley, guarded by sombre yews and cypresses and a splendid cross, which is framed by the C13 porch with a trefoiled arch and Purbeck marble shafts: in fact much of the work is earlier than the general run of Mendip churches, and this goes for the plain w tower. A spacious, light interior from which one looks out through plain glass windows to the gorse-covered slopes of the down. There is one of the C15 stone pulpits common round w Mendip, and an exquisite stained-glass panel of the Trinity high up in the E window. In all, a place that maintains a pervasive atmosphere of peaceful seclusion.

Compton Martin (545570): the settlement in the combe, belonging to Robert Martin temp. Henry I

A street village lying along the A368 under the steep slopes of Compton Wood into which the Combe plunges: a self-contained village nearly a mile long from the council houses to Georgian Highfield House. The street contains many pleasant colour-washed houses (such as Earls Farm and the Ring of Bells), behind which there is some discreet development. Up Rectory Lane there is an air of commuter prosperity spreading out from Bristol, but humbler settlements climb up Highfield Lane around that odd patch of unenclosed ground known as the Wrangle, with superb views over the Lakes. The centre of the village is marked by the pond with its old pump—once there was a paper mill here—the post office, the school (now the Church Room) and the church itself, perched on the Batch. The church is one of Mendip's prime glories, beautifully cared for and beautifully appointed, with good C17 woodwork and a sturdy Perpendicular tower, but primarily a Norman building with impressive ribbed vaulting in the chancel, deeply splayed windows and a famous twisted pillar in the nave. The parish stretches right up on to the high Mendip plateau and down into the valley, past the moated medieval Bickfield Farm, to include a third of the Chew Valley Lake, the building of which drowned the outlying hamlet of Moreton.

Cranmore: the cranes' mere or lake; cf Merehead where there is evidence that there was once a lake

The two villages lie pleasantly sheltered by the easy southern slopes of the main E Mendip ridge. Apart from the quarries—one abandoned

(Waterlip), the other in full production (Merehead)—they are purely agricultural villages.

East Cranmore (681438) consists of a few scattered farms and the large park belonging to Cranmore Hall, once the home of the Pagets, a Jacobean-neo-Jacobean mansion, now a private school. The little Gothic revival church (1846) by T. H. Wyatt has been declared redundant and converted into a dwelling. On the skyline 925ft above sea level stands Cranmore Tower, an Italianate Victorian folly also designed by T. H. Wyatt for the Pagets in 1862. The line of the Roman road from Charterhouse joins the main road just E of the toll-house built by the Shepton Mallet Turnpike Trust.

West Cranmore (668433) is more of a village, but a small one. The Perpendicular church built of Doulting stone has a good triple-windowed w tower with fan-vaulting. Southill House (late Georgian), for long the home of the Strodes, stands in its park beyond the railway. Cranmore station, once busy with stone traffic, now houses a Steam Centre as an attraction for railway fans.

Croscombe (591444): originally *corfweges* combe, the valley of the pass road

The parish stretches up to include parts of Maesbury Camp and the Mendip golf course, but Croscombe itself is a compact village, built along the river and climbing a little way up both sides of its narrow steep-sided valley. Viewed from Paradise Hill on the old Wells road, it seems focused on the spire of the parish church, round which clusters the older part of the village with its stone cross. From the churchyard there is a delightful roofscape of the old houses in the winding main street, mostly built of local Conglomerate, many of them with mullioned windows, including one or two notable larger houses such as the old manor at the E end. The river crosses and recrosses the road, various leats marking the sites of vanished mills, for Croscombe was a flourishing centre of the woollen industry until the C19, as evidenced by the roof bosses and the Bisse memorials in the church. This is basically a C15 building, outstandingly beautiful, light and airy, and full of Jacobean woodwork—screen, pulpit and box-pews—a magnificently impressive set of furnishings from the years of prosperity. Close to the church was the medieval manor house of the Paltons: part of it incongruously became a Baptist chapel, and is now being reconverted into a dwelling.

Cross (419548): referring to crossroads, or a wayside cross, or perhaps to Crook Peak

Now a considerable roadside hamlet towards the E edge of Compton Bishop parish, sheltered by Wavering Down to the N and looking down across the Axe on to the moors, Cross was formerly of some importance as a post town and coaching station on the Bridgwater road. Now mercifully it is bypassed by the A38. The two coaching inns survive, along with some older houses on the N side of the street, but to the s there is modern bungaloid development. Two former industries can be glimpsed in the abandoned quarry on the hillside and in traces of Collings' brewery incorporated in the buildings of a riding school.

Dinder (575446): Denrenn, the house in the valley (OE *denu*)

Though the parish includes half of Maesbury Camp, 958ft above sea level, Dinder is a village in a valley, lying snugly between the N slope of Dulcote Hill and the hanging woods of Lyatt and Sharcombe. The parklike feeling derives from two large houses: Sharcombe (c 1830), and Dinder House (1801–3 with harmonious Victorian additions)—for long the home of the Somervilles. Doulting water *(alias* the Sheppey) flows through the park over cascades and under a balustraded bridge. The village itself, quiet and tidy, stands off the main road, with a single-sided street and a number of lanes that are mainly cul-de-sacs, with pleasant cottages built of local Conglomerate and larger houses of various periods and styles sitting comfortably together. The C15 church stands a little apart, close to Dinder House: well restored and well cared for, plain but satisfying without and within.

Doulting (646431): like Dulcote, called after the river, a British name meaning dirty river

Standing at the source of the so-called River Sheppey on the main road to Frome, Doulting has several titles to fame: St Aldhelm died in the church here in 709; and for at least 800 years the honey-coloured oolite has been dug from the quarries as building stone of the highest quality. The village is at the centre of a large parish with many outlying hamlets, extending w to the Fosse Way, N to the Beacon, and s past Prestleigh to include most of the Bath and West Show ground and the lonely eminences of Maes Down and Whitstone Hill. On the latter the Hundred stone survives, as well as several old boundary stones on the perimeter of the parish.

Doulting is a seemly village, though it suffers from the heavy stone and holiday traffic along the A361: it is built almost entirely of the local stone—church, manor (formerly the vicarage), manor farm with its great C15 tithe barn, inn, school and cottages. Even the council estate along the road past the quarries blends in, though there is an unfortunate line of bungalows before Chelynch is reached. The exterior of the stone-tiled cruciform church is striking, with an elaborate s porch, and a spire—a great landmark—rising above an octagonal tower. The interior is disappointingly dark, and was over-restored in 1869, though it is worth careful examination: the Pagets of Cranmore were lords of the manor, and their memorials fill the s transept. Beyond the immaculately kept churchyard with its C15 cross is the Georgian manor; beyond that is St Aldhelm's Well, above the steep little valley which contains the remains of Coombs' edge-tool works.

Downhead (692462): the top of the down: rolling wooded landscape falling away from Cranmore Tower

A remote village with a few scattered farms and cottages; a tiny church, which has a small Perpendicular tower with splendid gargoyles (the body was rebuilt in 1751), stands beside the manor farm and has an uninterrupted view across gentle green fields. The basalt quarries are closed, but the new workings to the s and e threaten to advance upon the village.

Downside: to avoid confusion, it seems wise to distinguish between three distinct Downsides on e Mendip—all hillside settlements

(i) 624448: A hamlet immediately N of Shepton Mallet on the Bath road: some old grey houses, some modern bungalows, a small rope factory (with the remains of an old ropewalk), a pub and a farm or two, including outlying Millbrook, now the divisional office of the Bristol Waterworks, and Winsor Hill where the C17 mansion of the Longs crumbles into ruin beside the abandoned quarries and the abandoned railway. Downside House, where Monmouth rested for a few hours after Sedgemoor with Edward Strode, stands beside the main road.

(ii) 641504: The southern area of Chilcompton, a long ribbon of C20 housing, leading to the original Downside, a couple of farms, where in 1845 a church and vicarage were built as the centre of a new ecclesiastical parish carved out of Midsomer Norton, stretching past the Iron Age fortress on Blackers Hill down to the Nettlebridge river. The church is a plain single-cell building (by John Pinch junior, 1838) with a tiny chancel added later, the whole beautifully decorated and cared for.

(iii) 655508: The Benedictine monastery and public school for boys in the village of Stratton-on-the-Fosse. In 1814 the community of English monks in flight from Douai in Flanders bought the late C17 Downside House—then called Mount Pleasant—to which in the 1820s they added a church and domestic wing in prickly pointed Gothic. In 1873 the building of the abbey began, which continued in stages under Dunn, Hansom, Garner and Sir Giles Gilbert Scott until the tower was completed in 1938. It is a magnificent cruciform Gothic building in Bath and Doulting stone: simple, lofty and light, with much rich ornament in the numerous side chapels. (For full details of the buildings see Pevsner, and the *Guide* available at the abbey.) Immediately to the s are a very modern hexagonal glass-framed library, and the severe C19 monastery block with a split-level cloister leading into the school, a surprisingly harmonious congeries of styles, spanning the C19-20 with postwar additions: a complex series of open quadrangles with a large area of surrounding lawn, garden and playing fields. From the entrance off the Fosse Way, the whole community is rightly dominated by the great abbey tower, 166ft high, standing 600ft above sea level, from the top of which the whole of NE Mendip can be seen, as well as the Wiltshire downs, the Cotswolds beyond Bath, their outlier Dundry, and beyond that again the distant Welsh mountains.

Draycott (476513): the cottage or shelter on the stiff hill where great effort was required to drag or draw anything

Originally a hamlet belonging to Rodney Stoke, Draycott became an ecclesiastical parish in 1862. The church, consecrated in 1861, is a pleasant little Victorian building, lofty and light, with an apsidal chancel. Church, chapel, school, walls, gateposts, cottages, even the base of the Card memorial in the centre of the village, are made of local Dolomitic Conglomerate which was formerly quarried here and polished to make 'Draycott Marble'. The village is compact and populous: most of it except for the Batch lies to the s of the Wells road—a sort of grid plan with four parallel roads, The Street, Back Lane, Wet Lane and Bay Lane, joining up in Station Road, where the Bristol & Exeter station buildings have survived the closure of the Cheddar Valley line. The only industry is market gardening in the narrow fields of rich red loam, for the village basks in the sunshine under the steep s escarpment of the hill. One lane slips round Nyland Hill and across the moors to Wedmore: another (the New Road) climbs through a cleft in the hill to reach Priddy, with magnificent views over the moors and along w Mendip as far as Brean Down and Steep Holm.

Dulcote (564445): formerly Dultingcote, the cottage or shelter by the Doulting river

A neat hamlet on the road from Wells to Shepton Mallet, pleasantly situated between the wooded slopes of the main Mendip ridge and the façade of Dulcote Hill, the body of which has been destroyed by quarrying. Dulcote consists of farms and cottages built of limestone or Conglomerate—even the bus-shelter. There is a small mission church (1860) belonging to St Cuthbert's, Wells, but for long served by the students of the Wells Theological College; and a mellow redbrick Georgian mill house behind which survives the chimney of the paper mill, burned down in 1904—for Dulcote is on the lower reaches of the Doulting water which drove so many mills. Today there is much noise, with the quarry lorries rumbling through, and main road traffic negotiating the awkward bend by the fountain on its little island of grass.

Easton (513476): the settlement to the E of Westbury to which it is now joined by ribbon development

Once an attractive little hamlet under the steep s escarpment of Mendip—hence the strawberry fields with their rich red soil—snuggled along the 100ft contour where the hill falls sharply on to the moors; a mixture of limestone and Conglomerate, but now spoiled by sporadic modern houses and split in two by the heavy traffic on the narrow winding A371. The parish was carved from St Cuthbert Out in 1844 when the dreary little neo-Norman church was opened. The earlier Providence chapel (1831), built in the local stone, has been converted into a dwelling.

Elm (746493): Great Elm (for Little Elm see Chantry), named after the tree

The motorist sees only half of Great Elm, a grey limestone village along the road from Mells to Frome, centred upon a tiny green with a mullioned manor farm dated 1675 and the rambling old rectory: the school and the pub and the 1835 Providence chapel have all been closed. The humble exterior of the church, with its C13 saddleback tower above a beautiful w door, belies the richness and interest of the interior—one of the least spoiled and most charming on Mendip: a white plastered ceiling with delicate ribs and bosses, and much good woodwork, mostly C17—communion rails, pulpit, box-pews and a w gallery with outside staircase.

The rest of the village is perched on the steep hillside in the wooded gorge of the Mells river which widens out to make a picturesque pool for the ducks. In the valley are the remains of woollen mills and of Fussells edge-tool works, and it is now spanned by the railway line serving the quarry at Whatley.

Emborough (614513): the smooth hill or barrow

A thinly populated parish, 700ft up on the N slopes, and oddly shaped to include part of Binegar village. At Emborough there is no village, hardly even a hamlet, except at Old Down where the famous posting house is actually in Ston Easton parish. There are a few houses (including a toll-house) along the Bath–Wells road and a few scattered farms; Emborough Pond (once known as Lechmere Pool), sombre and beautiful, large worked-out quarries invisible from the road; and the forlorn little church on its smooth hillside, looking down to the great tower of the mother church at Chewton Mendip, and across the bare expanse of Chewton Plain to the hills above Blagdon Lake and the far Welsh mountains. A grey building with a whitewashed interior, Gothick windows, a plaster moulded ceiling, a splendid Gurney stove and many Hippisley memorials. They lived in the gabled and buttressed manor farm, and a sunken old road is still visible driving straight down to their larger and later mansion at Ston Easton.

Evercreech (649386): the *cruc* or hill of the boar—a Celtic name

The large village of Evercreech lies on the southernmost slope of Mendip, below Maes Down, looking across the Alham to Creech Hill. This is rich dairy country, hence the creamery whose chimney rivals the church tower as a local landmark. The parish stretches up on to the hills (and includes Chesterblade) and down to the Alham, where there is some industrial development round the old brickworks at what was once busy Evercreech Junction on the Somerset & Dorset main line.

The village is roughly central to the parish, and the church roughly central to the village: it stands on a green lawn surrounded by grey walls and grey buildings, and is famous for its graceful feminine tower, its ornate parapets and gargoyles and its fine ring of bells. Inside, it is unique among Mendip churches in retaining its N and s galleries complete with numbered box-pews: the gaily painted roofs emphasise the total effect of height and light in this noble Perpendicular building—though the chancel is earlier, and the s aisle was not added till 1843.

A pleasant civilised village, with a confusion of narrow winding streets with low grey cottages and paved alley-ways, and open spaces like Victoria Square or the pleasant place where the village cross stands opposite the w door of the church. Few of the houses are very old or very large, except for Evercreech House on the main street. There is a good deal of discreet new housing around the older core or interwoven with it, including several bungalow estates, decently planned and built of artificial stone which does not jar; also a little light industry, though the limeworks have gone, as has the silk mill which became a cheese store before being incorporated in the large dairy complex. Up towards Prestleigh is the permanent site of the Bath and West Agricultural Show, though this lies mostly in Doulting parish.

Stoney Stratton (656393): the settlement on the paved road across stony ground—presumably a vicinal Roman road leading to the site of the temple on Creech Hill

Parochially part of Evercreech, Stoney Stratton is really a village in its own right, and a charming village at that, with a pub and lots of old cottages and several largish houses, all built of local limestone. It lies to the N of the road to Westcombe and Batcombe under the slopes of Small Down. A jolly little stream comes down from Chesterblade, which supplied the brewery, some of whose buildings still survive.

Farrington Gurney (635557): the settlement where ferns grow; the manor belonged to the Gournays

Farrington lies below Chewton Plain where the A37 climbs Rush Hill out of the Cam valley. Pitway Lane follows the line of a Roman road W across Hollow Marsh, one of the least known and most atmospheric areas on the fringe of Mendip. Main Street runs W–E from the splendid old parsonage (now a hotel) fronting the main road to the gabled C17 manor where the Moggs lived for 300 years. The church stands completely isolated in green pastures, its beautifully kept graveyard protected by a little ha-ha: severe neo-Norman of 1844 by John Pinch junior, but C18 monuments, the stump of a medieval cross and an oddly primitive carving over the W door survive from an earlier building. The medieval village must have been sited here; the modern village is a mixture of Pennant Sandstone and White Lias which prevails in the ranks of miners' houses built down the valley towards Old Mills, past the dirt batch of Farrington colliery, closed in 1921., The market, for so long the Monday meeting place for the local agricultural community, was closed in 1971.

Frome (776481): called after the river, whose British name is identical with Welsh *ffraw*=fair, fine, brisk; formerly Frome-Selwood, from the forest in which grew many sallow or willow trees

Frome has for long been the largest Mendip town. In 1831, except for Bath, it was the largest town in Somerset, with a population of 12,240, and for the next 100 years this remained remarkably stable; even in 1971 it was only 13,400, though if the surrounding parish of Selwood is included, the true population is about 16,000—larger than Wells and Shepton Mallet put together.

A bustling market town which has been heavily industrialised for centuries without losing the feel of being a country town in close touch with the rhythm of its agricultural environment; a thriving commercial centre, full of schools, pubs, churches, shops and winding steep streets; a town with high density of population, on an awkward site, in which multifarious activities always seem to be taking place; a town with a strong social sense of community.

The medieval town, whose street-plan is still so clearly visible, grew uphill from the market place on the level ground near the river (earlier trackways had converged on Spring Gardens, a mile downstream, where before Domesday there was a village called Pikewell). Cheap Street, paved, with a central leat full of rippling water, leads to Church Steps; St John the Baptist, the parish church, is a building of many periods, mainly restored and decorated by the great Tractarian vicar, W. J. E. Bennett, between 1852 and 1866; past the church into Gentle Street, still cobbled and runnelled and lined with splendid old houses.

On top of the ridge, two important roads intersect at Gore Hedge by the ruins of the great Lamb brewery: the A361 from Bath and Trowbridge to Shepton Mallet and the West (a major holiday route), and the A362 from Radstock to Warminster and on over Salisbury Plain to London. Frome is thus a focal point for road transport, as indeed it was for rail, before the cut-off was built in 1933 and the local branches were closed; even now all Mendip's rail-borne stone gets away past Frome, just as Mendip's woollen cloth did in past centuries, as recalled by the Packhorse Inn at Badcox.

For Frome's old prosperity was based on woollens. Though few of the mills or the clothiers' houses survive, names like Dyers Close Lane, Welshmill Hill and Sheppards Barton are significant enough. Sheppards were the largest of the Frome clothiers; their factory at Spring Gardens closed in 1878, though the last cloth mill of all, at Wallbridge, worked until 1965.

From the market place, Stony Street and Catherine Street climb steeply to the complex road junction at Badcox. From Badcox to Gore Hedge was 'Behind Town', now Christchurch Street, and within this triangle, completed by Gentle Street and Cheap Street leading back to the market place, lay the old town. Eventually the clothiers began to build themselves grander houses a little way off, while to the NW there was a large new area of gridiron streets of early C18 artisan housing—some of it now cleared and redeveloped very delightfully, for instance, at The Mint. These were built, like most of the old town, of the friendly local Forest Marble, while the larger houses were built or faced with freestone from Doulting. New churches arrived—Christ Church (1818) and Holy Trinity (1838), to supplement some large nonconformist chapels.

The finest of these, Rook Lane Congregational (1707), now awaiting conversion to secular use, overlooks Bath Street, which was cut through the post-medieval jungle of alley-ways in 1810 to give a better way into the town for vehicles. In the C19 Frome began to spread over the s ridge, along Vallis Way, to Cottle's Oak (the traditional frontier of Mendip), through The Butts and along the ridge to Marston, or beyond Portway to absorb the old manors of Keyford, always within the enormous loop of the river. About 1900 a posher residential area had developed round Victoria Park. N of the river, along the Bath road beyond North Parade (cut in 1797), there were a number of big houses belonging to wealthier citizens on the very outskirts of the town: North Hill House, for example, now district council offices. Only in the present century has Frome spread rapidly and visibly northwards, incorporating Fromefield: here is the grammar school (now comprehensive), the sports centre and a large motel on the way down to the river at Oldford (Old Ford?).

New housing has spread along most of the other roads leading out of the town: the new industries, which replaced in course of time the woollen industry, are settled, sometimes on new sites, such as the Marston Trading Estate, or on old sites, often tucked away unobtrusively as at Merchants Barton. Even Singers seems to be cordoned off by the car-park and the market. Nearby is the new shopping centre, and even a new cinema, beside the newly canalised and landscaped river. Too much new stuff, say the conservationists who regret the large-scale demolition of buildings that had often been allowed to fall into a state of dereliction far beyond the wildest dreams of economic restoration.

There is more about Frome in the chapter on Industry; Pevsner's perambulation offers most of the sights of the town; Peter Belham's *The Making of Frome* tells the full story. But no visitor should miss seeing the Blue House beside the town bridge, or Willow Vale just beyond, or pedestrian Cheap Street, Gentle Street, Rook Lane Chapel and Catherine Street. There are wonderful roofscapes everywhere. For a distant view, go across the river to Innox Hill, where St Mary's has hardly altered since its building in 1863, and where there are some examples of early industrial housing built by Sheppards for their workers—and look back to the focal point of St John's spire that rises above the huddle of the old town clinging to its hillside. A town of tremendous character, well worth exploring throughly, on foot.

Green Ore (577503): formerly Greenworth, the green enclosure, referring to the Carthusians' grange and sheepwalks here, later corrupted to Green Ore by reason of the mining activity

A small hamlet strategically situated at the crossing of the Roman road from Charterhouse to Old Sarum and the Bristol–Wells turnpike road, Green Ore was a centre of lead mining from Roman times until the C17. There is still a lot of gruffy ground on the bare upland, but the hamlet consists merely of a pub and a few houses and outlying farms—and the ruined mansion of Hill Grove, once a sanatorium. The tiny church with its homely furnishings is dated 1848, but it was originally a cottage which was converted into a church and schoolroom c 1880, and was served by many generations of students from Wells Theological College.

Gurney Slade (623493): the *sleight* (hill-pasture or sheepwalk) or *slaed* (valley) belonging to the Gournays

A dour grey village lined along the A37, divided between the parishes of Ashwick and Binegar: abandoned quarries and cottages, perched or terraced where quarrying has allowed. The Methodist chapel has been converted into a dwelling, but the rest of the modern housing has hardly added to the amenity of the village, which shudders under the impact of continual traffic and of the noise and dust from the quarrying operations and the lime burning which has gone on here for at least a century.

East Harptree (565559): a personal name? or derived from *herepath*=the army road, through road

A large parish extending from the hamlets of Coley and Shrowl on the River Chew right up to the 950ft contour to include the Priddy Circles and the kennels of the Mendip Farmers Hunt; the village itself stretches over 1½ miles, from Townsend to the last cottages on Smitham Hill near the old lead mines, where the restored chimney is a notable landmark on the skyline. A village of considerable charm, despite much recent commuter building—Bristol is only 14 miles away—with the older houses, both cottages, farms and middling-sized houses, built sometimes of limestone, sometimes of Dolomitic Conglomerate. High Street climbs the hill as far as the Clock, then divides into three, Water Street, Middle Street and Church Lane, which reunite at Proud Cross and carry on up Smitham to the Castle of Comfort.

To the w, undecipherable fragments of Richmont Castle overlook the beautiful wooded combe which runs far up into Mendip. In the middle of the village is the Georgian court where lived the Kettlewells who were responsible for building the clock tower (1897), the village theatre, the Co-op and much of the school. Eastwood and its model farm are also a Victorian creation.

Down in the valley are a little Roman Catholic church (1883) and a more imposing Methodist church. The parish church stands aside from the village on a splendid site, looking across the Chew Valley Lake to the Dundry ridge. The porch with its Norman door and the Elizabethan monument to Sir John Newton attended by his twenty children is attractive enough, but the interior is disappointingly undistinguished.

West Harptree (561569)

Six roads converge on this neatly nucleated village on the N edge of an enormous parish extending from the middle of the Chew Valley Lake almost to Priddy. Only on the Bristol road is there any straggle, and many of the cottages here are old anyhow; the council houses are neatly sited off Ridge Lane. The open centre of the village is ringed by the church and vicarage, the pub, a garage, a post office stores, a bank and the school—giving the impression of a close-knit, self-sufficient community. Most of the buildings are of local Dolomitic Conglomerate, some of it very red as in the vicarage (c 1700) and in the two splendid C17 houses—Gournay Court and Tilly Manor—which face each other across the road to Weston. The church, guarded by a screen of five yew trees, has a squat Norman tower surmounted by a slated spire, but the body was rebuilt in 1864/5 and is without interest.

Holcombe (672498): the hollow or deep combe

A small parish to the E of the Fosse Way, with wooded valleys to the N and s-facing slopes looking across the Nettlebridge river to the main E ridge of Mendip. Holcombe is now a hilltop/hillside village, but the original settlement of which only the church, Moore's Farm and the Georgian rectory survive, stood on the edge of the deep wooded valley from which it derived its name. The small church is one of Mendip's gems, a tiny Perpendicular building with a Norman s door and unspoiled Georgian interior—clear glass, plaster roof, white box-pews, all one could wish for. Only occasional services are now held here in the summer, for a new church was built in 1885 (an uninspiring little building in Victorian EE) in the middle of the new village which succeeded the earlier settlement, traditionally abandoned after the Black Death. This new village grew up round a large brewery founded in 1800 and several collieries, the largest of which was Edford (1862–1915): ranks of houses stretch down the hill to the line of the abortive Dorset & Somerset Canal. A few older houses survive in un-usual pinkish or brownish stone; there is a large Methodist church, and a charming Catholic chapel converted from a stable at Flint House (and actually in Kilmersdon parish). For the rest, Holcombe, much disturbed by lorries from quarries and a large concrete works at Edford, is prosperously residential, almost suburban, loosely packed with private housing estates as well as council housing which includes an old people's estate at Scott's Close, pleasantly grouped round a green, while another green space is the recreation ground at the crossroads which is nearly the centre of the village, close to the remains of the brewery (now used as a garage) and the Georgian manor house.

Horrington; the earliest form is Horningdun, the horn-like down

Two distinct villages separated by the Wells–Bath road, lying halfway up the s slopes of Mendip with magnificent views, and until 1844 part of the huge Wells parish of St Cuthbert Out. Horrington parish extends to Green Ore and Masbury, and includes the Mendip Hospital, founded in 1848 with large grounds and a splendid range of buildings in Dolomitic Conglomerate by Gilbert Scott.

East Horrington (582467) is no more than a hamlet, but contained the parish church, an aisleless building in 1838 lancet style and the remains of a prebendal manor, half a mile E.

West Horrington (573475) perches higher on a steep hillside, a casual mixture of sturdy limestone vernacular and undistinguished modern housing. The old road up Biddle Combe joined the Bristol road near Pen Hill, passing the remains of an old buddle house, a link with lead mining days.

Hutton (353586): the settlement on the *hoh* or spur of a hill.

Seen from across the moor, Hutton lies snugly under the N slope of the great island mass of Bleadon Hill. Canada Combe leads on to lanes that climb over the hill to Christon and Loxton. There is a pleasant winding village street, once the main road from Banwell to Weston. Church Lane climbs a little higher, past the C15 court with its embattled tower, to the church, set against the backdrop of the wooded hillside: a building in Dolomitic Conglomerate with jolly gargoyles and a sober double-windowed tower under which there is good lierne vaulting: C15-16 brasses commemorate the Paynes who lived at the court; there is a beautiful stone pulpit; and waggon roofs throughout help to blend the original Perpendicular work with that of the 1849 restorers.

Kilmersdon (696524): originally Kunemersdon, the down belonging to Cynemaer

The down is Ammerdown, away to the E, where the Jolliffes, who acquired the estate by marriage in 1770, moved into the new mansion built by Wyatt in 1791. Kilmersdon itself is a village in a valley at the bottom of the long NE slope of Mendip: always a place of importance, a Hundred town (the magistrates used to sit in the large upper room at the Jolliffe Arms), and a large parish that included several manors and outlying hamlets as well as Coleford. A beautiful village in a beautiful setting, with its focal point a tiny square, surrounded by the church, the inn, the lock-up (now a bus shelter), some pleasing ranges of domestic buildings, Georgian or earlier, and not far away the old free school (1707), the gabled manor house (1674) and a disused Wesleyan chapel (1837). The church is a C15 building with surviving Norman details, and some good stonework inside and out, including a magnificent series of heraldic beasts on the exterior of the N aisle, added by the Botreaux family in the C15. The iron grille separating nave and chancel was made by Singers of Frome in 1878. Most of the buildings in the village are of mellow oolite, with many mullions and drip mouldings: the few newer houses are unobtrusive—even the garage is a converted stables—and the whole impression is of a well-kept estate: which of course it is, and the story of the village is admirably told in Lord Hylton's *Notes on the History of the Parish of Kilmersdon* (1910). The Twyfords, who preceded the Jolliffes, lived at Charlton 1 mile to the W on the road to White Post: their house is demolished, but the hamlet contains several good Georgian houses in local stone.

Langford (456603): long ford, presumably across the Yeo

Although neither a civil nor an ecclesiastical parish (it is split between Churchill and Burrington), Langford is a considerable village covering a large area.

Upper Langford is a hamlet lying along the road to Weston under the heavily wooded N escarpment of Mendip.

Lower Langford, a mile away to the N was once on the Bristol–Bridgwater road but is now mercifully bypassed by the A38, leaving unspoiled the civilised and charming village street with many excellent houses, some colour-washed, some of local stone, prosperous and well cared for. At the W end, the small church, a rather severe aisleless apsidal design of local Conglomerate, was built in 1900 as a memorial to the Simmons family. Langford Court in its park is mainly Georgian; Langford House, an Italianate villa of c 1850, now houses Bristol University's School of

Veterinary Science, where several modern blocks have been added.
Again to the N there is a certain amount of new housing, and a factory
where market gardening has escalated into mushroom growing and food
canning.

Leigh-on-Mendip (692473): the clearing or glade in the woodland up
on Mendip (Ligh Under Mendip on Morden's map 1695)

Perched 600ft up on the NE slope of the main ridge above the
Nettlebridge valley, the main street runs E–W for nearly a mile, containing much good building in local limestone, including a converted
Methodist chapel, and several houses bearing dates from C17 and C18:
the vicarage and Great House Farm are Elizabethan. The whole scene is
dominated by the church tower, triple-windowed Perpendicular,
similar in design to Mells but even more richly ornamented at the
crown. Beside it, in the beautifully mown churchyard, the body of the
church looks disproportionately meagre, though this is not so noticeable
inside: here the effect is of height and light, the creamy Doulting stone of
the tower contrasts with the random coursing of the other walls, and the
carved bench-ends and corbels, and the angels of the superb timber roof,
are the obvious eye-catchers. Leigh is an agricultural village, apart from
a timberyard which once specialised in making wooden handles for
agricultural tools, but now finds itself on the edge of the quarry belt.

Litton (594547): the settlement on the *hlyde* or torrent or on the *hlide* or
slope, or referring to the gate (*hlyd*) or opening of the narrow valley
coming down from Chewton Mendip

The village straddles the River Chew, here no more than a stream.
Along the green hillside towards Ford are plough lynchets. To the NW
the Chew was dammed in 1853 by Bristol Waterworks to form two small
reservoirs lying beautifully under the hill. Litton itself has remained
small, quiet and unspoiled, thanks in part to a bypass built in the 1920s.
The church (late C14 Perpendicular) has charm and is beautifully
maintained, but is architecturally undistinguished apart from an interesting set of gargoyles and corbels on the tower; it groups well with the
Georgian rectory and nearby Manor Farm and cottages. Parts of the
King's Arms date from the C15: elsewhere in the village and in the
outlying hamlets of Greendown, Ford and Sherborne are a number of
pleasant farms and cottages all built of local limestone.

Locking (363596): the settlement of Locc's people

Only just to be reckoned a Mendip village, looking across an unspoiled valley to the great mass of Bleadon Hill, with glimpses through to Wavering Down. At the highest point in the parish was the original hilltop settlement: church, manor, one or two farms and a tiny green. Northwards is an enormous area of modern housing and an RAF station that have together almost destroyed Locking's identity as a small village (population 116 in 1911 as against 4,200-odd today), now hemmed in by the roar of the Weston road and the M5. The church is interesting despite its forbidding grey stucco exterior—a C19 rebuild with Tuscan columns in the 1814 aisle, matching the legs on the communion table; a good C14 tower similar to that at Hutton; a splendid C11 square font with Celtic design; and a gaily painted stone pulpit.

Loxton (376558): Locc's settlement (cf Locking)

The small village, purely agricultural, climbs from the moor round the shoulder of Loxton Hill, and faces Crook Peak across the M5. Webbington, the half-timbered Edwardian house of the Tiarks family, now a Country Club, dominates from the E, though actually in Compton Bishop parish. To the s lie the moors, finally drained and reclaimed after the Act of 1802, and crossed by the new cut of the Axe. There are grey farms and farm buildings and a couple of larger houses. The church stands off the road, environed by farm buildings and effluvia: a much-restored church, undistinguished at a glance, but with several interesting features—a Norman s door, a squint for the bell-ringer in the porch beneath the oddly placed tower, some C14 glass, a stone pulpit hewn from a single block of stone and 'Draycott Marble' paving the floor.

Marston Bigot (755450): the settlement by the marsh, held by Richard le Bigot c 1200

The original village has disappeared: it may have been sited down in the valley, but the church was formerly in front of the present mansion which lies snugly under the last E ridge of Mendip, looking across the River Frome to the wooded Wiltshire escarpment. The church was re-sited in 1789, and rebuilt (except for the tower) in Victorian neo-Norman; the mansion with its 400ft long façade has a complicated architectural history, rebuilt and added to in the Georgian and Victorian periods by the Boyles, who acquired the manor in 1638 and owned it until 1905, becoming Earls of Cork and Orrery in the meantime. Only partly occupied, it has been threatened with demolition against which its architectural value and its historical and literary associations protest loudly. In 1822 Skinner found the situation unattractive 'as it looks over a flat expanse formerly marsh', but today Mendip's largest country house looks serenely down across the wooded park with its 20 acre lake on to peaceful, well-farmed countryside which is largely the creation of the ninth earl (1829–1904). A study of Marston House by Michael McGarvie appears in the *Somerset Archaeological Society's Proceedings*, 118 (1974).

Masbury or **Maesbury** (604473): originally Merkesbury, Maerec's burg or fort, or perhaps referring to a *mearc* or boundary

From the ring of fortifications guarding the Iron Age camp, there are magnificent views in every direction, from Exmoor to the Wiltshire downs, and from the Welsh mountains to Cranborne Chase and the Dorset Heights. Directly below lies the whole of the E Mendip plateau and all around, a varied landscape of ridges and valleys from which emerge the familiar landmarks of Dundry, Downside, Alfred's Tower, Glastonbury Tor—and Wells Cathedral, cradled by green hills. There is no village, only scattered farms and the former station building where the Somerset & Dorset main line from Bath breasted the summit of Mendip, 811ft above sea level.

Mells (728493): the mills

One of the most interesting and beautiful of the larger Mendip villages, Mells, designated a Conservation Area, is a curiously scattered and shapeless community: it was considerably larger when the woollen and edge-tool industries flourished. Quarrying is now the only local industry. New housing has not yet made good the loss of population. The village straddles the stream that emerges from the seclusion of Mells Park, past the ruined mill at Bilboa to the bridge at Woodlands End where five roads meet, and so into the deep wooded Wadbury valley—a network of lanes and cottages, many of them thatched or stone-tiled: the whole village from the squat square lock-up to the great manor house seems to be built of the local oolite. On the s bank the road climbs past Little Green to Mells Green where the village school stands, established by the Horners in 1830 in what had been weavers' premises; on the N bank, on a little plateau, stands the splendid group of church, manor, Georgian rectory, village pub, and New Street, a C15 attempt at town planning by Abbot Selwood of Glastonbury Abbey, which owned Mells.

The church is a magnificent Perpendicular building with a triple-windowed tower, similar to that at Leigh, and even loftier, a fan-vaulted porch and a two-storeyed vestry, once a chapel, dated 1485. The interior was heavily but well restored by the Victorians; much glass and the carved pew-ends were made in the village 1860–80. Work by Burne Jones, Munnings, Gill, Lutyens and William Nicholson enriches the building which is full of Horner memorials. The churchyard lawns spread out towards the open fields and up to the high-walled gardens of the Elizabethan manor house of the Horners. In the C18 they moved out to a new Georgian mansion in the park, but returned to the manor in the present century. Mells Park itself was rebuilt by Lutyens after a fire in 1917.

Midsomer Norton (662542): the settlement to the N of another settlement (? Stratton-on-the-Fosse) with reference to the midsummer festival of St John, the patron saint. The old name was Norton Friars or Norton Canonicorum, because it belonged to the Augustinians of Merton in Surrey

In 1933 Midsomer Norton was joined with Radstock to form the urban district of Norton–Radstock, but it has retained its separate identity and its distinct character, and its development has been very different from that of its neighbour. Midsomer Norton parish was once enormous, stretching s between Stratton and Chilcompton as far as the Nettlebridge valley where boundary stones can still be seen. By 1801 the population was 1,552, rising to 5,800 by 1901.

The original village lay along the valley of the so-called Somer (patently a back-formation) and on the little ridge separating it from the Wellow Brook. In the C19 the village grew into a small mining town almost surrounded by collieries at Welton, Old Mills and later at Norton Hill, where the s&D Railway had begun its long climb over Mendip on a gradient of 1 in 50. Fossilised remains of the old village, often in the shape of old bits of sandstone wall, can be deciphered, round the parish church, round the little square called The Island, and along High Street.

By 1900 a lot of new houses had appeared, built of the local grey lias: Redfield Road and Radstock Road, for example. In this century there has been enormous housing development, N into the Welton valley, w up the Clapton road and along the valley towards Chilcompton.

The central artery is High Street, running from the parish church to Stone's Cross (where Welton begins), along the river, now due to be culverted and roofed over to prevent persistent flooding and to provide a pedestrian precinct. There are some dignified houses on The Island, and on High Street The Hollies—a fine Georgian building—is now the district council offices. Pevsner comments on the town hall 'in an Italian Gothic style, but with an Italianate deep-eaved roof'; this sombre pile, the Greyhound Hotel and two bank houses were all built c 1860 by Thomas Harris Smith, a local architect.

In the town centre, three churches contrast vividly with each other: the solid Methodist church was built of local lias in 1859; the Anglican parish church is traditional Somerset Perpendicular at first glance, but apart from the C17 tower, it is mostly the work of John Pinch the younger c 1830—a dignified building, lofty and light within, with soberly painted plaster ceilings, islanded on a well-kempt lawn; but by far the most interesting is the Roman Catholic church, a C15 tithe barn of rich Red Stonestone, acquired by Downside Abbey in 1906, rescued from dilapidation and squalor, and restored by Giles Gilbert Scott. The massive buttresses, huge doorways, splendid timber roof, white-washed interior and the rich and varied furnishings, make it the outstanding building in the town.

Between Somervale School (1965) in the valley and Norton Hill School (the former grammar school of 1911 with modern additions) is the Somerset & Dorset Railway station, now adapted as a field study and project centre for local schools.

The rest of Midsomer Norton consists mostly of large areas of rather undistinguished modern housing and sporadic outbreaks of commercial or industrial premises: the old industries—coal, brewing and boot making—have given way to a variety of light industry and engineering, along Welton Vale towards the Five Arches, and up on Norton Hill to merge with Westfield.

In the centre there is still something of the atmosphere of a village rather than a town: essentially a friendly place, that has lost its two railways, that has never been on a main road, and never really allowed itself to become urbanised—despite the supermarkets. The best overall view perhaps is to be had from Clapton Road (where there is some of the best new housing) or from the footpaths on Folly Hill or Welton Hill, for like other Somerset mining settlements, Norton is surrounded by much pleasant green countryside.

Nunney (738457): the island of the nuns or of Nunna; OE *eg* often describes a piece of land beside a stream

All roads lead down into Nunney in its sheltered valley, where the village grew along the brook which was responsible for the prosperity brought by the woollen and edge-tool industries. Horn Street, High Street and Church Street (spanned by the sign of the George Inn) converge on the little market place and the stone bridge over the brook. Pleasing stone-built cottages retain their Georgian windows. At one end of the village, Nunney Court on its little bluff looks down on to the ruins of Fussells edge-tool works; at the other end Rockfield House takes its name from the Rack Field where cloth was stretched and dried. Now the village has climbed Berry Hill to the s, and long lines of council houses stretch as far as Nunney Catch where the main road from Frome to the West runs along the ridgeway. At the top of the combe are the huge Holwell quarries, but the lorries are mercifully routed away from the village.

Church and castle confront each other across the brook. The church tower is plain by Somerset standards but dignified, standing flush with the aisles to present a broad front to the street. Inside there is space and light, emphasised by the wide arches of transepts and arcades, and a general sense of a building well cared for since the restoration began in 1940. A huddle of de la Mare tombs includes that of Sir John who was licensed 'to fortify and crenellate his manor at Nunney' in 1373. The result was the only medieval castle to survive on Mendip, although it was slighted in 1645 during the Civil War. Very delightful it is, with its tranquil moat and smooth lawns and clustered circular towers at each corner. Behind the castle is the Manor Farm House, a handsome and civilised example of early C18 architecture—one of the best houses around Mendip.

Oakhill (636473); a precise descriptive name, like its neighbour Ashwick

The village lies cosily under the main E Mendip ridge, half a mile w of the Roman Fosse Way, between the Bath and Bristol roads; mainly a C19 industrial village, following the spectacular development of the brewery founded here in 1767. Its buildings dominated the main street which stretches as far as Little London, though only malting has been carried on here since the Great Fire of 1925. The Brewery Co built many houses, supplying much of the village with gas, water and sewerage. The Spencers who acquired the brewery built themselves mansions and a fine Congregational church (1873), now closed. The Methodist church (1825 Gothick) looks along the Bath road—by tradition on the ground where Wesley preached during numerous visits. The Anglican church—an aisleless, lofty, cold building by J. L. Pearson—dates from 1861, for Oakhill did not become a parish until 1866, and in 1923 the benefice was united with Ashwick, of whose civil parish it anyhow forms part.

Pilton (588408): the *tun* or settlement by the *pill* or creek

Its name implies that Pilton was once accessible from the sea—by tradition Joseph of Arimathea landed here—and indeed the road from Shepton Mallet to Glastonbury sweeps through the upper part of the village, down two steep hills, to reach the moors at Steanbow, less than 50ft above sea level. The motorist's impression is of a straggle of grey cottages and a vicious right-angled bend at the focal point where the pub and the shops are clustered—one of them occupying part of the old brewery building. Most of the village however lies along the valley below the main road: church and manor on the N, tithe barn on the s—for this was Glastonbury property, and there was a deer park here, the name Pilton Park surviving on the modern map, away to the s.

The valley is a network of steep narrow lanes, footpaths and little stone-arched bridges where the stream has been landscaped into a number of gardens: the older grey stone cottages lie about higgledy-piggledy, with some decent larger houses including two converted chapels, but there has been a good deal of infilling and a spread of new building away to the s, for Pilton is a large and popular residential village in the middle of an enormous parish which includes East and West Compton, Westholme with its Georgian mansion and park, and pseudo-Elizabethan Burford. Only the walls of the great C14 tithe barn now stand, for the building itself was gutted during a thunderstorm in 1963. Across the stream (which is actually one of the headwaters of the Whitelake river) are the fancifully crenellated and Gothicised manor, and the vineyards where Pilton Riesling is now produced and bottled. The lofty clerestoried church is a building of many periods from the Norman (s door) to the Tudor (chancel arch) with a magnificent wooden roof, only one of many interesting and beautiful features.

Priddy (528514): from the Welsh *pridd*=earth, soil

Priddy is unique—the one genuine village on the high Mendip plateau, 800ft up, lying in a sheltered hollow and centred on its green, where the stack of hurdles symbolises its famous sheep fair, held annually in late August ever since 1348. Really it is a scattered village stretching from Townsend to East Water, with some new housing developing along the Wookey Hole road, and with numerous outlying farms; a Mecca for cavers, and overlooked by hilltop burial mounds and other signs of early settlement. For centuries it was a centre of lead mining, and towards Wells the ruins of St Cuthbert's Leadworks which closed in 1908 can still be seen. Off the upper green stand the school and the church, an upland landmark, somewhat away from the village centre, with a sturdy grey C13 tower and a large expanse of mown churchyard: the body of the church is more spacious and more interesting than appears likely at first sight—a primeval font, a slim stone pulpit, a simple screen, and a tablet which records the mending of the tower and 'to pinikls' in 1705.

Radstock (689546): the *stoc*—place or settlement—near the road; the Fosse Way runs half a mile to the w

It is difficult to take in at a glance the amorphous sprawl into which Radstock has developed for very good historical and geographical reasons: Pevsner dismisses it as 'really desperately ugly'; Ian Nairn has found it fascinating. The site was—and to some extent still is—very beautiful: a basin where four steep-sided valleys converge, their streams uniting to form the Wellow Brook. Eight roads feed into this basin, causing notorious traffic problems which were accentuated until quite recently by two level-crossings 50yd apart.

The village grew up on the s edge of this basin at the foot of the NE extremity of Mendip. In 1801 it was a village of 500 people, already growing with the discovery of coal in 1763 and the arrival of a branch of the Somersetshire Coal Canal in 1799; by 1851 the population was about 1,800 and by 1901 this had nearly doubled. *Kelly's Directory* for 1889 says, 'The place is rapidly becoming a town'. Within a radius of 2 miles there were a dozen or so collieries at work and two lines of railway with feeder branches and attendant wagon works. 'Numerous dwellings and shops' had sprung up (like the Co-op), public buildings (like the Victoria Hall & Institute and Fortescue College, now the post office) and several chapels; the parish church had been rebuilt and enlarged in 1879, and long ranks of miners' houses, many of them built by the Waldegraves who during the C19 owned the most important group of collieries, stretching up the steep hillsides in various directions—to Clandown and Tyning and Haydon, along the Frome Road and the Fosse Way through Westfield, and along the valley towards Midsomer Norton with which Radstock was ultimately to be amalgamated, in 1933, to form the urban district of Norton–Radstock with a present population of 15,000.

Radstock had become the capital of the Somerset coalfield. The last colliery closed in 1973, but visually the abandoned spoil tips, known locally as batches, dominate the scene from many angles, and despite the appearance of new industries and new building, Radstock is still basically a C19–20 mining town: the old village has disappeared almost without a trace, but there is much pleasant countryside on the doorstep, penetrating right up to the town on the s and w.

The town centre is surprisingly un-urban; two small streets of shops separated by the railways from the Saturday market held by the road-side and in the covered market hall beside the old brewery. Radstock seems to lack a focal point: neither the Victoria Hall nor the modern Co-op have quite provided this, and even the UDC offices were at Mid-somer Norton. The parish church, a Victorian rebuilding except for the tower, and undistinguished at that, stands pleasantly on the edge of the town with its graveyard climbing a steep hillside above the brook that comes down from Charlton. There are several C19 nonconformist chapels and a Roman Catholic church—a converted barn built of local stone which was used as a printing house until 1926—with a delightfully simple white-washed interior.

Climbing the steep hills from the town centre, one looks down on the rather messy remains of a small industrial town that has had to change its way of life with the shut-down of its basic industry. Frome Old Road is more interesting than the modern Frome Road, and the same goes for Bath Old Road, which also leads on to Tyning, scattered around the spoil tips, where there is a lot of good new housing. For contrast there are the gaunt grey stone tenement blocks at Whitelands down the valley. Coomb End is an industrial area, and Haydon is virtually a separate mining village, grouped around Kilmersdon Colliery and built, like most of the older Radstock, of the local hard white lias. Of modern buildings there are the technical college, built on the site of Southill House, St Nicholas Primary School near the parish church, and Writhlington School (comprehensive) at the top of the Frome Road, from which one gets a fine panorama of the whole of E Mendip, focusing on the Beacon to which the Fosse Way laboriously climbed from the Radstock valley.

Rodney Stoke (482498): the *stoc* or place belonging to the Rodneys c 1300

A small village of considerable charm, both in itself and in its setting, though unlikely to be appreciated by motorists in a hurry to get from Cheddar to Wells. The parish climbs from the Axe, 20ft above sea level, to 883ft at Westbury Beacon; the village lies at the foot of the escarpment against the back drop of Stoke Woods, now a Nature Reserve, partly along the main road, partly along the street that drops downhill past the old mill towards the church. It is a village built largely of Dolomitic Conglomerate (except for the redbrick council houses along the main road). The church, a plain and simple building, stands alone on the last low ridge above the moors: it must be visited for the sake of the remarkable collection of Rodney monuments in the N chapel and some pleasant Jacobean woodwork.

Rowberrow (449586): the rough hill or barrow—with reference to the w slopes of Black Down, now covered by Forestry Commission plantations

Formerly a mining parish, with a much larger population who dug for calamine which was treated in Rowberrow Bottom, but now one of the smallest and least spoiled Mendip villages: an inn, a few cottages, and the old rectory and the former manor house, close to the church, which stands on the edge of a deep chasm that separates it from the stone ramparts of the Iron Age fortress of Dolebury. The church itself, smothered with roses in summer, is a small aisleless building, rebuilt in 1865 except for the tower.

Sandford (421595): sandy ford, presumably across the Towerhead Brook towards Banwell

The oldest part of the village lies along the noisy road to Weston, under the wooded slopes of Sandford Hill, though it is hardly visible under the ribbon development that extends from Churchill as far as the derelict railway station at the w end—a gabled Bristol & Exeter design in local Conglomerate. There are signs of traditional village industries: cider making, market gardening, corn milling. The church at the crossroads punctuates the long straggle: a simple aisleless building of 1885 in local limestone with stone carvings at the w end and a good wooden roof with gilded bosses and gaily painted beams. The village has extended s past the quarry that is rapidly eroding and destroying the wooded mass of Sandford Hill, towards which residential development has been allowed to creep: a shapeless area of suburban housing which imperceptibly merges into Winscombe.

Shepton Mallet (619436): the sheep farm or settlement held by the Malets c 1100

The Fosse Way bypassed Shepton to the E, so did the Somerset & Dorset Railway, so now does the A37 along Kilver Street, so that the town has escaped the worst problems set by modern traffic. The older parts of the town lie E–W along the valley bottom, and recent excavations during the redevelopment of the town centre revealed no early settlement round the parish church. The town grew uphill and flourished with the prosperity of the woollen trade: the market cross dates from 1500, and the period of greatest prosperity was C17-18, but Shepton (at one time considerably larger than Wells) never really recovered from the decline of the woollen trade, though silk and crape kept some of the mills going: the last (at Darshill) finally closed c 1930, and was recently demolished. Only today (ironically after the closure of both railway lines) has new industry come to Shepton, where redevelopment is giving a new look to what was perhaps the sleepiest and most old-fashioned of the Mendip towns. There is much charm in Shepton, but also much dereliction. Two areas have been cleared: N of the river, where the Hillmead flats climb above the valley with their restless skyline and blank windows in bleak white brick walls; and in the town centre, where a new stone-faced shopping centre is now complete, having been financed by Francis Showering, with a pedestrian precinct which has involved the building of relief and access roads.

The road from Bristol and Bath originally came down Cowl Street, past the splendid Unitarian chapel (1696/1785), now a play school, over the river at Longbridge, and steeply up narrow Town Street into the market place. Waterloo Road bridging the valley was opened in 1826. Downstream, Draycott Road passes some splendid but decayed houses—Sales House was once a convent—and peters out into a field path to Bowlish (where there is more dereliction and two outstanding Georgian clothiers' houses), and so on to Darshill with its bits and pieces of mills, some converted, some derelict, in the steep-sided valley.

Upstream from Longbridge, where a large gabled C17 house has been acquired for rehabilitation by the local Amenity Trust, Lower Lane runs beside the river as far as Leg Square, a civilised ambience of good Georgian houses; Garston Street carries on to the E, a pleasing line of much humbler dwellings, some of them skilfully restored, leading into the heart of the enormous Showering factory complex, and across Kilver Street to the twenty-seven-arch railway viaduct.

To the E of the market place stands the parish church, approached by paved footpaths, with the old grammar school (now the rectory) on the N and almhouses on the s–both founded by members of the Strode family, rich clothiers. The church itself is beautifully kept, and lighter and loftier since the early Victorian galleries and much stained glass were removed. Pevsner describes the roof as 'the most glorious of all the wagon-roofs of England', with its 350 carved panels and 306 bosses and 1,400 leaves, all different in design.

From the market place, High Street runs uphill, narrow at first, then a little wider—a friendly street lined with small shops—as far as the district council offices at Highfield House, and Townsend, to which the railway came in 1858 and Clarks shoe factory in 1956. Beyond the railway is Field where the medieval common fields must have stretched, now covered by an area of postwar housing except for the Mid-Somerset Show ground.

East of High Street is worth exploring: along Paul Street is the fine Methodist church of 1819, restored in 1969 with the room for worship now on the first floor at the level of the old galleries: beyond this are two good modern buildings—the telephone exchange and Whitstone Comprehensive School, whose name commemorates the Hundred in which Shepton stood. Also the prison, established here in 1610, grey and grim with a quite monumental N porch and towering walls past which narrow lanes creep down the hill. Uphill are the park and the new Roman Catholic church. The old church (Gothick of 1804) stands beside the Glastonbury road, towards West Shepton, which has something of the feeling of a village in its own right, dominated by the fine building that was originally the workhouse and is now a hospital—dated 1848, but still Georgian in style with a dignified grey stone façade and classical pediments—and so on to Wells by the old ridge road. Or back into the town along Board Cross, past the Anglo-Bavarian Brewery, now a trading estate, with its jumbled roofs and variegated brick chimney, past another fine Georgian chapel (now the Baptist church), and along Great Ostry into the market place again.

Shepton is a rambling and at present rather a messy town where many areas await redevelopment or conservation, and much would seem to depend upon the economic and social impact of the rebuilding of the town centre. It is hard to see the town as a whole. Like Frome it has grown up the hillside from its river, but unlike Frome there has been practically no development across the river. But it is a rewarding place to explore: one remembers in particular the steep stone-paved alleyways, the comfortable elegance of the Georgian mansions around Leg Square, the roof of the church, preferably viewed through binoculars; above all stands the fine late C14 tower, looking down towards the river that was for so long the life-blood of Shepton and from which the town has gradually moved away.

Shipham (443574): the sheep farm

An unusual site, 500ft up on the NW slopes of the main range, on the old turnpike road to Cheddar—there is a charming little toll-house just out of the village—and close to the track that came down from the

Charterhouse lead mines, through the Holloway, making towards the coast. The original settlement clustered round the church and the manor, a medieval stone-built house; the church, rebuilt in 1842, though pleasant enough outside, is gloomy and barnlike within. The village spread uphill beyond the green in the latter part of the C18: by then it had become the centre of mining for calamine. Many private shafts were sunk on individually-owned plots of land, hence the close-knit pattern of this area—a network of lanes and haphazard cottages, now mostly modernised, with discreet infilling. Hindpits Lane, the Miners' Arms, and the memorial window in the church to Hannah More recall this era; so do the large areas of gruffy ground, spoiled mining sites on the hillside, with fine views across to the coast and over the Bristol Channel into Wales.

Sidcot (428575): cottage or settlement on the hillside

Perched on the last w slope of the main Mendip ridge, and looking down into the Winscombe valley ringed by the hills, Sidcot was originally a hamlet of Winscombe. It has grown to be a sizeable village, lying to the E of the A38, and now linked with Oakridge, another of Winscombe's hamlets, where a certain amount of new housing has sprung up. The centre of Sidcot is the Quaker co-educational boarding school, founded in 1808, and successor to an earlier school and Meeting House on the same site throughout the C18. The school occupies an island of land surrounded by roads. To the original tall white Regency block with its striking deep eaves, various teaching blocks and boarding houses have accrued in the present century. A private bridge across the A38 leads to the playing fields, and behind the school is the hall, dating from 1817, which is also the local Friends' Meeting House.

Steep Holm (228607): the steep island, a Norse name commemorating the C10 raids of the Viking fleets in the Bristol Channel

Geologically part of Mendip, Steep Holm is an uninhabited limestone lump 3 miles WNW of Brean Down, and a detached portion of Avon—unlike its neighbour Flat Holm which belongs to Wales. Though always difficult of access—there is only one landing-place—it once housed a small Augustinian priory; later there was an extra-parochial inn much frequented by smugglers; in 1867, like Brean Down, it was fortified and garrisoned by the military, who again occupied it in World War II. It is now controlled by a Trust and visited by archaeologists, bird-watchers, and naturalists in search of the wild peony and other rare plants (see p 44).

Stoke St Michael (664469): *stoc* originally means place, perhaps an outlying homestead; the church is dedicated to St Michael, but the village was also known as Stoke Lane

A large parish, stretching from the Beacon ridge down to the Nettlebridge stream, with several widely scattered hamlets. The compact nucleus of the village lies in a sheltered fold of the hills where a little stream flows down to the old mill before disappearing underground into a slocker. It is a rather dour grey village, now straggling along the Oakhill road with a lot of new housing to the N and large quarries both to N and S. The finest building, right in the centre, where four roads meet, is the C17 Knatchbull Arms. The Knatchbulls held the Middle Manor, the Longs the East End Manor, where ruins of an Elizabethan house survive behind Manor House Farm. The church, now aisleless, was rebuilt in 1838 except for the low W tower, shortly after Stoke had become a separate benefice instead of being a chapelry of Doulting.

Ston Easton (624534): the settlement E of Chewton, the Hundred town: the dry stone walls show how close to the surface the limestone lies

Rather bleakly situated on the bare Chewton plateau, except for the well-wooded park and the sheltered valley that slips unobtrusively away NE, the parish stretches from Rush Hill to Old Down and E to Clapton. A roadside village of grey stone or colour-washed cottages with several farms and large houses but no real focal point: the church at the corner of Hay Street was rebuilt by Blomfield in 1890 with a heavy wooden roof and dormers. It contains memorials to the Hippisleys, squires here for four centuries, whose mansion in the park dates from the mid-C18. Somewhere here is a lost village, for early records speak of Easton Major and Minor: one possible site is near Whitchurch Farm, a fine C17 prebendal manor house (formerly in Binegar parish) out towards Clapton. Clapton itself (the hill settlement 642534) is a pleasant grey stone hamlet with a pub but no shop, on the very edge of the well-farmed plateau, just inside the present Somerset boundary.

Stratton-on-the-Fosse (659508): the settlement on the street or paved Roman road, the Fosse Way

A straggling village in the middle of a long parish which straddles the Fosse Way from White Post on the edge of Norton–Radstock to Nettlebridge. The S fringe, which was mined for coal from the C15 until 1968, was once much more thickly populated: Pitcot, Barlake and Benter were considerable hamlets 100 years ago, while Fernhill, where

200 people were living in 1791, has virtually disappeared. The nucleus of the village—parish church, manor house, a couple of farms and a few old cottages—lies to the E of the Fosse Way. Since 1814 Stratton has grown into a long roadside village largely dependent upon Downside Abbey and School (see under Downside). The passing motorist may with some justice dismiss it as a village of little charm: the earlier houses are built of the unattractive local White Lias, and there are three modern council house estates. The Catholic church, St Benedict's, a Gothic Revival building of 1857 by Charles Hansom, stands beside the Fosse Way attached to what was formerly the convent and village school. St Vigor's is snugly placed between the manor house and the old rectory with a rural outlook: the interior has recently been pleasantly refurbished. The C18 N chapel is full of memorials to the Longs and Knatchbulls whose fine house lies out in the fields to the N, now, like much of the parish, belonging to the Duchy of Cornwall.

Trudoxhill (746441): Truttoc's hill

Formerly an outlying hamlet of Nunney, in 1951 Trudoxhill became a civil parish which includes Marston Bigot, extending across the valley past Forest Farm to the Wiltshire boundary at Gare Hill in what was once Selwood Forest. Today Trudoxhill is very much a village in its own right, and a delightfully unspoiled village too, with a little stone-built mission church (1899), a couple of shops, and a pub at the strategic road junction. The street winds amiably down the hill, full of good stone cottages and farms into which newer housing blends unobtrusively. Easily mistaken for a cottage is a charming and tiny Congregational chapel dated 1699: plaster roof, plain windows, neat stained pews, pulpit and gallery, and a quiet graveyard beyond: a perfect example of an early nonconformist meeting house.

Ubley (529582): Ubba's *leah* or clearing in the woodland (cf Leigh, Whatley)

A village in the Yeo valley at the foot of the steep wooded N escarpment, though the parish stretches from the slopes of Breach Hill on the N almost to Charterhouse on Mendip, including the holiday centre at what was once the Nordrach Sanatorium. From the sawmills the village street falls sharply down to the church and the cross standing on its tiny green: lanes peter out into the fields towards the top end of Blagdon Lake where the trout hatcheries are situated. There are some good stone-built houses, notably the gabled manor house and the old rectory, and a strikingly modern group set amidst conventional council houses. The church is a low building with a reddish tower surmounted by a squat spire, a C15 building with Perpendicular aisles, simple and unrestored except for the chancel. Ubley has kept an air of quiet seclusion, lying on a loop road off the noisy highway to Weston.

Uphill (319588): the settlement above the *pylle* or creek off the River Axe

Leland described Uphill as the head 'wher al the water issueth to the Severne Se'. From the old windmill one looks down on Black Rock, the w boundary of Mendip, in the Axe estuary, and across sands and saltings to Brean Down (to which a ferry operates in the sumer months): beyond that to Flat Holm and South Wales—and to Weston lying against the background of Worlebury. s the view extends along Mendip as far as Glastonbury Tor; Brent Knoll rises from the moors beyond the glittering rhines, and far away is the long ridge of Quantock and Exmoor.

Now part of the borough of Weston-super-Mare, Uphill is still separated from it by the golf links and by the woods of Uphill Manor (castellated Gothic of 1828). The original village sheltering under the hill has been submerged by new housing. The parish church (Victorian Gothic) stands by the old main road, but the old church on the abrupt hill, predominantly Norman, has been restored as a mortuary chapel.

The pill—the tidal mouth of a rhine that comes down from Locking Head—was once a harbour where a wharf was specifically ordered by the Enclosure Act of 1813 for coasters bringing coal and iron. Now it is an anchorage for pleasurecraft. In fact some people may prefer to see Uphill in winter or early spring before the cars and caravans have flooded in.

Upton Noble (712394): the higher settlement belonging to the Noble family

Originally a hamlet of Batcombe, Upton Noble is a very small pastoral village on the last E slope of Mendip, looking across the headwaters of the Brue to Alfred's Tower on the Wiltshire escarpment, and within sight and earshot of the WR main line from Paddington to Penzance. The unpretentious little church, with its saddle-back s tower but heavily restored interior, stands above the village, which is rect- angular in shape: cottages of grey limestone, some with mullions and drip stones; a pub and a post office; one or two larger houses including the stone-tiled manor. There are few children to attend the new area primary school which has been built here. Away from the main road, the village maintains an atmosphere of isolation and quietness alien to the noisy modern world.

Vobster (705492): Fobb's tor

From Tor Rock one looks across the woodlands of Mells Park towards Cranmore Tower and the Beacon.

Upper Vobster, consisting of a rank or two of grey cottages and a grey chapel, was till lately a busy industrial site: the quarries are now silent and abandoned, the railway like the quarry plant is dismantled; a ditch along the hillside is the legacy of the abortive Dorset & Somerset Canal. Halfway down the hill, approached only by footpath, stands the church, on a green circular terrace, protected by a stone ha-ha. It is surprisingly spacious inside: an early Victorian period piece (1848) by Benjamin Ferrey, the diocesan architect, modelled on the chapel of Merton College, Oxford, with lofty hammer-beam roof, and carvings, both in wood and stone, by Edmund Stansfield, curate of Mells and first priest-in-charge, who was mainly responsible for building the church.

Lower Vobster consists of a shop, a farm and a few cottages by the river; but this too was once industrial with three collieries and a tramway clearly visible on the ground s of the river.

Wanstrow (710416): Waendel's tree

A main road village on the far E slopes where the Nunney Brook rises; but the main road was only built by the Bruton Turnpike Trust c 1810 and the old road still wanders round the E side of the village. The main street runs E–W, climbing gently from the brook to the church, and on to Weston Town, with sober stone-built cottages and a couple of nice arched bridges for foot-passengers against the flooding of the brook. The church, an undistinguished restoration of 1877, contains a memorial to John Yeoman (1745-1824) who lived in the crenellated Park House across the road and owned a pottery in Wanstrow. There was a brickyard here too until the present century. Wanstrow has lost its station, but heavy trainloads of stone still run down from the Merehead quarry over the East Somerset line.

Wells (551458): the springs (cf Fontanetum in an alleged charter of 725)

Wells was sited where strong springs break out from the roots of Mendip, on gently sloping dry ground well above the marshy Levels. By tradition King Ina of Wessex founded a collegiate church here at the suggestion of St Aldhelm who died in 709; in 909 it became the bishop's see for the whole of Somerset; and Ina's church was eventually superseded by the cathedral we see today. The fact that it became a city—its royal charter was granted in 1201—a market town, a tourist centre, and is now environed by light industry and considerable areas of residential development—all this is subservient to the fact that Wells is basically a town that grew up round about, and wholly dependent upon, a great ecclesiastical foundation and one that, unlike Glastonbury, was non-monastic.

The early borough developed round the parish church of St Cuthbert. The C15 hall of the Bubwith almshouses was the ancient Guildhall; the City Arms Inn was the gaol; High Street led from the parish church to the cathedral, probably aligned on the axis of the original church, and the town spread uphill so that the centre became the Market Place right under the walls of the Liberty of St Andrew, finally overspilling beyond it, up the Bath road, where a new parish church (St Thomas) was built by Teulon in 1856.

Between 1859 and 1870 three railways arrived, with separate termini at the bottom of the town, but no significant increase of population followed. There had been few changes in the medieval street-plan and little extension of the urban area. After 1918 there was some spread into the surrounding countryside, but until after World War II Wells remained a sleepy little town, dominated by its ecclesiastical establishment, with a population between 4,000 and 5,000, hardly larger than it had been a century before. Since 1947 extensive development has occurred and the medieval city has become engulfed in a mass of new housing, both council and private, on both sides of the Bath road, along the foothills of Stoberry and Beryl, along the Wookey Hole road and over the abandoned railways, and the population has risen to nearly 9,000.

Two superb approaches bring the traveller into Wells with hardly a hint of the new developments: the Bristol road, dropping sharply down through Georgian New Street into the heart of the city; and the approach from Shepton, either by the footpath across The Park leading directly to the palace moat, or by Tor Hill which provides an incomparable glimpse of the E end of the cathedral church and its associated buildings.

From the top of the tower (187ft; 247 steps) the whole of the medieval layout of the town can be grasped, and all around lies the complex of ecclesiastical buildings within the boundary of the ancient Liberty, whose walls were pierced by three gateways into the town. To the s is the Bishop's Palace, crenellated and moated in the C14 against attacks from the town which never materialised; to the N is the college of vicars generally known as the Vicars' Close, a C14 street of forty-two cells provided for the Priest Vicars and the Vicars Choral, together with a chapel and dining hall. Along the N side of the Cathedral Green are a series of fine buildings which once housed the Quinque Personae, the chief cathedral dignitaries: the old deanery, for example, now diocesan offices; the chancellor's house, now the museum, founded and cared for over the years by H. E. Balch, greatest of Mendip archaeologists; the archdeacon's house, later the theological college which has now removed to Salisbury. The outer Liberty contains many more fine houses, Georgian or earlier.

Even if it is always crammed with cars, there is much to admire in the market place: the fine gateways from the cathedral precinct; the 'New Works' of Bishop Beckington along the N side, their medieval origin disguised by their Georgian façade; the C17 Crown Hotel; the town hall built by Paty of Bristol in 1779; and the post office (formerly the market hall) of 1835. Several streets run more or less parallel down the hill: High Street, widening out and still partly cobbled, with rivulets of clear water in the gutters, and plenty of good building to look at above the shop fronts; Chamberlain Street, decorously residential; and South Street, very much a back lane, eventually meeting Silver Street and becoming Southover, which was once the main road out of town towards Glaston-bury.

There are other good buildings scattered about: the C15 Bishop's Barn on the edge of the recreation ground; the Tudways' mansion also built by Paty in 1759, and now the Cathedral School; the Priory Hospital on the Glastonbury road, built as the workhouse in 1837; the new Blue School (now comprehensive) looking down across Mundy's Meadow from its hillside site; and, best of all, St Cuthbert's, the largest parish church in Somerset, soaring Perpendicular, its C16 roof richly carved and decorated, and restored and gaily painted in 1963.

Today Wells is a bustling market town, full of shoppers and sightseers, often uncomfortably full and choked by traffic. Every scheme proposed for bypasses and relief roads has so far been rejected by the local authority on one ground or another. The best time of year to enjoy Wells is in the winter, when the crowds have gone home; the best time of day is a sunny Sunday morning, when Wells is once again a haven of peace in a noisy world, a city of bells declaring the glory of God and reminding us that the cathedral is more than a stately (ecclesiastical) home to be sauntered round on holidays.

For the cathedral *is* Wells: many hundreds of thousands of words have been lavished on it (Pevsner devotes thirty-two pages to it out of fifty-three on the whole of the city), and here one can only hint at a few of the riches which no visitor can afford to miss: the overwhelming splendour of the w front; the boldness of the inverted arches at the crossing, in-serted in 1338 to buttress the tower against further subsidence; the exquisite Bubwith and Sugar chantries in the nave; the chapter house steps and the perfect proportions of the octagonal chapter house itself; the retrochoir and Lady chapel with their shifting vistas of slender columns and the richness of their stained glass; and so out through the cloister and the Camery churchyard to see where the great springs rise to fill the moat and to flow down through the streets of the city to which they have given their name.

Westbury-sub-Mendip (499487): western burg or fort, w of Wells

Most people see Westbury as a long straggling village on the A371, stretching from Easton to a horrible agglomeration of redbrick council houses and utterly inappropriate modern development along the Stoke road. By far the largest and most attractive part of the village lies above the main road: past the cross there are pleasant areas like the Hollow and the Square, surrounded by old houses, colour-washed or of local Conglomerate. Lanes like Perch Hill and Kites Croft climb away up the lower Mendip slopes and peter out in fields, or double round, like Back Lane: everywhere is a close-knit texture of old and new. Old Ditch with its roadside crags climbs towards the skyline quarry and the Beacon, 892ft above sea level. The church stands below the main road, well screened by trees: a plain exterior and a plain interior, mostly restored or rebuilt in 1887. Lower still lies the derelict station, with a fine group of Bristol & Exeter buildings, now desecrated by a graveyard for motor-cars. A lane leads past Windmill Hill and Lodge Hill on to the moors—the Axe is the parish boundary—and looking back one sees the village comfortably spread about at the foot of the great s escarpment of Mendip.

Westfield (673538): on the site of Radstock's West Field or common

As the Fosse Way climbs slowly sw, Radstock merges into Westfield and Westfield into Norton Hill so that this C20 development of Norton–Radstock has little visible identity: there are council housing estates, private estates and an industrial area. The landmarks are the Elm Tree, Clarks' new factory (1956), and the nave of the parish church, built in 1953 when Westfield became an ecclesiastical parish, and as yet uncompleted. The interior belies the stark exterior: lofty and narrow, well-furnished and decorated—a strangely satisfying conception.

Whatley (734476): the *leah* or glade where wheat was grown (there was a Roman villa here)

A small scattered community on one of the last E outliers of Mendip, looking across Nunney Brook over softer elm-studded country to the Longleat woods. At Lower Whatley is the rebuilt portion of what was a fine Georgian mansion, before a disastrous fire. Southfield, another aesthetically satisfying Georgian house, is where the Rev John Skinner used to visit Peter Hoare. Nearer the church are a handful of cottages and several prosperous-looking stone-built farmhouses, including the dignified Manor Farm, approached through a medieval gatehouse; and also the rectory where R. W. Church lived for 19 years before becoming Dean of St Paul's. The church spire is a striking landmark, but the building itself was heavily restored in the Victorian period: little survives from earlier days except for the C14 crumbling effigy of Sir Oliver de Servington in the s transept. Close by to the N are the spoil heaps of the enormous New Frome Quarry, served by its own line of railway.

Winscombe (412566): Wine's combe or valley

Church Knoll on the N slope of Wavering Down is as good a point as any from which to observe how a number of scattered settlements have gradually coalesced to form modern Winscombe. Immediately below the church one gets the feel of the remains of an older Winscombe. The Green at Woodborough was once another village centre. The coming of the Cheddar Valley branch line in 1869 encouraged the growth of Woodborough on the floor of the valley; the coming of the motor-car made the area a pleasant dormitory for Bristol; and postwar housing development has turned the valley into a shapeless residential area with a population of 3,500, skirted by the A38, threaded by the road from Wells to Weston, and split in two by the derelict railway. Yet green areas survive among the blocks of suburban houses, and looking out across a thickly wooded landscape, beyond Banwell Hill one catches glimpses of the Bristol Channel coast at Worlebury and Clevedon. The triple-windowed church tower is an eye-catcher from almost anywhere in the valley: the church itself is a C15 building, lofty, light and full of good workmanship, notable for its stained glass, both medieval and Victorian. The large parish includes Sandford and Sidcot.

Witham Friary (744411): Witta's *ham* or homestead, given by Henry II to Carthusian monks: Friary=frary (French *frérie*), the residence of the lay brothers as distinct from the charterhouse itself

A remote village reached by circuitous lanes, at the foot of the last E Mendip slope and on the headwaters of the River Frome, but a place full of historical interest. Here the Roman road to the Charterhouse lead mines entered Somerset. The site of the first Carthusian monastery in England, near Witham Hall Farm, has only recently been identified and excavated; the stones were used by the Wyndhams for an C18 mansion and again removed by Beckford to build Fonthill Abbey.

The church belonged to the lay brothers and is unique on Mendip—severe, stone-vaulted and apsidal in the French style, simple and beautiful, dating from c 1180 when St Hugh of Lincoln was still Prior of Witham; from 1458 it was also used as a parish church; in 1876 it was well restored and lengthened. The glass in the E windows (1909) and in the s wall (Comper 1923) portrays episodes from the history of the Carthusians. An impressive building with its high-pitched roof, deep-splayed Norman windows, buttresses (copied from Lincoln) and lofty bellcote. The Victorian architect William White successfully retained the austere atmosphere of the early Middle Ages. The monastic fishponds survive down the valley, and the dovecote is the village reading room.

The village itself is small and compact: many of the cottages with their neat gables and porches were built on the Duke of Somerset's estate—the Seymour Arms proclaims his lordship of the manor—in local stone with unusual brick facings, probably the product of the C19 brickworks at Holt. Before the Beeching era, one changed trains at Witham, where the Wells branch train waited patiently in the bay. The station has gone, but a lonely signal box controls the stone traffic from Merehead, fitting the trains in between the expresses on the main line to the West.

Wookey Hole (532476): from the Celtic *ogof*, a cave

Wookey Hole, which is quite distinct from Wookey nearly two miles s, was for centuries a hamlet in the Wells parish of St Cuthbert Out. By 1610 there was a paper mill here, close to where the Axe debouches from the bowels of Mendip. The village we see today was developed by the Hodgkinsons: after a fire in 1855 they rebuilt the mill, and were responsible for the school, some good housing for the mill hands, the village club and their own neo-Tudor Glencot—all built of local Conglomerate, as was the church, consecrated in 1874 and notable for its spacious and richly furnished chancel, and for the various Hodgkinson memorials. In the present century the Hodgkinsons opened up the caves, which had been visited by curious travellers for many centuries, and built the amenities which have attracted tourists from all over the world. Down the valley St Cuthbert's paper mill is still at work, but

Hodgkinsons' mill, now being transformed into a museum and entertainment centre, was very much the heart of the village, with its fine façade looking across the bowling green and down the village street. Despite ribbon development along the Wells road and some council housing up Milton Lane, Wookey Hole is still a small village, though apt to be overcrowded in the holiday season, on a cramped site along the River Axe, sheltered by wooded hills, with the tremendous rampart of Mendip rising behind the ravine that leads to the caves. Off the Priddy road, which climbs up over Deerleap, lie Ebbor Rocks, the deep wooded gorge now owned by the National Trust.

North Wootton (564418): the settlement near the N wood of Pilton, of which it was a chapelry until 1846

Kelly's Directory neatly describes North Wootton as 'standing by a stream at the entrance of a valley surrounded by curiously formed hills'. The stream is the Redlake river, and down the valley from the remains of the hamlet of Worminster with its fine wayside cross winds what was once the turnpike road from Wells to the SE, skirting the edge of Queen's Sedgemoor. This lane passes the new vineyard and the old Queen's Head Inn, now Manor Farm, and then splits into two, the village lying between the two lanes—a small complex of lanes, farms, stone-built cottages and a little unobtrusive new housing, for the population has remained remarkably stable for over a century: a purely agricultural village set among orchards, with a ford and a neat stone bridge across the river. Nearby is the church, a C15 building of local Lias with a low simple W tower and a pleasing and well-kept interior, including several interesting examples of the work of local craftsmen. The 1830 nonconformist chapel is now a carpenter's workshop, the mill and the school no longer fulfil their original functions, and Tanyard Lane is another reminder of the past.

Notes References and Sources

Mendip Today: Robin Atthill

Mendip is covered on the One-inch os map by Sheets 165 (Weston-super-Mare) and 166 (Frome); on the 1:50,000 map by Sheets 172 (Bristol & Bath), 182 (Weston-super-Mare & Bridgwater) and 183 (Yeovil & Frome); and on the first edition of the One-inch os (1809/1817, reprinted 1969) by Sheets 75 (Bridgwater) and 76 (Bath & Wells). Day & Masters' One-inch map of Somerset (1782) and Greenwood's (1822) are both invaluable.

An overall picture of the area will be found in the County Development Plan (1953) and the First Review (1964), published by the Somerset County Council, which has also published *Wells: The Future,* and brochures on the Designated Conservation Areas at Axbridge and Mells, and (in preparation) those at Frome, Nunney and Shepton Mallet.

Much information is to be found in the works of the old topographers: Collinson's *History and Antiquities of Somerset* (1791), Rutter's *Delineation of the North Western Division of Somersetshire* (1829), and Phelps's *History and Antiquities of Somersetshire* (1836). Green's *Bibliotheca Somersetensis* (1902) and Humphreys's *Somersetshire Parishes* (1906) are exhaustive bibliographies in themselves. Two volumes of the *Victoria County History* were published in 1906 and 1911.

F. A. Knight's *The Seaboard of Mendip* (1902) and *The Heart of Mendip* (1915) are the classic studies of the west end of the hill, but only Coysh, Mason and Waite's *The Mendips* (1954, third edition 1971) and the Mendip Society's *Man and the Mendips* (1971) attempt to deal with the region as a whole. Robin Atthill's *Old Mendip* (1964, second edition 1971) covers various aspects of Mendip history—see specific references in the Notes to Chapters 6 and 7. Of the general guidebooks to Somerset, the best is Bryan Little's *Portrait of Somerset* (1969), but there is some evocative writing in Edward Hutton's *Highways and Byways in Somerset* (sixth edition, 1955). Further books of local interest are mentioned in the introduction to the Gazetteer (p 214).

No major work of literature seems to have been inspired by Mendip. In the first tale of Hardy's *A Group of Noble Dames* (1891), Falls-Park is Mells, and *Our Exploits at West Poley* (1952) is loosely identified with Wookey Hole, where the story was filmed, and Wookey Hole also features in J. C. Powys's *A Glastonbury Romance* (1933). Walter Raymond's *Two Men o' Mendip* (1899) is a minor classic, as are the dialect stories of Jarge Balsh (William Marchant Jones of Coleford) such as *Jarge Balsh at Bristol Zoo* (1934), *Our Village Parliament* (1967) and his *Somerset Songs and Verse* (1930). Ethelbert Horne's *Idylls of Mendip* (1922), *Somerset Folk* (1938) and *Stories of West Country Folk* (1948) are more serious pieces, based upon Fr Horne's long years as a parish priest at Stratton-on-the-Fosse.

Lynn Brock's *The Mendip Mystery* (1929) and John Jarmain's *Priddy Barrows* (1944) are both set on the high plateau, but unlike Elizabeth Goudge's *A City of Bells* (1936, reprinted 1970), in which Torminster is Wells, they are virtually unobtainable today. So are Emma Marshall's novels such as *Under the Mendips* (1886), Edward Tylee's *The Witch Ladder* (1911) and Francis Brett Young's *The Young Physician* (1919). Copies of these and other pieces of fiction and imaginative writing can be consulted at the Local History Library, Taunton Castle.

The memoirs of Frances Horner, *Time Remembered* (1933) describe Mells, as do *Goodly Pearls* (1926) and *Pleasant Places* (1934) by George A. Birmingham (Canon J. O. Hannay), and Christopher Hollis's two autobiographical volumes, *Along the Road to Frome* (1958) and *The Seven Ages* (1974). The early chapters of Arthur Waugh's *One Man's Road* (1931) are set in Midsomer Norton.

CHAPTER 2

(Pages 18–49)

I   The Physical Environment of Mendip: D. I. Smith

Atkinson, T. C. 'The dangers of pollution of limestone aquifers with special reference to the Mendip Hills, Somerset', *Proc Univ Bristol Spelaeol Soc*, 12, No 3 (1971), pp 281–90

Atkinson, T. C., Smith, D. I., Lavis, J. and Whitaker, R. J. 'Experiments in tracing underground waters in limestone', *J Hydrology*, 19 (1973), pp 323–349

Atkinson, T. C., Bradshaw, R. and Smith, D. I. *Quarrying in Somerset: Supplement No 1, Hydrology and Rock Stability of the Mendip Hills* (1973)

Donovan, D. T. 'Geomorphology and hydrology of the central Mendips', *Proc Univ Bristol Spelaeol Soc*, 12, No 1 (1969), pp 63–74

Down, C. G. and Warrington, A. J. *The History of the Somerset Coalfield* (1971)

Findlay, D. C. 'Soils of the Mendip district of Somerset', *Mem Soil Gt Brit* (1965)

Ford, D. C. and Stanton, W. I. 'The geomorphology of the south-central Mendip Hills', *Proc Geol Assoc London*, 79 (1969), pp 401–27

Godwin, H. 'Botanical and geological history of the Somerset Levels', *Advmt Sci London*, 12 (1955), pp 310–22

Gough, J. W. *The Mines of Mendip* (1930, reprinted 1967)

Green, G. W. 'The central Mendip lead-zinc orefield', *Bull Geol Survey Gt Brit* 14 (1958), pp 70–90

Green, G. W. and Welch, F. B. A. 'Geology of the country round Wells and Cheddar', *Mem Geol Survey UK* (1965)

Hannell, F. G. 'Climate', in *Bristol and Its Adjoining Counties*, (1955), pp 47–65

Hanwell, J. D. and Newson, M. D. *The Great Storms and Floods of July 1968 on Mendip* (Wessex Cave Club, Occasional Publication, Series 1, No. 2, 1970)

Hawkins, A. B. and Kellaway, G. A. 'Field meeting at Bristol and Bath with special reference to new evidence of glaciation', *Proc Geol Soc London*, 82 (1971), pp 267–92

Savage, R. J. G. (ed). *Geological Guide to the Bristol Region* (manuscript)

Smith, D. I. and Drew, D. P. (eds). *Limestones and Caves of the Mendip Hills* (1975)
Somerset County Council. *Quarrying in Somerset* (1971)
Stanton, W. I. 'Mendip Quarries', in *Man and the Mendips* (1971)
Van de Kamp, P. C. 'The Silurian volcanic rocks of the Mendip Hills, Somerset', *Geol Mag*, 106 (1969), pp 542–53

II   *Natural History and Ecology*: A. J. Willis

Appleyard, J. 'A bryophyte flora of North Somerset', *Trans Br Bryol Soc*, 6 (1970), pp 1–40
Bassindale, R. 'Fauna', in *Bristol and Its Adjoining Counties*, Chapter 5, pp 73–90 (1955)
Bridgewater, P. 'The vegetation of Steep Holm, Bristol Channel', *Proc Bristol Nat Soc*, 32 (for 1970), pp 73–9
Brown, A. D. R. 'A review of the butterflies in the Bristol area', *Entomologist's Record*, 83 (1971), pp 101–8, 210–15, 236–40, 316–22
Burton, J. 'Somerset butterflies and their conservation', *Somerset Trust for Nature Conservation, Seventh Annual Report* (1971), pp 13–18
Davis, H. H. 'A revised list of the birds of the Bristol district', *Proc Bristol Nat Soc*, 27(4) (for 1947), pp 225–68
Godwin, H. 'Prehistoric wooden trackways of the Somerset Levels: their construction, age and relation to climatic change', *Proc Prehist Soc*, 26 (1960) pp 1–36
Hope-Simpson, J. F. 'Mendip rare plants in the context of their wider distribution', *Somerset Trust for Nature Conservation Tenth Annual Report* (1974), pp 17–22
Hope-Simpson, J. F. and Willis, A. J. 'Vegetation', in *Bristol and Its Adjoining Counties*, Chapter 6, pp 91–109 (1955, reprinted with Appendix, pp 340–2, 1973)
Knight, F. A. *The Seaboard of Mendip* (1902)
Knight, F. A. *The Heart of Mendip* (1915, reprinted 1971)
Matthews, L. H. *et al.* 'A survey of Steep Holm', *Proc Bristol Nat Soc*, 8 (4) (for 1938), pp 438–78
Moss, C. E. *Geographical Distribution of Vegetation in Somerset: Bath and Bridgwater District* (1907)
Palmer, E. M., Ballance, D. K. *et al. The Birds of Somerset* (1968)
Rogers, M. H. *et al.* 'Cheddar Gorge Survey', *Proc Bristol Nat Soc*, 31 (for 1969), pp 635–50
Smith, C. E. D. 'Natural History' in *Man and the Mendips* (1971), pp 59–64
Tetley, H. 'Land mammals of the Bristol district', *Proc Bristol Nat Soc*, 9 (4) (for 1940), pp 100–42
White, J. W. *The Flora of Bristol* (1912, reprinted 1972)
Willis, A. J. 'Further studies on a filamentous saprophyte from Wookey Hole', *Proc Univ Bristol Spelaeol Soc*, 9, No 2 (1961), pp 137–44

Articles on plants (Bristol Botany), Lepidoptera (Lepidoptera Notes, Bristol District), birds (Bristol Bird Report) and mammals (Mammal Survey, Bristol District) are included annually in the *Proceedings of the Bristol Naturalists' Society*, and a great deal of information about the distribution of plants and animals is available from these sources.

ACKNOWLEDGEMENTS

I am grateful to many botanists and zoologists for the supply of information, and in particular to Mr P. J. M. Nethercott, Dr M. H. Martin (limestone heath vegetation), Dr R. S. Wilson (animal life), Mr J. F. Burton (insects) and Mr S. M. Taylor (birds). Dr M. C. F. Proctor kindly supplied photographs 4 and 5.

CHAPTER 3

(Pages 50–74)

Early Mendip: P. J. Fowler

SELECT BIBLIOGRAPHY

In such a short resumé of Mendip's prehistory and early history, footnotes are unnecessary since, while the author's own fieldwork in the area has contributed in part to the chapter, the main sources can best be indicated in three groups: general and site bibliographies, and a list of museums with relevant material. *PUBSS* is an abbreviation for the *Proceedings of the University of Bristol Spelaeological Society*, without which there would be no early Mendip to write about sensibly.

General Bibliography
ApSimon, A. M. '1919–1969: Fifty Years of Archaeological Research', *PUBSS* 12 (1) (1969), pp 31–56
Archaeological Review 1–7, 1966– 72 (Dept of Extra-Mural Studies, Bristol University)
Barrington, N. and Stanton, W. I. *The Complete Caves of Mendips* (second edn. 1972)
Branigan, K. *The Romans in the Bristol Area* (1969)
Branigan, K. and Fowler, P. J. (eds). *The Roman West Country* (1976)
Burrow, E. J. *Ancient Earthworks and Camps of Somerset* (1924)
Campbell, J. *et al. The Mendip Hills in Prehistoric and Roman Times* (1970)
Collinson, J. *The History and Antiquities of Somersetshire* (1791)
Cunliffe, B. W. *Iron Age Communities in Britain* (1974)
Dobson, D. P. *The Archaeology of Somerset* (1931)
Donovan, D. T. 'A bibliography of the Palaeolithic and Pleistocene sites in the Mendip, Bath and Bristol area', *PUBSS*, 7 (1) (1954), pp 23–34; 'First Supplement' (to the above), *PUBSS*, 10 (2) (1964), pp 89–97
Eichholz, D. E. 'The Bristol region in the Roman period' in MacInnes, C. M. and Whittard, W. F. (eds). *Bristol and Its Adjoining Counties* (1955), pp 163–77
Fowler, P. J. (ed). *Recent Work in Rural Archaeology* (1975)
Gough, J. W. *Mines of Mendip* (second edn, 1967)

Grinsell, L. V. (ed). *A Survey and Policy concerning the Archaeology of the Bristol Region, Part I to the Norman Conquest* (1964)
Grinsell, L. V. *Prehistoric Sites in the Mendip, South Cotswold and Bristol Region* (1966)

Grinsell, L. V. *Prehistoric Bristol* (1969)

Grinsell, L. V. 'Somerset barrows, Part II: North & East', *Proc Somerset Archaeol Natur Hist Soc*, 115 (1971), pp 43-137

Hebditch, M. and Grinsell, L. V. *Roman Sites in the Mendip, Cotswold, Wye Valley and Bristol Region* (revised edn 1974)

Neale, F. A. 'Mendip: the fourth dimension' in Hall, W. G. (ed). *Man and the Mendips* (1971), pp 8-38

Phelps, W. *The History and Antiquities of Somersetshire* (1836)

Rahtz, P. et al. *Medieval Sites in the Mendip, South Cotswold and Bristol Region* (1969)

Rahtz, P. and Fowler, P. J. 'Somerset AD 400-700' in Fowler, P. J. (ed). *Archaeology and the Landscape* (1972), pp 187-221

Savage, R. J. G. 'Pleistocene mammal faunas', *PUBSS*, 12 (1), 1969, 57-62

Standing, P. A. 'Author index to Proceedings, volumes 1-12 (1), 1920-1969', *PUBSS*, 12 (1), 1969, pp 89-97

'Site index to archaeological notes in Proceedings', *PUBSS*, 12 (1) (1969), pp 97-8

Tratman, E. K. 'The prehistoric archaeology of the Bristol region' in MacInnes, C. M. and Whittard, W. F. (eds). *Bristol and Its Adjoining Counties* (1955), pp 147-62

'Some ideas on Roman roads in Bristol and north Somerset', *PUBSS*, 9 (3) (1962), pp 159-76

Wainwright, G. J. 'Three microlithic industries from SW England and their affinities', *Proc Prehist Soc*, 26 (1960), pp 193-201

Wymer, J. (ed). *Gazetteer of British Mesolithic Sites* (forthcoming)

Site Bibliography

AVELINE'S HOLE: Davies, J. A. (Reports on excavations at), *PUBSS*, 1 (2) (1921), pp 61-72; 1 (3), pp 113; 2 (1), pp 5-15; 2 (2) (1925), pp 104-14; see also 11 (3) (1968), pp 237-42

BATH: Cunliffe, B. W. *Roman Bath* (1969)

BREAN DOWN: Taylor, H. and E. E. 'An early beaker burial (?) — —, *PUBSS*, 6 (1) (1949), pp 88-92

ApSimon, A. M. et al. 'The stratigraphy and archaeology of the late-glacial and post-glacial deposits at — —', *PUBSS*, 9 (2) (1961), pp 67-136

ApSimon, A. M. et al. 'The Roman temple at — —, *PUBSS*, 10 (3) (1965), pp 195-258

A plan of the westernmost field system is in Fowler, P. J. (ed). *Recent Work in Rural Archaeology* (1975), fig 85

BURLEDGE CAMP: ApSimon, A. M. 'Excavations at — —', *PUBSS*, 8 (1) (1957), p 40

BURRINGTON CAMP: Tratman, E. K. 'Burrington Camp, Somerset', *PUBSS*, 10 (1) (1963) pp 16-21

BUTCOMBE: Fowler, P. J. 'Excavation of a Romano-British settlement at Row of Ashes Farm, Butcombe, north Somerset, 1966-67', *PUBSS*, 11 (3) (1968), pp 209-36

Fowler, P. J. 'Fieldwork and excavation in the Butcombe area, north Somerset, 1968-69', *PUBSS*, 12 (2) (1970), pp 169-94

Rahtz, P. A. and M. M. 'T.40: Barrow and windmill at ——', *PUBSS*, 8 (2) (1958), 89–96

CADBURY CONGRESBURY: Fowler, P. J. *et al. Cadbury Congresbury, Somerset, 1968* (1970)

CAMERTON: Wedlake, W. J. *Excavations at Camerton, Somerset* (1958)

CHARTERHOUSE: Gray, H.StG.the excavation of the amphitheatre at Charterhouse-on-Mendip', *Proc Somerset Archaeol Natur Hist Soc*, 55 (1909), 118–37

Boon, G. C. 'A Roman field-system at ——', *PUBSS*, 6 (2) (1951), pp 201–4

Budge, A. R. *et al.* 'Excavations and fieldwork at Charterhouse-on-Mendip, 1960–67', *PUBSS*, 13 (3) (1974), pp 327–47

CHEWTON MENDIP: Williams, A. 'Bronze Age barrows near ——', *Proc Somerset Archaeol Natur Hist Soc*, 93 (1947), pp 39–67

CHEW VALLEY LAKE: Rahtz, P. A. and Greenfield, E. *Excavation Report* (forthcoming)

GORSEY BIGBURY: Jones, S. J. *et al.* 'The excavation of ——', *PUBSS*, 5 (1) (1938), pp 3–56

ApSimon, A. M. '——, The Second Report', *PUBSS*, 6 (2) (1951), pp 186–200

Tratman, E. K. '—— The Third Report', *PUBSS*, 11 (1) (1966), pp 25–30

GOUGH'S CAVE: Donovan, D. T. 'The Pleistocene Deposits at ——', *PUBSS*, 7 (2) (1955), pp 76–104

Hawkes, C. J. *et al.* 'Decorated piece of rib bone from the Palaeolithic levels at Gough's Cave, Cheddar, Somerset', *PUBSS*, 12 (2) (1970), pp 137–42

Tratman, E. K. *et al.* '—— Rescue Dig ——' *PUBSS*, 13 (1) (1972), pp 49–60

GREEN ORE: Palmer, L. S. and Ashworth, H. W., 'Four Roman pigs of lead from the Mendips', *Proc Somerset Archaeol Natur Hist Soc*, 101 (1957), pp 52–88

Ashworth, H. W. W. *Report on Romano-British settlement and metallurgical site, Green Ore, Wells. Somerset'* (1970)

HAY WOOD CAVE: Everton, A. and R. 'Hay Wood cave burials ——', *PUBSS*, 13 (1) (1972), pp 5–29

KINGSDOWN CAMP, MELLS: Gray, H. St G. 'Excavation at ——', *Archaeologia*, 80 (1930), pp 59–98

MAESBURY CASTLE: Tratman, E. K. *PUBSS*, 8 (3) (1959), pp 174–78

PAGANS HILL, CHEW STOKE: Rahtz, P. A. 'The Roman temple ——', *Proc Somerset Archaeol Natur Hist Soc*, 96 (1951), pp 112–142

Rahtz, P. A. and Harris, L. G. 'The temple well ——', *Proc Somerset Archaeol Natur Hist Soc*, 101/2 (1956-7), pp 15–51

Rahtz, P. A. *et al.* 'Three post-Roman finds from the temple well——', *Medieval Archaeol*, 2 (1958), pp 104–11

ApSimon, A. M., *et al.* 'The Iron Age A ditch and pottery at ——', *PUBSS*, 8 (2) (1958), pp 97–105

PICKEN'S HOLE, CROOK PEAK: Tratman, E. K. '—— a Pleistocene site', *PUBSS*, 10 (2) (1964), pp 112–15; see also, *Catalogue of Fossil Hominids* (British Museum), p 34

PRIDDY CIRCLES: Tratman, E. K. 'The Priddy Circles, Mendip, Somerset. Henge monuments', *PUBSS*, 11 (2) (1967), pp 97–125

PRIDDY LONG BARROW: Phillips, C. W. and Taylor, H. 'The Priddy Long Barrow, Mendip Hills, Somerset', *PUBSS*, 13 (1) (1972), pp 31–6

READ'S CAVERN: Tratman, E. K. 'Final report ——', *PUBSS*, 4 (1) (1931), pp 8–10

SMALL DOWN CAMP, EVERCREECH: Gray, H. St. G. 'Excavation at ——', *Proc Somerset Archaeol Natur Hist Soc,* 50 (1904), pp 1–18

STAR VILLA: Barton, K. J. 'Star Roman Villa, Shipham, Somerset', *Proc Somerset Archaeol Natur Hist Soc,* 108 (1964), pp 45–93

TYNING'S FARM BARROW GROUP: Taylor, H. 'Second and third reports', *PUBSS,* 4 (2) (1933), pp 67–127; 6 (2) (1951), pp 111–73

WESTBURY-SUB-MENDIP: Heal, G. J. 'A new Pleistocene mammal site, Mendip Hills, Somerset', *PUBSS,* 12 (2) (1970), pp 135–36

Bishop, M. J. 'A preliminary report on the Middle Pleistocene mammal bearing deposits of ——', *PUBSS,* 13 (3) (1974), pp 301–18; see also *Nature.* (10 January 1975), pp 253, 95

WHITE WOMAN'S HOLE: Barrett, J. H. and Boon, G. C. 'A Roman counterfeiters' den. Part I White Woman's Hole, near Leighton, Mendip Hills, Somerset; Part 2 Romano-British counterfeiters on Mendip and in South Wales ——', *PUBSS,* 13 (i) (1972) pp 61–82

WOOKEY HOLE: Balch, H. E. *Wookey Hole: Its Caves and Cave-dwellers* (1914)

Tratman, E. K. *et al.* 'The Hyaena Den, Wookey Hole, Somerset', *PUBSS,* 12 (3) (1971), pp 245–79

Museums

The numbers after most of the museums indicate the volume no, the number within the volume, and the date of the *Bulletin* of the Bristol Archaeological Research Group containing a brief catalogue of the museum's contents as then existing.

AXBRIDGE: King John's House (2, 9, 1967)

BATH ROMAN MUSEUM: The Pump Room (2, 9, 1967; 3, 8, 1970)

BRISTOL CITY MUSEUM: Queen's Road

Grinsell, L. V. *Guide Catalogue to the South Western British Prehistoric Collections* (1968)

Hebditch, M. *Guide Catalogue to the Roman Collections from South Western Britain,* I (1970)

BRISTOL UNIVERSITY SPELAEOLOGICAL SOCIETY MUSEUM, University Road (3, 9, 1970; 4, 1, 1971)

CHEDDAR CAVES MUSEUM: (3, 5, 1969)

FROME MUSEUM: St John's Church Steps (2, 9, 1967)

SHEPTON MALLET MUSEUM: to be rehoused in new town centre (3, 2, 1968)

SOMERSET COUNTY MUSEUM: The Castle, Taunton (no catalogue available)

WELLS MUSEUM: Cathedral Green (3, 1, 1968)

WESTON-SUPER-MARE MUSEUM: (3, 6, 1969; 3, 7, 1970)

WOOKEY HOLE MUSEUM: (3, 2, 1968)

ACKNOWLEDGEMENTS

The assistance received from Professor E. K. Tratman, L. V. Grinsell and Mrs A. Everton is gratefully acknowledged. Without the work and publications of the university of Bristol Spelaeological Society, this chapter could not have been written.

CHAPTER 4

(Pages 75–101)

Saxon and Medieval Landscapes: Frances Neale

BIBLIOGRAPHY

NB *SANHS* refers to Proceedings of Somerset Archaeological and Natural History Society

Archaeological Review (CBA Group 13/University of Bristol Dept of Extra-Mural Studies)

Aston, M. and Leech, R. *Historic Towns in Somerset* (CRAAGS 1976—Committee for Rescue Archaeology in Avon, Gloucestershire and Somerset)

Axbridge Caving Group and Archaeological Society: Newsletters and Journals

Banwell Society for Archaeology: Journal *Search*

Batt, M. C. '*The Burghal Hidage*—Axbridge', *SANHS*, 119 (1975)

Beachcroft, G. and Sabin, A. 'Two compotus rolls of St Augustine's Abbey, Bristol', *Bristol Record Society*, 9 (1938)

Belham, P. *The Making of Frome* (1973)

Birch, W. de G. 'Collections towards the history of Stanley Abbey, Wilts.', *Wiltshire Archaeological Magazine*, 15 (1875), pp 239–307

Bristol Archaeological Research Group: *Field Guide no. 3, 'Medieval Sites'* (1969)

Coleman, J. 'Historical notes on Priddy and its leadmines', *SANHS*, 55 (1909), pp 138-161

Darby, H. C. and Finn, R. W. *Domesday Geography of South-West England* (1967)

Davidson, J. B. 'On the charters of King Ine', *SANHS*, 30 (1884), pp 1–29

Dickinson, F. H. 'The Banwell Charters', *SANHS*, 23 (1877), pp 49–64

Dobson, D. P. *Archaeology of Somerset* (1931)

Fowler, P. J. and Rahtz, P. A. 'Saxon estates' in Wilson, D. (ed). *Anglo-Saxon Archaeology* (forthcoming)

Finberg, H. P. R. *The Early Charters of Wessex* (1964)

Gough, J. W. 'The Witham Carthusians on Mendip', *SANHS*, 74 (1928), pp 87-101

Grinsell, L. V. 'Somerset barrows part II', *SANHS*, 115 (1971), supplement pp 44-137

Grundy, G. B. *Saxon Charters of Somerset* (1935)

Hearne, T. (ed). *John of Glastonbury: Chronicle of Glastonbury*, 2 vols (1726)

Hearne, T. (ed). *Adam de Domerham: History of Glastonbury*, 2 vols (1727)

Historical Manuscripts Commission. *Calendar of MSS. of Dean & Chapter of Wells*, 2 vols (1907 and 1914)

Hobhouse, Bishop. 'On a map of Mendip', *SANHS*, 41 (1895), pp 65–72

Hope, W. H. St. J. 'On the first Cathedral Church of Wells and the site thereof', *SANHS*, 55 (1909), pp 85–96

Hylton, Lord. *Notes on the History of the Parish of Kilmersdon* (1910)

Jackson, J. E. *Liber Henrici de Soliaco, 1289* (1882)

Maxwell Lyte, H. 'An outline of the manorial history of Shepton Mallet and Croscombe', *SANHS*, 53 (1907), pp 64-7

Morland, S. C. 'Some Domesday manors', *SANHS*, 99-100 (1954-5), pp 38-48

Morland, S. C. 'Further notes on Somerset Domesday', *SANHS*, 108 (1963-4), pp 94-8

Neale, F., (ed). *Wrington Village Records* (1969)

Neale, F. 'Mendip: the fourth dimension', *Man and the Mendips* (1971)

Notes and Queries for Somerset and Dorset

Porter, H. M. *The Saxon Conquest of Somerset and Devon* (1967)

Porter, H. M. *The Celtic Church in Somerset* (1971)

Potter, K. R. *Gesta Stephani: The Deeds of Stephen* (1955)

Rahtz, P. A. 'The Saxon and Medieval Palaces at Cheddar', *SANHS*, 108 (1963-4), pp 99-112

Rahtz, P. A. 'Cheddar Vicarage 1965', *SANHS*, 110 (1965-6), pp 52-84

Rahtz, P. A. 'Cheddar Vicarage 1970', *SANHS*, 117 (1973), pp 65-96

Robinson, J. A. 'The foundation charter of Witham Charterhouse', *SANHS*, 64 (1918), pp 1-28

Savory, J. H. 'An ancient map of Mendip', *Wells Natural History and Archaeological Society Proceedings* (1913)

Somerset Archaeological and Natural History Society Proceedings (SANHS)—retitled *Somerset Archaeology and Natural History* from vol 112 onwards

Somerset Record Society. Volumes of particular relevance to medieval Mendip are:

   Medieval Bishops' Registers: vols 1 (1887), 9 (1895), 10 (1896), 13 (1899), 29 (1913), 30 (1914), 31 (1915), 32 (1916), 49 (1934), 50 (1935), 52 (1937), 54 (1939), 55 (1940)

   Kirby's Quest for Somerset: vol 3 (1889)

   Pre-Reformation Churchwardens' Accounts: vol 4 (1890)

   Glastonbury Abbey Records: vols 5 (1891), 26 (1910), 59 (1947), 63 (1952), 64 (1956)

   Medieval Feet of Fines: vols 6 (1892), 12 (1898), 17 (1902), 22 (1906)

   Bath Priory Cartularies: vol 7 (1893)

   Medieval Pleas: vols 11 (1897), 36 (1921), 41 (1926), 44 (1929)

   Wills: vols 16 (1901), 19 (1903), 21 (1905), 40 (1925), 62 (1952)

   Mendip Mines and Forest Bounds, and Mining Orders: vol 45 (1930) and supplement (1973)

   Wells City Charters: vol 46 (1931)

   Wulfric of Hazelbury: vol 47 (1932)

University of Bristol Spelaeological Society Proceedings

Ward, R. B. *Bleadon Parish* (typescript thesis, College of St Matthias, Bristol, 1972)

Wells Natural History and Archaeological Society Proceedings and Reports

ACKNOWLEDGEMENTS

This study seeks to complement rather than to repeat previously published work on medieval Mendip, a range of which is included in the Bibliography. It is based as far as possible on materials already in print. Mendip is fortunate in that the dominance of its medieval ecclesiastical landlords has meant the survival of many of its original records, to be published by local and national record societies and so made more readily available to the interested reader. However, an intrinsic part of such a study is fieldwork on the ground, some of which has not, at the time of writing, yet been finally published. For valuable discussions on this, the writer is most grateful to her co-authors and many other colleagues in local archaeological societies, and in particular to M. Aston, M. C. Batt, D. Bromwich, Anne Everton, M. St. J. Forrest, C. J. Hawkes and Dr R. D. Reid.

CHAPTER 5

(Pages 102-25)

Mendip Farming: the last three centuries: Michael Williams

BOOKS AND ARTICLES

Acland, Sir Thomas Dyke. 'On the Farming of Somersetshire', *Journal of the Royal Agricultural Society of England*, 11 (1850), p 666. Reprinted the following year with William Sturge's essay and entitled *The Farming of Somersetshire* (1851)

Best, R. H. and Coppock, J. T. *The Changing Use of Land in Britain* (1962), particularly pp 72-98, 'The Changing Arable in England and Wales, 1870-1960'

Billingsley, John. 'Account of the culture of carrots; and thoughts on burn-baiting on Mendip-hills', *Letters and Papers of the Bath and West of England Society*, 1 (1788), pp 214-19

Billingsley, John. 'On the culture of potatoes', *Annals of Agriculture*, 21 (1793), pp 1-32

Billingsley, John. *A General View of the Agriculture of Somerset* (1798, 2nd edn)

Billingsley, John. 'Remarks on the utility of the Bath and West Society with an account of the progress and improvements in the county of Somerset', *Letters to the Bath and West of England Agricultural Society*, 10 (1805), pp 238-46; see also the editorial remarks about Billingsley's activities appended to this article

Billingsley, John. 'An essay on waste lands', *Letters of the Bath and West of England Agricultural Society*, 11 (1807), pp 2-93

Billingsley, John. 'On the best method of inclosing, dividing and cultivating waste lands', *Letters and Papers of the Bath and West of England Society*, 11 (1809), pp 1-27

Dallas, J. W. 'Farming in Somerset', *Agriculture, the Journal of the Ministry of Agriculture*, 65 (1958/9), pp 172-6

Darby, Joseph. 'The farming of Somerset', *Journal of the Bath and West of England Society*, 5 (1873), pp 96-172

Findlay, D. C. *The Soils of the Mendip District of Somerset*, Memoirs of the Soil Survey of Great Britain, H.M.S.O. (1965)

Great Britain, Parliament. Royal Commission on Agriculture. Report on Devon, Cornwall, Dorset and Somerset, *British Parliamentary Papers*, 14 (1881), p 423

Haggard, Sir Rider. *Rural England*, 2 vols (1909)

Holsworthy, R. (ed). *The Hearth Tax for Somerset*, E. Dwelly's National Records, 1 (1916); see also Manuscripts below

MacInnes, C. M. and Whittard, W. F. (eds). *Bristol and Its Adjoining Counties. A Handbook for the British Association* (1955); see in particular 'Agriculture and horticulture', by W. E. Jones, J. W. Dallas, W. J. Brimacombe and R. Garside, pp 111-23

Ross, Colin D. 'Some aspects of West Country farming', *Journal of the Royal Agricultural Society of England*, 118 (1957), pp 7-13

Somerset Record Society, 'The proportion Roll for Somerset', *Somerset Record Society*, 3 (1889)

Stuart-Menteath, T. 'Somerset', being part 86 of *The Land of Britain* (1938), ed L. Dudley Stamp

Sturge, William, see Acland, T. D. above

Tate, W. E. *Somerset Enclosure Acts and Awards* (1948)

University of Bristol, Reconstruction Research Group. *Land Classification: Gloucestershire, Somerset, Wiltshire* (1947)

Walker, F. *The Bristol Region* (1972)

Williams, Michael. 'The 1801 crop returns for Somerset', *Proceedings of the Somersetshire Archaeological and Natural History Society*, 113 (1969), pp 69–85

Williams, Michael. *The Draining of the Somerset Levels* (1970)

Williams, Michael. 'The enclosure and reclamation of the Mendip Hills, 1770–1870', *Agricultural History Review*, 19 (1971), pp 65–81

Williams, Michael. 'The enclosure of waste land in Somerset, 1700–1900', *Transactions of the Institute of British Geographers*, 57 (1972), pp 99–123

MANUSCRIPTS

Ministry of Agriculture, Parish Statistics (1968)

Public Record Office (PRO), Home Office Documents, HO 67/2, The Agricultural Returns for Somerset, 1801

Public Record Office, Exchequer documents EL79/354, for portions of the Hearth Tax for Somerset, 1664–5

Somerset Record Office, the Enclosure Awards for Somerset. Each has a number, and those which affected Mendip, in chronological order (after East and West Cranmore which had no number) are numbers 62, 58, 27, 134, 132, 18, 21, 71, 22, 72, 73, 81, 65, 42, 38, 13, 23, 33, and 161

Somerset Record Office, DD/SAS PR 86, Locke's *Survey*. Portions of the Survey are printed in F. Madeline Ward, *Supplement to Collinson's History of Somerset* (1939)

ACKNOWLEDGEMENTS

The author wishes to thank the Ministry of Agriculture for access to the parish summaries of the Agricultural Census, and the editor of the *Agricultural History Review* for permission to reproduce material which first appeared in an article in Vol 19 (1971), entitled 'The enclosure and reclamation of the Mendip Hills, 1770–1870'.

CHAPTER 6

(Pages 126–44)

Transport and Communications: Robin Atthill

BOOKS

Roads

Atthill, Robin. *Old Mendip* (1971), Chapters 8–10 on turnpike roads

Margary, I. D. *Roman Roads in Britain* (1973)

Maps: Day & Masters' Somerset (1782); Greenwood's Somerset (1822); One-inch OS (1817, reprinted 1969) Sheets 75 and 76

The Somerset Record Office at Taunton has a large collection of Minute Books, statements of accounts, deposited plans and maps relating to the Mendip Turnpike Trusts.

Canals
Clew, Kenneth R. *The Somersetshire Coal Canal and Railways* (1970)
Clew, Kenneth R. *The Dorset & Somerset Canal* (1971)
Hadfield, Charles. *The Canals of South West England* (1967), Chapter 7

Railways
Atthill, Robin. *The Somerset & Dorset Railway* (1967)
Atthill, Robin. *Picture History of the Somerset & Dorset* (1971)
Atthill, Robin. *Old Mendip* (1971), Chapter 13 on industrial railways
Bradley, D. and Milton, D. *Somerset & Dorset Locomotive History* (1973)
MacDermot, E. T. (revised Clinker, C. R.). *History of the GWR* (1964)
Peters, Ivo. *The Somerset & Dorset* (1974)
Smith, P. W. *Mendips Engineman* (1972)
Thomas, D. St J. *Regional History of the Railways of Great Britain* Vol 1 (third edition, 1966)

ARTICLES

Atthill, Robin. 'The Downhead Railway', *Industrial Archaeology*, 8, No 4 (1971), pp 419–20
Clinker, C. R. 'The Cheddar Valley Railway', *Railway Magazine* (April 1950), pp 224–7
Clinker, C. R. 'The Wrington Vale Light Railway', *Railway Magazine* (November 1959), pp 741–4
Gilson, R. G. and Quartley, G. W. 'Some technical aspects of the Somerset coal canal tramways', *Industrial Archaeology*, 5, No 2 (1968), pp 140–61
Maggs, Colin G. 'The East Somerset Railway', *Railway Magazine* (July 1958), pp 460–4
'A Somersetshire Light Railway' (Oakhill Brewery), *The Locomotive* (15 November 1920)

CHAPTER 7

(Pages 145–79)

Industry: Robin Atthill

Lead etc
Buchanan, Angus and Cossons, Neil. *The Industrial Archaeology of the Bristol Region* (1969), Chapter 5
Gough, J. W. *The Mines of Mendip (1930, reprinted 1967)*
Green, G. W 'The central Mendip lead-zinc orefield', *Bulletin of the Geological Survey of Great Britain*, 14 (1958), pp 70–90
Hawtin, Frank. 'Industrial archaeology at Charterhouse-on-Mendip', *Industrial Archaeology*, 7, No 2 (1970), pp 171–5
More, Martha. *Mendip Annals* (ed. Roberts, second edn 1859)
Coal
Buchanan and Cossons. *Op cit*, Chapter 4

Bulley, John A. 'To Mendip for coal', *Proc Somerset Arch & Nat Hist Soc,* 97 and 98 (1952 and 1953)

Down, C. G. and Warrington, A. J. *The History of the Somerset Coalfield* (1971), containing a full bibliography

Hylton. *History of Kilmersdon* (1910), Chapter 3

Stone

Somerset County Council. *Quarrying in Somerset* (1972) and *Draft Policy for Quarrying* (1974)

Stanton, W. I. 'Mendip quarries', *Man and the Mendips* (1971); also 'The quarrying industry on Mendip' by Amalgamated Roadstone Corporation

Wallis, F. S. 'Draycott Stone and Marble', *Proc Bristol Nat Soc,* 32 (3) (1973), pp 275–80

Wallis, F. S. 'Additional notes on Draycott, Somerset, Stone and Marble', *Annual Report of Wells NH & Arch Soc* for 1973 and 1974

Cloth

Belham, Peter. *The Making of Frome* (1972)

Carus-Wilson, E. M. 'Aulnage accounts: a criticism', *Econ Hist Rev,* 2 No 1 (January 1929), pp 114–23

Cobbett, William. *Rural Rides,* see 2 September 1826

Gray, H. L. 'The production and exportation of English woollens in the fourteenth century', *Eng Hist Rev,* 39 (1924), pp 13–35

Mann, J. de L. *The Cloth Industry in the West of England from 1640–1880* (1971)

Ponting, Kenneth G. *The Woollen Industry of South-West England* (1971)

Victoria County History: Somerset Vol 2, pp 405–23

Iron

Atthill, Robin. *Old Mendip* (1971), Chapter 6

Paper

Atthill, Robin. *Op cit,* Chapter 5

Shorter, A. H. 'Paper and board mills in Somerset', *Notes and Queries for Somerset and Dorset,* 25 (March 1950), pp 245–57

Brewing

Barnard, Alfred. *A Short Account of the Anglo-Bavarian Brewery* (c 1888)

Pudney, John. *A Draught of Contentment: The Story of the Courage Group* (1971)

Tabrett, B. A. 'Banwell Brewery', *Search,* Journal of the Banwell Soc of Arch, 11 (1971–2), pp 9–14

Clock Makers

Bellchambers, J. K. 'Somerset clockmakers', Antiquarian Horological Soc Monographs, 4 (1968)

Hobbs, J. L. 'Former clock & watch makers of Somerset to ca. 1850' — typescript at Local History Library, Taunton Castle

CHAPTER 8

(Pages 180–201)

Recreation: Robin Atthill

1   Hulbert, N. F. 'A survey of Somerset fairs', *Proc Somerset Arch & Nat Hist Soc,* 82 (1936), pp 83–159

Jones, I. F. 'Somerset fairs', *op cit,* 91 (1946), pp 71–81

2   Bull-baiting and cock-fighting: see Atthill, Robin. *Old Mendip*
    (1964/1971), Chapter 15
3   See Fuller, Margaret. *West Country Friendly Societies* (1964); Hylton. *History
    of Kilmersdon* (1910), pp 174-5; Kettlewell, F. B. *Trinkum Trinkums of
    Fifty Years* (1927), pp 60-1
4   Brooke, L. E. J. *Somerset Newspapers 1725-1960* (1960)
5   Further accounts of hunting on Mendip are to be found in Fairfax-
    Blakeborough, J. (ed). *The Hunting & Sporting Reminiscences of H. W. Selby
    Lowndes* (1926); Batten Pooll, A. H. *A West Country Potpourri* (1969);
    Tiarks, Herman. *Hunting Reminisences of an ex-MFH* (c 1936)
6   Knight, F. A. *The Heart of Mendip* (1915), pp 62, 257, 353; *The Seaboard of
    Mendip* (1902), pp 75, 76, 258; Wickham, J. D. C. *Records by Spade and
    Terrier* (c 1912), p 100, Plates XI, XII
7   Full details of the various facilities for recreation, and of the necessary
    permits, are obtainable from the Bristol Waterworks Co, Recreations
    Dept, Woodford Lodge, Chew Stoke, Bristol
    See also Jones, F. C. *Bristol's Water Supply and Its History* (1946) and 'Birds of
    the reservoirs' by Brian Rabbitts in the *Somerset Trust for Nature Conserva-
    tion Annual Report* (1974)
8   Some early tourists' accounts of Mendip—also referred to in Chapter 5, pp
    102/104, can be found in Leland, J. *Itinerary* (ed Toulmin Smith,
    1907/1964); Fiennes, C. *Journeys* (ed Morris, 1947); Defoe, D. *Tour ... of
    Great Britain 1724-7* (ed Cole, 1927); Gilpin, W. *Observations on the
    Western Parts of England* (1798); Maton, W. G. *Observations ... of the
    Western Counties of England* (1797); Warner, R. *A Walk through some of the
    Western Counties of England* (1800)
9   Hobhouse, E. (ed). *Diary of a West Country Physician* (1934), p 54

Caves and Caving: D. I. Smith

Baker, E. A. and Balch, H. E. *The Netherworld of Mendip* (1907)
Balch, H. E. *Wookey Hole. Its Caves and Cave-Dwellers* (1914)
Balch, H. E. *The Caves of Mendip* (1927)
Balch, H. E. *The Mendip Caves* (1948) This single volume comprises the second
    editions of three earlier books.
Barrington, N. and Stanton, W. I. *The Complete Caves of Mendip* (second edn,
    1972)
Hanwell, J. D. 'Memorandum on caving in the Mendip Hills', in *Quarrying in
    Somerset* (1971), pp 256-7
Johnson, P. *The History of Mendip Caving* (1967)
Smith, D. I. and Drew, D. P. (eds). *Limestones and Caves of the Mendip Hills* (1975)
Stanton, W. I. *Pioneer under the Mendips* (Wessex Cave Club, Occasional
    Publication, series 1, no 1, 1969)

In addition to the references above, there are numerous articles in journals
published by individual caving societies. For more detail the reader is par-
ticularly referred to the *Journal of the Mendip Nature Research Committee*, the
Proceedings of the University of Bristol Spelaeological Society and the *Journal of the
Wessex Cave Club*. These can be consulted in the Central Reference Library,
College Green, Bristol.

CHAPTER 9

(Pages 202–13)

The Changing Face of Mendip: Robin Atthill

1   The complete figures from the census returns 180–1901 are listed (by Hundreds) in the *Victoria County History: Somerset,* Vol 2, pp 338–52
2   Changes in the landscape are considered by Hanwell, J. D. 'Agriculture on Mendip', *Man and the Mendips* (1971).
3   Information about National Trust properties can be obtained from their Wessex Regional Office at Stourton, Warminster, Wiltshire; about the National Nature Reserves from the sw Regional Office of the Nature Conservancy Council at Roughmoor, Bishop's Hull, Taunton; and about the Somerset Trust for Nature Conservation from their office at Fyne Court, Broomfield, Bridgwater.

EDITOR'S NOTE AND ACKNOWLEDGEMENTS

This book was conceived at a meeting between publisher and editor early in 1971. Since then I have travelled many hundreds of miles all over and around Mendip, and talked and corresponded with innumerable friends both old and new, importuning them for information and advice without which this book could not have been written. My fellow contributors have been in constant touch with each other and with me, and I am profoundly grateful for their co-operation and patience under persistent editorial pressure. We are, however, responsible neither for each other's opinions nor for the mistakes that must inevitably creep into a symposium such as this.

It would be impossible to name all those who have so readily (and often unwittingly) helped me with my own parts of the book, but I must record my grateful thanks to those who kindly read sections of the book in typescript and offered invaluable comment and criticism: Mr Peter Belham; Dr Alan Blanford; Dr R. W. Dunning; Mr G. A. V. Foster; Mr Hugh Hobhouse; Mr C. L. Keeler; Mr John Luff; Miss J. de L. Mann; Mr D. Morgan; Mr G. T. Moysey; Dr R. D. Reid; Mr Michael Saul; Dr C. E. D. Smith; Mrs K. A. Tonkin and Mr Brian Vincent. I am also grateful to members of the Mendip Society with whom I have discussed many problems, and to the County Archivist and the County Planning Officer and members of their staffs who have supplied me with essential information. Mrs Pauline Noble has typed and retyped my manuscript; Mr K. F. Marchant took many photographs at my request; and from my publisher and his staff at Newton Abbot I have received constant encouragement and advice.

The photographs in this volume are reproduced by kind permission of the following:
John Cornwell: plates 29, 39; Frome Society: plate 28; F. Green: plate 12; J. E. Hancock: plate 11; F. A. Hardwick: plate 32; D. H. James: plates 33, 49; Locomotive & General Railway Photographs: plate 22; K. F. Marchant: plates 13, 18, 30, 31, 37, 38, 42, 43, 44, 45, 46, 47; Richard Neale: plate 10; Ivo Peters: plate 25; Dr. M. C. F. Proctor: plates 4, 5; Somerset Education Committee:

Index

Page numbers in italic indicate illustrations.